A Level
Advancing
Physics
for OCR
Revision Guide

Lawrence Herklots
John Miller

OXFORD
UNIVERSITY PRESS

Great Clarendon Street, Oxford, OX2 6DP, United Kingdom

Oxford University Press is a department of the University of Oxford. It furthers the University's objective of excellence in research, scholarship, and education by publishing worldwide. Oxford is a registered trade mark of Oxford University Press in the UK and in certain other countries

British Library Cataloguing in Publication Data
Data available

978 0 19 834095 9

10 9 8 7 6 5 4 3 2 1

Paper used in the production of this book is a natural, recyclable product made from wood grown in sustainable forests. The manufacturing process conforms to the environmental regulations of the country of origin.

Printed and bound by CPI Group (UK) Ltd, Croydon, CR0 4YY

Acknowledgements

COVER: DR JUERG ALEAN/SCIENCE PHOTO LIBRARY

p40: G. Muller, Struers Gmbh/Science Photo Library; **p42**: Philippe Plailly/Science Photo Library; **p78(T)**: 36Clicks/ iStockphoto; **p78(B)**: Jose Gil/Shutterstock; **p80**: Tonybaggett/ iStockphoto

Artwork by Q2A Media

AS/A Level course structure

This book has been written to support students studying for OCR A Level Physics B. It covers all A Level modules from the specification. These are shown in the contents list, which also shows you the page numbers for the main topics within each module.

AS exam

A level exam

Year 1 content

1 Development of practical skills
2 Fundamental data analysis
3.1 Imaging, signalling, and sensing
3.2 Mechanical properties of materials
4.1 Waves and quantum behaviour
4.2 Space, time, and motion

Year 2 content

5.1 Creating models
5.2 Matter
6.1 Fields
6.2 Fundamental particles

A Level exams will cover content from Year 1 and Year 2 and will be at a higher demand. You will also carry out practical activities throughout your course.

Contents

How to use this book

Specification references

→ At the beginning of each topic, there are specification references to allow you to monitor your progress.

Revision tips

Prompts to help you with your understanding and revision.

Synoptic link

These highlight the key areas where topics relate to each other. As you go through your course, knowing how to link different areas of physics together becomes increasingly important. Many exam questions, particularly at A Level, will require you to bring together your knowledge from different areas.

 ## Practical

Support for the practical components of the exam.

Key term

Pulls out key terms for quick reference.

 ## Worked example

Step-by-step worked solutions.

Common misconception

Common misunderstandings clarified.

Maths skills

A focus on maths skills.

Model answers

Sample answers to exam-style questions.

Summary Questions

1 These are short questions at the end of each topic.

2 They test your understanding of the topic and allow you to apply the knowledge and skills you have acquired.

3 The questions are ramped in order of difficulty. Lower-demand questions have a paler background, with the higher-demand questions having a darker background. Try to attempt every question you can, to help you achieve your best in the exams.

1 A wire has a breaking stress of z Pa. What is the breaking stress of a wire made from the same material which is twice as long and of half the [initial] wire?

[A ... B] $\frac{z}{2}$ **C** z **D** $2z$ (*1 mark*)

2 [Which of the follo]wing terms does not apply to a ceramic material?

[A ... B] hard   **C** strong   **D** tough   (*1 mark*)

3 Copper has a density of $8960 \, \text{kg m}^{-3}$. The mass of a copper atom is $1.068 \times 10^{-25} \, \text{kg}$.

  a Estimate, by calculation, the diameter of a copper atom. Show your working and analysis clearly.   (*3 marks*)

  b When a dislocation moves through a crystalline material such as copper the planes of atoms move across each other by one atomic spacing. Use your answer to **a** to calculate the number of dislocations that have occurred when a sample of copper is permanently deformed by 2 mm.   (*2 marks*)

4 The energy stored in a stretched wire is given by the equation $E = \frac{1}{2} Fx$ where F is the tensile force on the wire and x is the extension.

  a Consider a wire of length L and cross-sectional area A. Use the equation $E = \frac{1}{2} Fx$ to show that the energy stored per unit volume is given by $\frac{1}{2}$ *stress × strain*.   (*2 marks*)

  b Show that the units J m^{-3} are equivalent to Pa.   (*1 mark*)

  c A wire of original length 1.2 m and diameter 1.5 mm is extended elastically by a force of 250 N. The Young modulus E of the wire is 1.8×10^{11} Pa.

    Calculate the energy stored per m^3 in the stretched wire.   (*3 marks*)

5 Figure 1 shows a graph of force against extension for a wire of original length 2.0 m and diameter 0.4 mm.

  a Calculate the energy stored when the wire is extended by 1.5 mm.   (*2 marks*)

  b Use data from the graph to find the Young modulus of the material.   (*2 marks*)

  c The yield stress of the wire is $3.7 \times 10^8 \, \text{N m}^{-2}$. Calculate the force required to make the wire yield.   (*2 marks*)

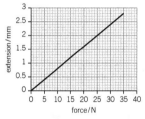

▲ Figure 1

6 Figure 2 shows a representation of the microscopic structure of pure iron and a steel alloy. Describe and explain the effect alloying has on the mechanical properties of the alloy. You should explain any technical terms you use in your answer.   (*6 marks*)

▲ Figure 2

45

1

IMAGING
1.1 Bending light with lenses
Specification references: 3.1.1a(i), 3.1.1b (ii), 3.1.1c(ii)

Wave-fronts and curvature

Wave-fronts are imaginary lines that move along with a wave. In water waves, the line of the crest of the wave can be thought of as a wave-front. You can think of wave-fronts of light spreading from a small source (such as an LED) resembling ripples in water spreading out when you throw a stone in a pond.

Maths skill: Wave-fronts and curvature

The curvature of the circumference of a circle is the reciprocal of its radius.

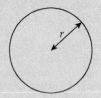

▲ **Figure 1** *The curvature of the circumference of this circle is $\frac{1}{r}$*

As the radius of the circle approaches infinity, the curvature approaches zero.

Rays and wave-fronts – two ways of thinking about light

A ray of light is an imaginary line that points along the direction of motion of the wave-front. Rays are always at right angles to the wave-front.

Ray point of view

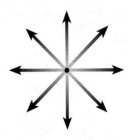

Light travels in straight lines from a small source.

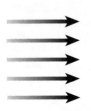

Light in a parallel beam, or from a very distant light source, has rays (approximately) parallel to one another.

Wave point of view

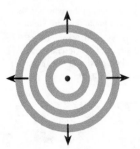

Light spreads out in spherical wave-fronts from a small source.

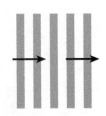

Wave-fronts in a parallel beam, or from a very distant light source, are straight (not curved) and parallel to one another.

▲ **Figure 2** *Rays and waves – two ways of picturing light*

Light from a distant source through a converging lens

Ray description: a converging lens bends rays from a distant source, bringing them together at the focus.

Wave-front description: a converging lens changes the curvature of the plane waves into spherical wave-fronts that converge on a focus.

Lens power

The power of a lens, measured in dioptres (D) is the reciprocal of the focal length f in metres.

$$\text{lens power (D)} = \frac{1}{f\,(\text{m})}$$

The dioptre is equivalent to m^{-1}.

Common misconception: Converting units

To calculate the power of a lens in dioptres you must use the focal length in metres. Short focal lengths are often given in millimetres. These must be converted into metres before calculating the lens power.

Worked example: The power of a lens

The lens in a smartphone has a focal length of 3.8 mm. Calculate the power of the lens.

Step 1: Convert the focal length into metres.

3.8 mm = 0.0038 m

Step 2: Write down the equation, substitute and solve.

$$\text{lens power (D)} = \frac{1}{f\,(\text{m})} = \frac{1}{0.0038\,\text{m}} = 260\,\text{D (2 s.f.)}$$

Remember that your final answer should be given to the same number of significant figures as the data you are given. Strictly, you should write your answer as 2.6×10^2 D to make it clear that you are only quoting to two significant figures.

Summary questions

1   A circle has curvature of $280\,\text{m}^{-1}$. Calculate the radius of the circle. *(2 marks)*

2   The radius of the Earth is about $6.4 \times 10^6\,\text{m}$. Calculate the curvature of a circle of this radius. *(2 marks)*

3   A lens has a power of 16.0 D. Calculate the focal length of the lens in millimetres. *(2 marks)*

4   Draw a diagram showing plane wave-fronts passing through a lens and focusing at a point behind the lens. Mark the focal length on your diagram.
    Draw a second diagram showing plane wave-fronts of the same wavelength passing through a lens of twice the power of the first lens. Compare the focal length of the two lenses. *(4 marks)*

Wave point of view:
The lens adds curvature to the waves, centering them on the focus.

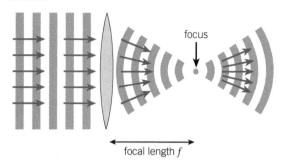

Ray point of view:
The lens bends the rays, bringing them to a focus

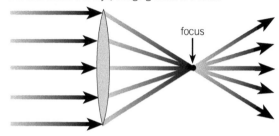

▲ **Figure 3** *Rays and waves – two ways of representing light travelling through a converging lens*

Key term

Focal point and focal length: The focal point of a converging lens is the point where light from a very distant object on the axis of the lens is brought to a focus.

The focal length f of a lens is the distance from the lens to the focal point. This distance is the radius of the wave-fronts just after passing through the lens.

Revision tip:

A high power lens has a short focal length.

1.2 Finding the image

The action of a converging lens described in Topic 1.1, Bending light with lenses, can produce clear images of objects. This is how images of the world around us are formed on the back of our eyes.

The lens equation

The lens equation links:

- u, the distance from the object to the lens (object distance). This distance is *negative*.

- v, the distance from the lens to the image (image distance). This distance is *positive*.

- f, the focal length of the lens. This distance is *positive*.

$$\frac{1}{v} = \frac{1}{u} + \frac{1}{f}$$

Common misconception: A focused image

The distance between the lens and the position of a focused (or clear) image is *not* the same as the focal length unless the object distance is much greater than the focal length. This confusion happens because people often talk about an image being 'in focus' but this does not mean that the image is at the focal point of the lens.

Worked example: Calculating the focal length of a lens

A lamp 28 cm from a converging lens produces a clear image 1.2 m from the lens. Calculate the focal length of the lens.

Step 1: Identify the variables, remembering that u is negative. Convert all distances to m.

$u = -0.28\,\text{m}, v = 1.2\,\text{m}$

Step 2: Substitute values into the lens equation and rearrange.

$$\frac{1}{1.2\,\text{m}} = \frac{1}{0.28\,\text{m}} + \frac{1}{f}$$

$$\therefore \frac{1}{f} = \frac{1}{1.2\,\text{m}} + \frac{1}{0.28\,\text{m}}$$

Step 3: Evaluate.

$$\frac{1}{f} = \frac{5}{6}\,\text{m}^{-1} + \frac{25}{7}\,\text{m}^{-1} = \frac{185}{42}\,\text{m}^{-1}$$

$$f = \frac{42}{185}\,\text{m} = 0.23\,\text{m}$$

Revision tip:

You may find it easier to keep the values of $\frac{1}{u}, \frac{1}{v}$, and $\frac{1}{f}$ as fractions to avoid problems with rounding intermediate answers but remember to convert to a decimal value for the final answer and give your value to the correct number of significant figures.

The lens equation and curvature

The lens equation can be considered in terms of the curvature of the waves passing through the lens.

The equation $\frac{1}{v} = \frac{1}{u} + \frac{1}{f}$ is interpreted as:

| *Curvature of waves leaving the lens* | = | *curvature of waves entering the lens* | + | *curvature added by the lens* |

In this interpretation, the curvature of the waves entering the lens is considered to be *negative*. The power of the lens ($\frac{1}{f}$) is simply the curvature the lens adds to the waves as they pass through the lens.

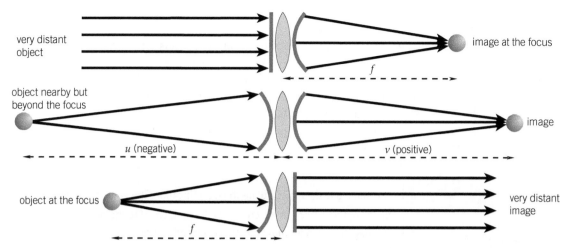

▲ **Figure 1** *The effect of a converging lens on light from objects at varying distance. Wave-fronts of light entering and leaving the lens are shown*

🖩 Worked example: The lens equation and curvature

A lens of focal length 0.160 m produces a clear image at a distance of 0.250 m from the lens.

Calculate **a** the curvature added by the lens, **b** the curvature of waves leaving the lens, **c** the curvature of waves entering the lens, and **d** the object distance.

Step 1: Take the reciprocal of the distances given to find the values of **a** and **b**. Include the sign of the value in your answers.

a curvature added by lens $= \dfrac{1}{f} = \dfrac{1}{0.160\,\text{m}} = +6.25\,\text{D}$

b curvature of waves leaving the lens $= \dfrac{1}{v} = \dfrac{1}{0.25\,\text{m}} = +4.00\,\text{D}$

Step 2: Use the wave-curvature interpretation of the lens equation to find the curvature of the waves entering the lens.

c $+4.00\,\text{D} =$ curvature of waves entering the lens $+ 6.25\,\text{D}$

curvature of waves entering the lens $= +4.00\,\text{D} - 6.25\,\text{D} = -2.25\,\text{D}$. Notice that this is negative.

Step 3: Take the reciprocal of the curvature of waves entering the lens to find the object distance.

d object distance $u = \dfrac{1}{-2.25}\,\text{D} = -0.444\,\text{m}$

Magnification

Linear magnification is also related to the object distance (u) and image distance (v) by:

$$\text{linear magnification } m = \frac{\text{image distance } v}{\text{object distance } u}$$

Magnification does not have units as it is a ratio of two lengths. You must be careful that you use the same units for both lengths in the equation.

Model answer: Calculating the focal length of a lens

A camera has a lens of focal length = 50 mm. It produces an image of height 12 mm at an image distance of 70 mm. Calculate the height of the object.

$f = 0.05\,\text{m}, v = 0.07\,\text{m}$

$$\frac{1}{v} = \frac{1}{u} + \frac{1}{f}$$

$$\therefore \frac{1}{u} = \frac{1}{0.07\,\text{m}} - \frac{1}{0.05\,\text{m}}$$

$$\frac{1}{u} = -\frac{40}{7}\,\text{m}^{-1}$$

$$\therefore u = -\frac{7}{40}\,\text{m}$$

magnification $= \dfrac{v}{u} = \dfrac{0.07\,\text{m}}{-7/40\,\text{m}} = (-)0.40$

linear magnification $m = \dfrac{\text{image height}}{\text{object height}}$

$$0.4 = \frac{0.012\,\text{m}}{\text{object height/m}}$$

object height $= \dfrac{0.012\,\text{m}}{0.40} = 0.030\,\text{m}$

> This answer has a clear structure. This is particularly important in a multi-stage calculation like this. The first task is to calculate the object distance. It is always helpful to gather the data you have been given and write down the equation you are using. Notice that the distances have been converted to metres.

> The second task is to calculate the magnification. The value for $\frac{1}{u}$ has been kept as a fraction which avoids the problem of rounding errors. The negative sign for magnification is placed in brackets and is not necessary for the answer.

> The value for the magnification is now used to calculate the object height. This is a useful example of a well-structured answer that records all the intermediate steps.

Practical: Determining the power and focal length of a converging lens

- A small filament lamp is used as an object. A converging lens projects an image of the glowing filament onto an opaque screen as shown in Figure 2.

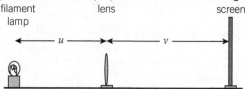

filament lamp   lens   screen

▲ **Figure 2** *Experimental set-up*

- The object distance is changed several times. The screen is moved until a clear image is formed.
- The image distance v is recorded for each object distance u.
- Values of $\frac{1}{v}$ (y-axis) and $\frac{1}{u}$ (x-axis) are plotted.
- This straight-line graph gives intercepts of $\frac{1}{f}$ on both axes.
- This method is better than calculating f from pairs of u and v values because drawing a careful best fit line reduces the uncertainty in the final value.

Summary questions

1 A projector forms a clear image on a screen 3.7 m from the lens. The distance between the projector lens and the illuminated object is 7.0 cm. Calculate the magnification of the image. *(2 marks)*

2 A converging lens of focal length 38 mm produces a clear image of a filament lamp. Calculate the distance from the lamp to the lens (u) that gives an image distance (v) of 90 mm. *(2 marks)*

3 A digital projector uses a lens of focal length $f = 0.064\,\text{m}$. The distance from the illuminated object to the lens is 0.065 m. Calculate the magnification of the image produced. *(3 marks)*

1.3 Storing and manipulating the image

Specification references: 3.1.1 a (ii), 3.11 b (i), 3.1.1 c (i), 3.1.1 c(vi)

Bits, bytes, and pixels

Topic 1.2, Finding the image, described how converging lenses form images. In digital cameras, the lens forms a real image onto sensitive microchips called charge-coupled devices (CCDs). These convert variations of light intensity into variations of electric charge that can be given numerical values. The image becomes an array of numbers.

A CCD will typically have millions of light detectors on its surface. Each light detector corresponds to an individual pixel in the final image and its electric charge is represented by a single number.

Numbers in computers (and camera memories) are stored as binary values. The two values can be thought of as two digits, 1 and 0.

If a pixel simply records light intensity as 'high' (1) or 'low' (0) it will require one bit of memory to store this information.

A pixel will often record 256 levels of light intensity, with each level represented as a number from 0 to 255.

This number of alternatives (256 possible values) is stored on 8 bits, or one byte of memory.

Number of bits and number of alternatives

One bit gives two alternatives, 0 or 1. Two bits give four alternatives: 00,01,10,11. Three bits give eight alternatives.

The number of alternatives N can be calculated using the equations:

$N = 2^b$ or $b = \log_2 N$ where b is the number of bits.

 Worked example: Calculation using bits

Calculate the number of bits needed to give 100 000 possible alternatives.

Step 1: Identify the equation.

$b = \log_2 N$

Step 2: Substitute values and evaluate.

$b = \log_2 100\,000 = 16.6 = 17$ bits required

The number of bits must be a whole number (you can't possibly have 6.6 bits, for example) and the number of bits is rounded *up* to ensure that you have sufficient memory to store the number of alternatives required. 17 bits will give 2^{17} alternatives = 131 072, but 16 bits only gives $2^{16} = 65\,536$ alternatives.

Image resolution

The resolution of an image is given by the equation

$$\text{resolution of image} = \frac{\text{distance represented in the image}}{\text{number of pixels in that distance}}$$

It is important to remember that resolution is a quantity associated with the image, not the device that made the image. The resolution of an image from a particular system changes as the distance represented in the image changes. Your mobile phone will give a better resolution when used for a 'selfie' than for a photograph of distant mountains because the distance represented is smaller for the 'selfie' than for the mountains but the number of pixels in the image remains the same.

Synoptic link

Light intensity is considered in more detail in Topic 7.2, Quantum behaviour and probability.

Key term

Pixel: A pixel is a single 'picture element'.

Key term

Bit: A bit is the smallest unit of digital information, representing either a single 1 or a single 0. A byte is a group of eight bits.

Maths skill: Finding log2*N* on a calculator

'$\log_2 N$' means 'log to base two of N'. You can find the log to base 2 of a number N on your calculator by using the button that looks like:

log ▪□ . Enter '2' in the black square and value 'N' in the larger rectangle.

Key term

Resolution: The resolution of a digital image is the size of the smallest detail that can be distinguished.

Revision tip

'Good' or 'high' resolution is a small number. For example, resolution of 0.5 mm per pixel is a 'better' resolution than 0.9 mm per pixel.

Summary questions

1   A digital image consists of 1024 × 512 pixels. Each pixel is coded with 8 bits. How many bits of memory are needed to store the image? How many bytes?
    (2 marks)

2   How many alternatives *N* can be coded by 10 bits?
    (1 mark)

3   A 'selfie' has 512 pixels across an image of a face that is approximately 0.2 m across. What is the resolution of the image?
    (1 mark)

4   How many bits are required to give 2 million alternatives? *(2 marks)*

5   The memory card in a digital camera can store 2 GB (gigabytes). There are 8 megapixels in each image. Each pixel codes 24 bits of information. How many images can the memory card store? Assume that 1 GB = 8×10^9 bits *(2 marks)*

6   A digital image has random bright dots scattered across it. These are 'noise'. The noise can be removed by replacing the value of each pixel in the image with the median value of its neighbours. Suggest how this process removes the bright dots and suggest a limitation of this method. *(2 marks)*

 Worked example: Resolution of an image

An image of Pluto from the New Horizons spacecraft is 1024 pixels across. The diameter of the dwarf planet is 2.37×10^6 m. Calculate the resolution of the image.

Step 1: Identify the correct equation required.

$$\text{resolution of image} = \frac{\text{distance represented in the image}}{\text{number of pixels in that distance}}$$

Step 2: Substitute and evaluate.

$$\text{resolution of image} = \frac{2.37 \times 10^6 \, \text{m}}{1024} = 2.31 \times 10^3 \, \text{m pixel}^{-1}$$

Information in an image

The amount of information in an image is the number of bits that represent (or 'code') the image.

amount of information in image (bits) = number of pixels × number of bits per pixel

 Worked example: Information in an image

An image of Pluto from the New Horizons spacecraft has 1024 × 1024 pixels. Each pixel is coded by 12 bits. Calculate the image size in bits and in bytes.

Step 1: Identify the correct equation required.

number of bits = number of pixels × number of bits per pixel

Step 2: Substitute and evaluate.

number of bits = 1024 × 1024 × 12 = 12 582 912

$$\text{number of bytes} = \frac{12\,582\,912}{8} = 1\,572\,864$$

Note that this is a precise answer as there is no uncertainty in the original data.

Image processing

Because each pixel in a digital image is coded by a number, the appearance of an image can be changed by changing the number assigned to any of the pixels. This means that images can be processed using mathematical operations. This is how camera phones edit photographs.

The table shows examples of ways digital images can be processed.

▼ **Table 1** *Image processing*

Changing brightness	A dim image can be brightened by increasing the value on each pixel by the same amount until the brightest pixel in the image is coded at 255.
Removing noise	Noise in images refers to the random speckles across the image. This can be reduced by smoothing, where the value of each pixel is replaced with the median or mean of its value and those around it.
Edge detection	To enhance edges in an image the average value of the pixel's neighbours is subtracted from each pixel. This removes uniform areas of brightness and picks out the places where the gradient of the brightness changes abruptly – at the edges.
Changing contrast	An image with little contrast will not use the full range of pixel values. An image may only use the values between 75 and 150. To improve the contrast this range is stretched across the 256 possible values so the value 75 becomes 0 and 150 becomes 255.

1.4 Polarisation of electromagnetic waves

Specification references: 3.1.1 a (iv), 3.11 b (i), 3.1.1 b (iii), 3.1.1 c (v), 3.1.1 d(ii)

Light is a transverse wave and can be polarised.

This property is used in many applications including sunglasses, camera lenses, and 3D cinema.

The wave equation

Light is an electromagnetic wave. Three wave properties, speed v (m s^{-1}), frequency f (Hz) and wavelength λ (m) are related by the equation:

$$v = f\lambda$$

Frequency, the number of waves passing a point in a second, is the inverse of the time period T, the time for one complete oscillation of the wave:

$$f = \frac{1}{T}$$

Diagrams of wave-forms

Figure 1 shows how the displacement of a wave from its equilibrium position (y-axis) varies with the displacement along the wave (x-axis). This is a snapshot of the wave.

The variation of wave displacement with time is shown in Figure 2.

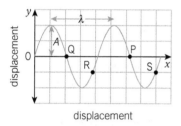

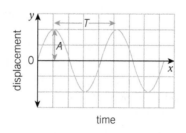

▲ **Figure 1** *A snapshot of a wave at an instant in time*

▲ **Figure 2** *The position of a particle P on a wave plotted against time*

Note that the distance between crests represents the wavelength in Figure 1 and represents the time period in Figure 2.

Electromagnetic waves

Electromagnetic waves are waves of oscillating electrical and magnetic fields. The fields oscillate at right angles to each other and to the direction of travel of the wave.

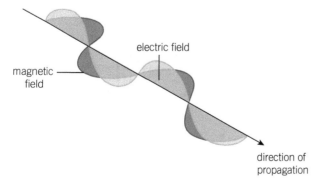

▲ **Figure 3** *An electromagnetic wave*

Electromagnetic waves are transverse and so can be polarised as represented in Figure 4.

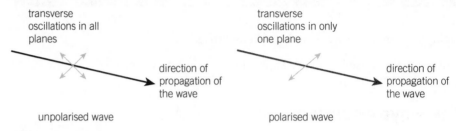

▲ **Figure 4** *Polarised and unpolarised waves*

Summary questions

1 The velocity of light in air is $3.0 \times 10^8 \, \text{m s}^{-1}$. Calculate the frequency of light of wavelength 690 nm. *(1 mark)*

2 The velocity of a deep ocean wave is given by the equation $v = \sqrt{\dfrac{g\lambda}{2\pi}}$ where g is the acceleration due to gravity $(9.8 \, \text{m s}^{-2})$.

  a Show that $\sqrt{\dfrac{g\lambda}{2\pi}}$ can be expressed in the units m s^{-1}. *(1 mark)*

  b Calculate the frequency of a deep-ocean wave with velocity $= 10 \, \text{m s}^{-1}$. *(2 marks)*

3 Polarising ski goggles use polarising lenses to cut out the glare from sunlight reflecting off the snow. Sunlight is partially polarised when it reflects. Explain how the polarising glasses cut out glare from the snow and suggest and explain how the glare you observe would change if you tilted your head so that the glasses were vertical rather than horizontal. *(5 marks)*

Practical: Demonstrating polarisation with light and with microwaves

Light:

- A beam of unpolarised light is passed through a polarising filter.
- The beam is observed through a second polarising filter.
- The observer looks through the second filter as it is rotated.

It is observed that the brightness of the transmitted light varies as the filter is rotated. This is explained as follows: the first filter only transmits the component of oscillation in a particular plane. In Figure 5 the first filter transmits the vertical component.

When both filters transmit the vertical component the brightness of the light observed is a maximum. When the second filter is rotated so that it transmits the horizontal component (as shown in the figure) there is no light transmitted because the light passing through the first filter is fully polarised in the vertical direction.

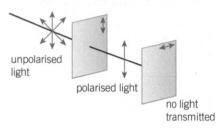

▲ **Figure 5** *The effect of polarising filters on polarised light*

Microwaves:

A similar demonstration can be performed using microwaves. A metal grille acts like the second filter in the demonstration with light. The strength of the signal at the receiver can be varied as the metal grille is rotated, showing that the microwaves emitted are polarised.

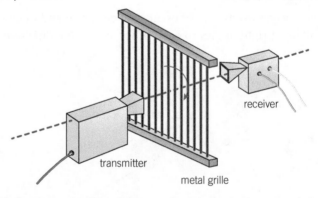

▲ **Figure 6** *Demonstrating that microwaves from the transmitter are polarised*

Chapter 1 introduced the idea of digitising images. This chapter covers digitising audio signals and introduces aspects of digital signalling.

A digital signal is a stream of binary digits (1s and 0s). Digital signals can be transmitted through space, through the air (wireless), through cables, or optical fibres.

Two advantages of digital signals

1 Digital signals can be edited and manipulated easily and quickly. (The manipulation of digital images has already been covered. Digital audio can be manipulated in a similar manner.)

2 Noise can be removed from digital signals without loss of detail.

Analogue signals vary continuously. When analogue signals are amplified the noise in the signal is also amplified. The noise in this context is the random variation on the signal – the hiss on a poorly tuned radio, for example. Turning up the volume of the radio doesn't improve the sound because the hiss is also amplified. Filtering out noise from an analogue signal produces a loss of detail. This is not a problem for digital signals. The signal can be 'regenerated' with the noise removed.

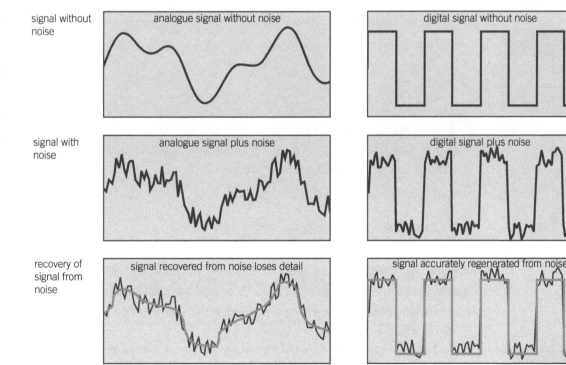

▲ **Figure 1** *Signals and noise*

Sampling and analogue to digital conversion

Figure 2 gives an example of the process of sampling. In this case there are eight quantisation levels; eight different values that the sample can take. Each sample requires three bits of memory. The process is not completely accurate because there are quantisation errors where the original signal is between quantisation levels at the moment the sample is taken. Increasing the number of quantisation levels gives a more accurate sample but more levels use more memory.

Key term

Sampling: The process in which the displacement of a continuous (analogue) signal is changed into a string of binary numbers (samples) by measuring the displacement at small time intervals.

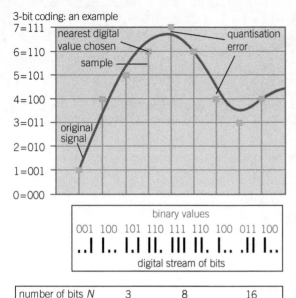

3-bit coding: an example

```
7=111
6=110     nearest digital              quantisation
          value chosen                 error
5=101       sample
4=100
3=011     original
          signal
2=010
1=001
0=000
```

binary values

001 100 101 110 111 110 100 011 100

..| |.. |.| ||. ||| ||. |.. .|| |..

digital stream of bits

number of bits N	3	8	16
number of levels 2^N	$2^3 = 8$	$2^8 = 256$	$2^{16} = 65536$

▲ **Figure 2** *Digitising a signal*

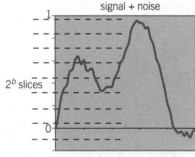

signal + noise

2^b slices

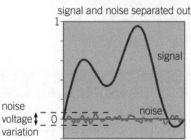

signal and noise separated out

signal

noise voltage variation

noise

▲ **Figure 3** *Signal, noise, and quantisation levels*

Resolution of a sample

Sampling involves a varying potential difference (voltage) because the original signal (for example, sound level) is changed into a continuously varying potential difference by a microphone or other sensor.

 Worked example: Resolution of a sample

A signal varies over a range from −1.00 V to 1.00 V. Each sample is represented by a 5-bit number. Calculate the resolution of the sample.

Step 1: Identify the number of quantisation levels = 2^5 = 32. Remember that this includes the zero level, so the number of quantisation levels above zero = 31. When you are considering large numbers of quantisation levels you can simply use the total number, including the zero level.

Step 2: Identify the equation required.

$$\text{resolution of a sample} = \frac{\text{potential difference range of signal}}{\text{number of quantisation levels in sample}}$$

Step 3: Substitute and evaluate: $\text{resolution} = \frac{1.00\,\text{V} - (-1.00\,\text{V})}{31} = \frac{2.00\,\text{V}}{31}$

$$= 6.45 \times 10^{-2}\,\text{V}$$

Signal, noise, and quantisation levels

Figure 3a shows a noisy signal. Figure 3b shows the smoothly varying signal and the noise separated out.

The presence of noise in a signal puts a limit on the number of useful quantisation levels. There is no point having better resolution than the level of noise.

$$\text{maximum useful number of levels} = \frac{\text{total noisy signal variation}}{\text{noise variation}} = \frac{V_{\text{total}}}{V_{\text{noise}}}$$

$$\therefore 2^b = \frac{V_{\text{total}}}{V_{\text{noise}}} \text{ where } b \text{ is the maximum useful number of bits}$$

$$\therefore 2^b = \log_2 \frac{V_{\text{total}}}{V_{\text{noise}}}$$

Worked example: Noise in a signal

A signal has a maximum total variation of 1920 µV. The noise variation is 120 µV. Calculate the maximum useful number of bits per sample.

Step 1: Identify the equation required: $b = \log_2 \frac{V_{\text{total}}}{V_{\text{noise}}}$

Step 2: Substitute and evaluate: $b = \log_2 \frac{1920\,\mu\text{V}}{120\,\mu\text{V}} = 4$

Summary questions

1. How many bits are required to represent: **a** 512 quantisation levels **b** 1000 quantisation levels? *(2 marks)*

2. The 3-bit sampling system illustrated in Figure 2 is used to sample a signal over a 10.00 V range. Calculate the resolution of the sample. *(2 marks)*

3. The potential difference range of a signal is 24.0 V. A 6-bit sample of the signal is produced.
   a Calculate the resolution of the sample. *(2 marks)*
   b How many bits are required in the sample to halve the resolution in **a**? *(1 mark)*

4. A noiseless signal has a potential difference variation of 126.0 µV. When transmitted the signal picks up a noise variation of 2.0 µV. Calculate the maximum number of bits to code the received signal. *(2 marks)*

2.2 Sampling sounds and sending a signal

Specification references: 3.1.1a(iii), 3.1.1 c(vii), 3.1 c(viii)

Topic 2.1, Digitising a signal, showed that the resolution of a sample depends on the number of bits in the sample. The accuracy of a sample of a signal that varies with time (such as a sound wave) also depends on how many times the signal is sampled per second.

Minimum sampling rate

- If the sampling rate is too low, high frequency detail is lost.
- If the sampling rate is less than twice the highest frequency variation of the signal, spurious low frequencies (called aliases) can be created when the sample is reconstructed.

Sampling too slowly misses high frequency detail in the original signal

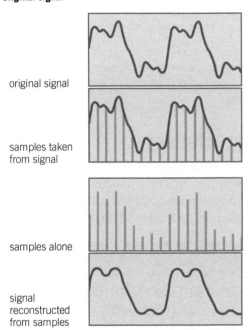

original signal

samples taken from signal

samples alone

signal reconstructed from samples

▲ **Figure 1** *Losing high frequency detail*

Sampling too slowly creates spurious low frequencies (aliases)

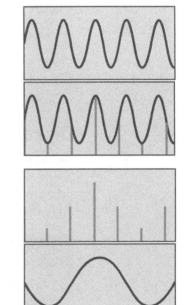

original signal

samples taken from signal

samples alone

signal reconstructed from samples

▲ **Figure 2** *Aliasing*

To avoid aliasing: minimum sampling rate > highest frequency component of the signal

Bit rate

The bit rate is the number of bits that are sampled per second:

bit rate (bit s^{-1} or Hz) = samples per second × bits per sample.

For example, CD quality sound uses 16 bits per sample at a sample rate of 44.1 kHz for each of the two stereo channels. This produces a bit rate of 1.4 Mbit s^{-1} or 1.4 MHz.

The bit rate of a signal can also be used to calculate the duration of a signal:

$$\text{duration of signal (s)} = \frac{\text{number of bits in signal}}{\text{bit rate (bit s}^{-1}\text{ or Hz)}}$$

This equation can be used to calculate the time to upload or download files over a broadband link.

Worked example: Uploading a digital photograph

The upload rate of a broadband link is $2.9 \times 10^6\,\text{bit s}^{-1}$. Calculate the time taken to upload a 5 megapixel image. Each pixel is coded by 24 bits.

Step 1: Calculate the size of the image (number of bits in the image).

image size = number of pixels × bits per pixel = $5 \times 10^6 \times 24\,\text{bits} = 1.2 \times 10^8\,\text{bits}$

Step 2: Identify the equation required.

$$\text{duration of signal (s)} = \text{upload time} = \frac{\text{number of bits in signal}}{\text{bit rate (bit s}^{-1}\text{)}}$$

Step 3: Substitute and evaluate.

$$\text{upload time} = \frac{1.2 \times 10^8\,\text{bits}}{2.9 \times 10^6\,\text{bits}^{-1}} = 41\,\text{seconds}$$

This answer may seem very large. In practice, digital images (and other data) are 'compressed' so that the number of bits transmitted (the file size) is reduced. This greatly reduces the upload or download time.

Disadvantages of digital technology

Digital technology gives almost instantaneous access to information and is therefore a great benefit to many. However, this ease of access brings problems of security of information. Similarly, the ability to edit photographs and other digital files calls into question how 'real' these digital images are.

Summary questions

1 A music streaming service transmits at a bit rate of $0.16\,\text{Mbit s}^{-1}$. How much memory is required to download a track lasting $3\frac{1}{2}$ minutes? Give your answer in bits and in bytes. *(3 marks)*

2 A premium streaming service operates at $0.32\,\text{Mbit s}^{-1}$ rather than $0.16\,\text{Mbit s}^{-1}$. Explain how this higher streaming rate improves the signal received. *(2 marks)*

3 Each individual character (a letter, number, or other character) on a computer keyboard can be encoded by one byte. A wireless link from a tablet pc transmits data at $10\,\text{MHz}$. Calculate the duration of a signal for 3000 characters (about a page of text). *(2 marks)*

Chapter 1 and 2 Practice questions

1   People with long sight require glasses for reading.

    A comfortable distance to read is about 25 cm from the text to the eye.
    Annie is long-sighted and is not able to focus on objects closer than 80 cm.

    a   Calculate the curvature of waves from an object 25 cm from
        the eye.   *(1 mark)*

    b   Calculate the curvature of waves from an object 80 cm from
        the eye.   *(1 mark)*

    c   Use your answers to **a** and **b** to explain why a lens of power +2.75 D
        will allow Annie to read a book held at 25 cm from her eyes.   *(3 marks)*

2   A lamp is placed 30 cm from a converging lens. The lens makes a clear,
    real, image of the lamp on a distant screen. The image is magnified 2.7
    times. Calculate the focal length of the lens.   *(3 marks)*

3   An imaging system on a surveillance drone has a square sensor of
    1.8×10^9 pixels. It images an area of 6 km × 6 km. Calculate the
    minimum length that can be resolved by the system.   *(3 marks)*

4   A real image of a lamp is formed on a screen by a
    converging lens. The height of the image is recorded as
    the screen is moved further from the lens. The distance
    between the lamp and the lens is changed so that the
    image on the screen is always clear.

    The student takes the results shown in Table 1.

    a   Copy and complete the graph of the results shown
        in Figure 1.   *(2 marks)*

    b   Give the value of the *x*-axis intercept and explain
        why this is equal to the focal length of the lens.
                                                        (3 marks)

    c   Explain why the height of the image is the same
        as the height of the object at a lens–screen distance
        of 0.40 m.   *(3 marks)*

5   The camera on a mobile phone has a power of 220 D.

    The distance between the lens and the light-sensitive
    surface of the camera is 4.5 mm.

    a   Calculate the focal length of the lens.   *(1 mark)*

    b   Explain why the camera can produce a clear image of an object at a
        distance of 1.0 m from the lens but cannot produce a clear image of an
        object 0.1 m from the lens.
        You should include calculations in your answer.   *(3 marks)*

    c   Look at the data about the phone camera.

        Number of pixels per image = 1200 × 1000
        3 colours per pixel
        Each colour is coded with 256 levels of intensity
        Memory available = 4.5 GB

        Calculate the number of images that can be stored in the
        memory of the camera.   *(3 marks)*

6   A mobile phone is used to record video. Each image consists of
    3.6×10^5 pixels. Each pixel is coded with 24 bits. The camera can
    record and transmit 18 frames a second.

    a   Calculate the bit rate for transmitting video images.   *(2 marks)*

▼ **Table 1**

lens–screen distance / m	height of image / mm
0.26	10
0.28	12
0.30	15
0.33	20
0.40	30
0.60	60
0.70	75

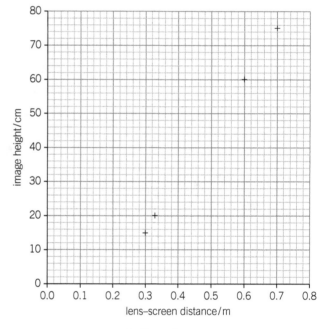

▲ **Figure 1**

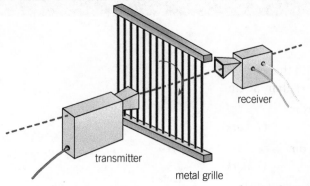

▲ Figure 2

b The phone samples sound at a sample rate of 20 000 Hz.
Each sample is coded with 6 bits.
Calculate the bit rate for sampling sounds. *(1 mark)*

c State the maximum frequency that can be
accurately sampled. Explain your answer. *(2 marks)*

7 A metal grille is placed between a microwave transmitter
and receiver as shown in Figure 2.

a The frequency of the microwaves is 10 GHz.
Calculate their wavelength. ($c = 3.0 \times 10^8 \text{m s}^{-1}$) *(1 mark)*

b As the metal grille is rotated the amplitude of the waves detected
behind the grille varies.

i Describe the variation of the detected waves as the grille
is rotated. *(2 marks)*

ii Explain why the detected amplitude varies in the manner
you have described and explain why this demonstration
shows that microwaves are transverse waves. *(4 marks)*

8 The graph shown in Figure 3 shows part of a sampled waveform.
The sample points are represented by the circles on the waveform.

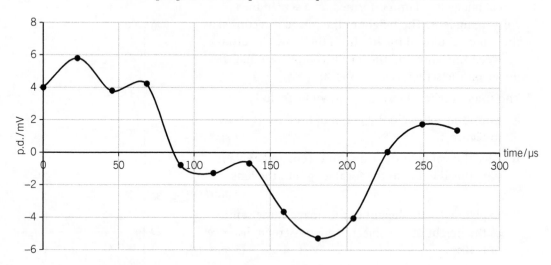

▲ Figure 3

a Use the graph to show that the sampling rate is between 40
and 50 kHz. *(2 marks)*

b There are 64 000 voltage levels between +6.0 mV and −6.0 mV.
Calculate the resolution of the system. *(1 mark)*

c Calculate the number of bits required to code for 64 000 levels. *(2 marks)*

d The sample rate for CD quality music is 44.1 kHz. Each sample requires
16 bits for each of the two channels in a stereo recording. The bit rate
of the CD quality playback is the same as the bit rate for the recording.

A music streaming system streams music at a rate of 0.16 Mbit s⁻¹.
Explain, using calculations and ideas about sampling rate and
quantisation levels, why the quality of the playback will be lower than
a CD recording. (This is a level of response question.) *(6 marks)*

3

SENSING
3.1 Current, p.d., and electrical power
Specification references: 3.1.2a(i), 3.1.2a(ii), 3.1.2a(v), 3.1.2a(ix), 3.1.2b(i), 3.1.2c(i), 3.1.2c(ii)

Electric current and charge

If there is a p.d.(potential difference) between two points and those points are joined by a conducting path, then a current I will be present in the conducting path. This current is the rate at which the charge flows through any part of the path. The charge is made of very many charged particles, usually electrons.

If the conducting path splits into two or more branches, so that charge can go one way or the other, then:

the total charge into the junction = the total charge out of it (Kirchhoff's first law)

Maths skill: Numbers of electrons and standard form

The moving charges are often electrons, of charge 1.6×10^{-19} C. The number of electrons passing each second will be very high, so standard form must be used.

Worked example: The number of electrons passing through a bulb each second

Calculate the number of electrons passing each second through the filament of a torch bulb carrying 0.25 A.

Step 1: Write the current in coulombs per second.

$0.25\,A = 0.25\,C\,s^{-1}$

Step 2: Divide this value by the charge of one electron in coulomb.

$$0.25\,A = 0.25\,C\,s^{-1} = \frac{0.25\,C\,s^{-1}}{-1.6 \times 10^{-19}\,C\,electron^{-1}}$$

$$= -1.5625 \times 10^{18} \frac{s^{-1}}{electron^{-1}} = -1.56 \times 10^{18}\,electron\,s^{-1}\,(2\ s.f)$$

(The minus sign reminds you that the negative electrons are moving in the opposite way to the conventional current direction.)

Common misconception: Flow in a circuit

People often mistakenly write 'current flows around a circuit.' It is charge that flows around the circuit: current is the name for the flow.

Potential difference and energy

The potential difference (p.d.) or 'voltage' between any two points is the potential energy difference ΔE for every unit of charge moving between those two points: ΔE is the work done, W. When a charge Q flows across a p.d. V:

$$W = QV$$

This work often heats components, dissipating the energy.

Synoptic link

The study of electrical circuits is the study of moving charges. You will meet stationary charges and their behaviour in Topic 17.1, Uniform electric fields, and Topic 17.3, Charged spheres.

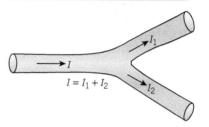

$I = I_1 + I_2$

▲ **Figure 1** *Current dividing at a junction*

Key terms

Kirchhoff's first law: At any junction in an electrical circuit, the sum of all currents entering the junction is the same as the sum of all currents leaving the junction.

Current and charge: $1\,A = 1\,C\,s^{-1}$

Key term

Dissipation: In any energy transfer, some energy is 'wasted'. For motion, this will be against forces such as friction, and for electrical circuits this will be electrical heating. These unwanted energy transfers are referred to as dissipation.

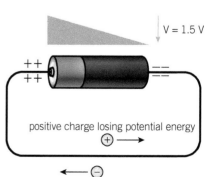

▲ **Figure 2** *Potential energy changes for charges in a circuit*

Key term

p.d., energy, and charge:
$1 V = 1 J C^{-1}$

 Worked example: The energy dissipated in a bulb

A 6.0 V battery is connected to a bulb which draws a current of 300 mA. Calculate the energy dissipated in the bulb filament in two minutes.

Step 1: Calculate the charge flowing across the 6.0 V in this time.

Charge in C = current in C s^{-1} (A) × time in s

$Q = It = 300 \times 10^{-3}$ A × (2×60) s = 36 C

Step 2: Calculate the energy dissipated.

$W = QV = 36$ C × 6.0 V = 216 J = 220 J (2 s.f.)

Power, current, and p.d.

$$P = \frac{W}{t} = \frac{QV}{t} = \frac{Q}{t}V = IV$$

$P = IV$ is a useful equation. It gives an alternative way of solving the final Worked example.

 Worked example: The energy dissipated in a bulb (using $P = IV$)

A 6.0 V battery is connected to a bulb which draws a current of 300 mA. Calculate the energy dissipated in the bulb filament in two minutes.

Step 1: Calculate the power.

$P = IV = 300 \times 10^{-3}$ A × 6.0 V = 1.8 W

Step 2: Calculate the energy dissipated in the two minutes.

$P = \dfrac{W}{t} \Rightarrow W = Pt = 1.8$ W × (2×60) s = 216 J = 220 J (2 s.f.)

Summary questions

1   A 1.5 V battery cell delivers a current of 0.35 A for 24 s. Calculate:
    a   the charge Q flowing   (2 marks)
    b   the potential energy ΔE lost by the cell.   (2 marks)

2   An electric kettle has a heating element with a power rating of 2.1 kW. It is connected to the 230 V mains electrical supply. It takes 5 minutes and 12 seconds to heat up the water it contains. Calculate:
    a   the current I in the heating element   (2 marks)
    b   the charge Q flowing through the heating element   (2 marks)
    c   the work W done in heating the water.   (2 marks)

3   A lightning strike from a cloud to the ground lasts for a time of 0.4 ms. The average current in this time is 25 kA. The p.d. between the cloud and the ground is 35 MV.
    a   Calculate the energy dissipated in the lightning strike.   (3 marks)
    b   Compare the power released during the strike with the output of the large Drax power station (currently 4.0 GW). (2 marks)

3.2 Conductors and resistors

Specification references: 3.1.2a(iii), 3.1.2a(vi), 3.1.2b(i), 3.1.2b(ii), 3.1.2b(iii), 3.1.2c(i), 3.1.2c(ii), 3.1.2d(i)

Resistance, conductance, and Ohm's law

Many conductors obey Ohm's law. For these ohmic conductors the ratio of I to V is constant providing that the temperature does not change. This ratio can be written two ways:

$$\text{conductance in siemen (S) } G = \frac{I}{V}$$

$$\text{resistance in ohm } (\Omega)\ R = \frac{V}{I}$$

where I is in amps (A) and V is in volts (V). Good conductors have large G and small R, and poor conductors have the opposite.

From the definitions above: $G = \dfrac{1}{R}$ and $R = \dfrac{1}{G}$

Worked example: Resistance and conductance of a bulb filament

At its working temperature, the current taken by a 6.0 V torch bulb is 50 mA. Calculate its resistance and conductance.

Step 1: Convert the current from mA to A (the p.d. is already in V).

$50\,\text{mA} = 50 \times 10^{-3}\,\text{A}$

Step 2: Substitute I and V into the equations for R and G.

$R = \dfrac{V}{I} = \dfrac{6.0\,\text{V}}{50 \times 10^{-3}\,\text{A}} = 120\,\Omega$

$G = \dfrac{I}{V} = \dfrac{50 \times 10^{-3}\,\text{A}}{6.0\,\text{V}} = 0.0083\,\text{S} = 8.3\,\text{mS (2 s.f.)}$ (or $G = \dfrac{1}{R} = \dfrac{1}{120\,\Omega} = 0.083\,\text{S (2 s.f.)}$)

Series and parallel combinations of conductors

A parallel combination has the same p.d. across the conductors, but they share the total current. The conductance G of the combination is found by adding the conductances G_1, G_2, etc. of the separate components. As an alternative, you can find the resistance R of the combination using the equation:

$$\frac{1}{R} = \frac{1}{R_1} + \frac{1}{R_2} + \dots$$

A series combination has the same current through the conductors, but they share the total p.d. The resistance R of the combination is found by adding the resistances R_1, R_2, etc. of the separate components. As an alternative, you can find the conductance G of the combination using the equation:

$$\frac{1}{G} = \frac{1}{G_1} + \frac{1}{G_2} + \dots$$

Maths skill: Reciprocals and calculators

Although parallel combinations are more easily analysed in terms of conductance, some students prefer to use resistances. If you prefer this approach, remember (1) to convert $k\Omega$ etc. to Ω, (2) to make proper use of the reciprocal [x^{-1}] key of your calculator. Practise adding $3\,\Omega$ in parallel to $6\,\Omega$:

$3\,[x^{-1}] + 6\,[x^{-1}] = [x^{-1}] =$ should give you the right answer: $2\,\Omega$.

Synoptic link

The study of electrical circuits is the study of moving charges. You will meet stationary charges and their behaviour in Topic 17.1, Uniform electric fields, and Topic 17.3, Charged spheres.

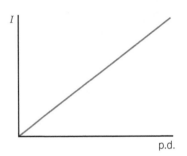

▲ **Figure 1** *Current against p.d. for an ohmic conductor*

Key terms

Ohm's law: Ohm's law states that current is directly proportional to p.d., $I \propto V$.

Ohmic conductors: An ohmic conductor (e.g., a metal at constant temperature) is one that obeys this law.

Revision tip

When converting resistance to conductance or vice versa, make sure you take account of prefixes like k, M, m. Write the values in standard form, so $120\,\text{k}\Omega = 1.2 \times 10^5\,\Omega$.

Revision tip

In the Worked example you can find G from I and V or from your calculated value of R. The first of these is safer, as you may have made an error in your calculation of R. In examinations, 'error carried forward' marking is applied so this should not matter, but using an incorrect value of R may make further calculations harder.

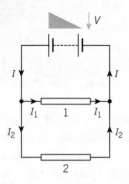

▲ **Figure 2** *Parallel conductors*

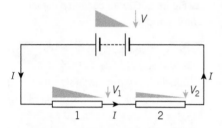

▲ **Figure 3** *Series conductors*

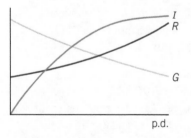

▲ **Figure 4** *Variation of current, resistance, and conductance with p.d. for a filament bulb*

Complex networks

In an examination, there will not be time to analyse very complex networks, but the principles are the same whenever there are more than two components:

- Two components in series can be combined by adding their resistances: $R = R_1 + R_2$
- Two components in parallel can be combined by adding their conductances: $G = G_1 + G_2$

Applying these rules will allow you to reduce the number of components one by one until there is just one component.

Worked example: Simplifying a complex network

In the circuit shown in Figure 4, each of the components X_1 to X_8 has a resistance of $10\,\Omega$, which is a conductance of 0.1 S.

Calculate the resistance and conductance of the combination.

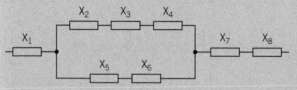

▲ **Figure 4** *Circuit for analysis*

There are many ways of doing this! Here is one approach.

Step 1: In the parallel combination, add the two strings of series resistances and find the conductance of each.

X_2, X_3, and X_4: $10\,\Omega + 10\,\Omega + 10\,\Omega = 30\,\Omega$ which is a conductance of $\dfrac{1}{30\,\Omega} = 0.03333\ldots$ S

X_5 and X_6: $10\,\Omega + 10\,\Omega = 20\,\Omega$ which is a conductance of $\dfrac{1}{20\,\Omega} = 0.050$ S

Step 2: These conductances are in parallel, so they add. Then use $R = \dfrac{1}{G}$ on the sum to find the resistance of the combination of X_2 to X_6.

conductance $= 0.03333\ldots$ S $+ 0.050$ S $= 0.08333\ldots$ S so the resistance $= \dfrac{1}{0.08333\ldots\,\text{S}}$ $= 12\,\Omega$

Step 3: The network now has four resistances in series, so they add.

$R = 10\,\Omega + 12\,\Omega + 10\,\Omega + 10\,\Omega = 42\,\Omega$ so $G = \dfrac{1}{42\,\Omega} = 0.02380\ldots$ S $= 0.024$ S (2 s.f.)

Temperature changes

Ohm's law applies to conductors such as metals only if the temperature is constant, and current in a resistance dissipates energy in it, raising the temperature. This has the effect of increasing the resistance.

If the p.d. across such a conductor, such as the wire in a filament bulb, is increased, the current will increase. This increases the temperature further, making the resistance rise and conductance fall.

Investigating *I–V* characteristics

You will expect to obtain a graph of current against p.d. for the component. This will be a straight-line if the component is ohmic, when the gradient of the best-fit line will give the resistance or conductance. If the component is non-ohmic, the resistance and conductance will change as the p.d. changes. You should also reverse the component: it may conduct differently if the p.d. is in the opposite direction.

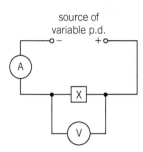

▲ **Figure 5** *Investigating an electrical component*

Summary questions

1 A resistor of resistance 22 kΩ is connected to a battery of p.d. 9.0 V. Calculate the current drawn by the resistor. *(2 marks)*

2 A car starter motor takes a current of 80 A when first connected to 12 V car battery. Calculate the resistance and conductance of the motor under those conditions. *(3 marks)*

3 Calculate the conductance of a parallel combination of a 12 Ω resistor and a 6 Ω resistor. *(3 marks)*

4 Calculate the resistance of a series combination of a 0.25 S conductor and a 0.40 S conductor. *(3 marks)*

5 Three identical 60 Ω resistors can be combined in a network in four different ways. Calculate the resistance and conductance of each of these networks. *(7 marks)*

6 The resistance of iron increases by 0.65% of its value at 0 °C for every degree rise above 0 °C. An iron wire has a resistance of 300 Ω at 0 °C. Calculate its resistance at 25 °C. *(2 marks)*

7 In an experiment to investigate the *I–V* characteristics of a component, the data shown in Table 1 were obtained.

▼ **Table 1**

V / V	0	1.0	2.0	3.0	4.0	5.0	6.0
I / mA	0	26	49	77	98	110	117

Plot an *I–V* graph and describe the behaviour of the component, with calculation where appropriate. *(8 marks)*

3.3 Conductivity and resistivity
3.4 Conduction under the microscope

Specification references: 3.1.2a(viii), 3.1.2b(i), 3.1.2b(iii), 3.1.2c(iii), 3.1.2d(ii)

Key terms

Electrical conductivity σ and resistivity ρ: These are constants for a particular material, allowing calculation of conductance G and resistance R, given by the equations $G = \dfrac{\sigma A}{L}$ and $R = \dfrac{\rho L}{A}$. L and A are the length and mean cross-sectional area respectively of a sample of that material.

Revision tip

The Greek letters sigma σ and rho ρ are used for different variables in other parts of physics – when studying materials, σ is used for tensile stress and ρ is used for density.

Revision tip

Be careful not to use the diameter instead of the radius in πr^2.
In this example, note that the answer should be rounded to two significant figures to match the data, but that it is best to round at the very end, as here.

Conductivity and resistivity

The resistance of a sample of conductor depends on three factors: the length L of the conductor in the direction of current, the mean cross-sectional area A and the type of material used. A greater length will increase resistance (like having resistors in series). A greater cross-sectional area will decrease resistance (like having resistors in parallel). Furthermore, different materials conduct differently: a copper wire will have a much lower resistance than a steel wire of identical dimensions. These three factors are combined in the equation:

$$R = \frac{\rho L}{A}$$

where the electrical resistivity ρ (rho) is a constant which depends on the material of the conductor. The S.I. units of resistivity are $\Omega\,\text{m}$. Resistivity varies across a huge range: for metals it is typically about $10^{-8}\,\Omega\,\text{m}$, while for insulators such as polythene it is greater than $10^{12}\,\Omega\,\text{m}$.

In the same way, the conductance of conductor is given by:

$$G = \frac{\sigma L}{L}$$

where the electrical conductivity σ (sigma) is related to resistivity by:

$$\sigma = \frac{1}{\rho} \text{ or } \rho = \frac{1}{\sigma}$$

The S.I. units of conductivity are $(\Omega\,\text{m})^{-1}$, which are $\Omega^{-1}\text{m}^{-1} = \text{S}\,\text{m}^{-1}$.

🖩 Worked example: The resistance or conductance of a long wire

A resistor consists of a 5.0 m wire of constantan alloy of diameter 0.19 mm. The resistivity of constantan is $4.9 \times 10^{-7}\,\Omega\,\text{m}$. Calculate the conductance of this resistor.

Step 1: Calculate the cross-sectional area A of the wire.

$r = \dfrac{1}{2} \times d = 0.095\,\text{mm} = 9.5 \times 10^{-5}\,\text{m}$ so $A = \pi r^2 = \pi \times (9.5 \times 10^{-5}\,\text{m})^2 = 2.835 \times 10^{-8}\,\text{m}^2$

Step 2: Calculate the resistance.

$R = \dfrac{\rho L}{A} = \dfrac{4.9 \times 10^{-7}\,\Omega\,\text{m} \times 5.0\,\text{m}}{2.835 \times 10^{-8}\,\text{m}^2} = 86.42\,\Omega$

Step 3: Calculate the conductance.

$G = \dfrac{1}{R} = \dfrac{1}{86.42\,\Omega} = 0.001157\,\text{S} = 0.012\,\text{S}$ (2 s.f.)

(or **Step 2:** use $\sigma = \dfrac{1}{\rho}$ calculate the conductivity σ of constantan, then **Step 3:** use $G = \dfrac{\sigma A}{L}$ to find G.)

Models of conduction

In metals, each atom has ionised to give one or more electrons to a cloud of free electrons which move freely about the lattice of positive ions, 'knitting' all the positive ions together with strong forces. The large number of free electrons present means that metals are good electrical conductors. The number density of free electrons is very large.

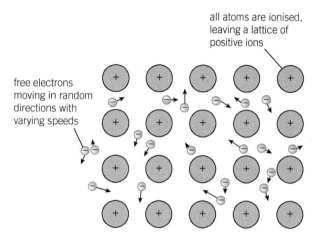

all atoms are ionised, leaving a lattice of positive ions

free electrons moving in random directions with varying speeds

▲ **Figure 1** *A simple model of the ions and electrons in a metal*

Insulators lack mobile charges, while semiconductors such as silicon or germanium have conductivities between conductors and insulators, due to having some (very few) mobile charges. The number density of free electrons in semiconductors is very much less than for metals.

Temperature effects

When the temperature of a metal is raised, the increased vibration of the positive ions impedes the movement of free electrons, increasing the resistivity/decreasing the conductivity.

When the temperature of a semiconductor is raised, more and more atoms receive enough energy for electrons to be released. This number increases rapidly with temperature, causing a great decrease in resistivity/increase in conductivity.

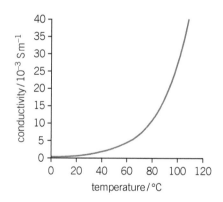

▲ **Figure 2** *The relationship between temperature and conductivity for a semiconductor*

Measuring resistivity or conductivity

This activity consists of finding the resistance or conductance of a metal in the form of a wire of known length and thickness. This will involve using a long, thin specimen so that the resistance is not too small, or the conductance too large. A small resistance/large conductance would result in the p.d. across the specimen giving a current which heats the wire, changing its resistance or conductance.

One approach would be to measure the current for different p.ds. across the measured length which should give a straight-line graph through the origin if the resistance or conductance is constant. The gradient of the I–V graph will give R or G, which will then give ρ or σ. Another approach would be to measure the p.d. across different lengths of a long wire with a constant current I, when the graph of V against L would be a straight-line graph whose gradient will give the resistivity and hence the conductivity.

Summary questions

1 A 2.4 m length of nichrome wire has a cross-sectional area of 2.0×10^{-7} m^2. The resistivity of the metal alloy nichrome at room temperature is 1.1×10^{-6} Ω m. Calculate:
   a the resistance of the wire   (2 marks)
   b the conductance of the wire.   (1 mark)

2 The heating element for an electric kettle needs to dissipate 2.0 kW from a mains p.d. of 230 V.
   a Using data from Question 1, calculate the length of nichrome wire of diameter 0.32 mm that would be needed to construct the element.   (4 marks)
   b Explain why the kettle will dissipate a value of power less than 2.0 kW at the boiling point of water.   (2 marks)

3 A semiconductor device constructed of silicon of conductivity 1.8 S m^{-1} measures 2.6 mm in length and has a rectangular cross-section measuring 0.15 mm × 0.48 mm. Calculate the current in mA drawn by this device when the p.d. across it is 3.4 V.   (4 marks)

3.5 Potential dividers

Specification references: 3.1.2a(vii), 3.1.2b(i), 3.1.2c(iv), 3.1.2d(iii), 3.1.2d(iv)

Sharing voltages in series

As you saw in Topic 3.2, Conductors and resistors, two components R_1 and R_2 in series have the same current I, and the total p.d. V across the pair of components is equal to the sum of the two p.ds. across the two components:

$$V = V_1 + V_2$$

The p.d.s across the two resistors in Figure 1 are in the same ratio as their resistances, with the larger resistor having the larger p.d. They form a potential divider:

$$\frac{V_1}{V_2} = \frac{R_1}{R_2}$$

It is often more useful to compare one of the two p.ds. with the total battery voltage, V:

$$\frac{V_2}{V} = \frac{R_2}{(R_1 + R_2)} \Rightarrow V_2 = \frac{R_2}{(R_1 + R_2)}V$$

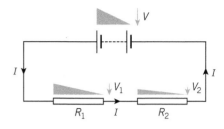

series
- same current
- p.d. shared
- resistances add

▲ **Figure 1** *The potential divider circuit*

 Worked example: The p.d. across a resistor in a potential divider

In Figure 1, the battery voltage is 4.5 V, $R_1 = 100\,\Omega$ and $R_2 = 470\,\Omega$. Calculate the p.d. across R_1.

Step 1: Substitute the values into the equation and calculate V_2.

$$V_2 = \frac{R_2}{(R_1 + R_2)}V = \frac{470\,\Omega}{[100\,\Omega + 470\,\Omega]} \times 4.5\,V = \frac{470\,\Omega}{(570\,\Omega)} \times 4.5\,V = 3.71\,V$$

Step 2: Use V_2 with the battery voltage to calculate V_1.

$$V = V_1 + V_2 \text{ and } V = 4.5\,V \text{ so } 4.5\,V = V_1 + 3.71\,V$$

$$V_1 = 4.5\,V - 3.71\,V = 0.79\,V$$

Potential dividers and sensors

Many sensor circuits consist of two resistors sharing the battery p.d. V, which is the input p.d. V_{in}. The p.d. V_2 across one resistor is then the output p.d. V_{out}, so:

$$V_{out} = \frac{R_2}{(R_1 + R_2)}V_{in}$$

A sensor circuit is normally drawn with the battery on the left and the potential divider vertical. One of the two resistors is a fixed resistor and the other varies with an environmental variable such as temperature or light intensity.

Either R_1 or R_2 can be the fixed resistor in this circuit. In Figure 2, the fixed resistor has been chosen to be R_2. In this case, the output p.d. has been taken across R_2, but it could be taken across R_1: the p.d. across R_1 decreases with temperature rise, so that across R_2 will increase as the two p.d.s add to give V_{in}.

Revision tip
It is also possible to use the total resistance $R_1 + R_2$ to calculate the current I and then use $V = IR$ for each resistor.

Key term
Potential divider: A potential divider consists of two (or more) components in series. Components in series share the total p.d. across them, with the p.d. across each component proportional to its resistance.

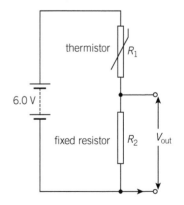

▲ **Figure 2** *Temperature-sensing circuit*

Worked example: Finding the resistance of a thermistor

In Figure 2, the fixed resistor has resistance 120 Ω. Calculate the resistance of the thermistor if V_{out} = 4.3 V.

Step 1: Identify the values given.

$$R_2 = 120\,\Omega, R_1 = \text{thermistor resistance}, V_{in} = 6.0\,\text{V and } V_{out} = 4.3\,\text{V}$$

Step 2: Substitute values into the correct equation and evaluate R_1.

$$V_{out} = \frac{R_2}{(R_1 + R_2)} V_{in} \Rightarrow 4.3\,\text{V} = \frac{120\,\Omega}{(R_1 + 120\,\Omega)} \times 6.0\,\text{V}$$

$$(R_1 + 120\,\Omega) = \frac{120\,\Omega \times 6.0\,\text{V}}{4.3\,\text{V}} = 167.44...\,\Omega$$

$$R_1 = 167.44...\,\Omega - 120\,\Omega = 47.44...\,\Omega = 47\,\Omega\ (2\ \text{s.f.})$$

Calibration and use of sensors

In most cases, you should expect to use a component whose resistance changes with the environment, quite possibly a light-dependent resistor (LDR) or thermistor. In each case, an increase in the internal energy of the component frees more mobile charges, so the resistance drops.

Before use in a measurement circuit, the approximate range of the resistance of the component needs to be estimated or measured, so that an appropriate value of the fixed resistance R_2 can be chosen.

Once R_2 has been chosen, the circuit can be calibrated. The output p.d. V_{out} must be measured over a range of values of the environmental measurement (e.g., temperature or light intensity). This will involve a separate measuring instrument (e.g., thermometer or light-meter) so that a graph of V_{out} against this variable value can be obtained. This is a calibration curve for the circuit. Use of the calibration curve will allow conversion of any value of V_{out} into the environmental variable it is intended to measure.

Summary questions

1. A 330 Ω resistor and a 470 Ω resistor are connected in series to a 4.5 V battery. Calculate the p.d. across each resistor. *(2 marks)*

2. A light-dependent resistor and a thermistor are connected in series with a battery. When they are set up on the laboratory bench, the p.d. across each is 3.0 V. Without calculation, explain what would happen to the two voltages if the room became cooler and more brightly lit. *(2 marks)*

3. A thermistor has resistance which drops as it is heated, from 1100 Ω at 20 °C to 95 Ω at 100 °C. It is connected in series with a fixed resistance R_2 to a 6.0 V battery. The temperature of the thermistor is gradually raised from 20 °C to 100 °C. Calculate the minimum and maximum p.d.s across the fixed resistor R_2:
   a. for a 50 Ω fixed resistor *(2 marks)*
   b. for a 500 Ω fixed resistor *(1 mark)*
   c. for a 5000 Ω fixed resistor. *(1 mark)*

3.6 E.m.f. and internal resistance

Specification references: 3.1.2a(iv), 3.1.2b(i), 3.1.2c(i), 3.1.2c(i), 3.1.2d(v)

Electric sources and e.m.f.

Electrical sources, such as batteries, generators, solar cells, or thermocouples provide p.d. which will make charges move. The energy provided by the source for each unit of charge that moves is called the e.m.f.

Kirchhoff's second law and internal resistance

Kirchhoff's first law (see Topic 3.1, Current, p.d., and electrical power) describes what happens to currents at a junction in a circuit. Kirchhoff's second law is about conservation of energy: the energy given to each coulomb of charge by the source (the e.m.f.) is equal to the sum of the energies transformed by that coulomb as it moves around the circuit (the p.ds.).

In any source of e.m.f., some energy is dissipated within the source itself. This is best thought of as resistance inside the source: internal resistance.

In Figure 1 the e.m.f. is shown in dark grey and the p.d. drops across resistances are shown in light grey. By Kirchhoff's second law, the sum of the 'light grey' p.d. drops = the sum of all 'dark grey' e.m.f.s.

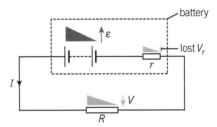

▲ **Figure 1** *A source of e.m.f. with internal resistance r*

Because there is a p.d. drop inside the battery itself, measuring the p.d. across the battery terminals will give a reading less than the e.m.f. if there is any current in the circuit. The p.d. drop across the internal resistance is sometimes called 'lost volts'.

Battery current and terminal p.d.

When a battery of e.m.f. ε and internal resistance r is connected to an external resistance R, Kirchhoff's second law tells us:

$$\varepsilon = \text{'lost volts' across } r + \text{p.d. across } R = Ir + IR$$

where I is the current in the circuit.

The battery terminal p.d. V = p.d. across $R = IR$ so $\varepsilon = Ir + V$ where ε and r are constants.

The equation can be re-arranged into:

$$V = -rI + \varepsilon$$

This is in the form $y = mx + c$ for a straight line of gradient m and y-axis intercept c as shown in Figure 2.

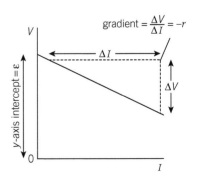

▲ **Figure 2** *Variation of terminal p.d. with current*

Revision tip

Note that the final values are quoted to two significant figures, the same as the least precise measurements in the data (the current). Each answer is rounded as late as possible in the calculation.

 ## Worked example: Finding the e.m.f. and internal resistance of a battery

The p.d. across the terminals of a battery cell is 1.95 V when the battery is connected to a 5.00 Ω resistor, delivering a current of 0.39 A. When the battery cell is connected to a 10.0 Ω resistor, the p.d. is 2.07 V and the current is 0.21 A. Calculate the e.m.f. and internal resistance of the battery cell.

Step 1: Write the equation $\varepsilon = Ir + V$ twice, once for each pair of variables, numbering each equation .

$$\varepsilon = 0.39\,\text{A} \times r + 1.95\,\text{V} \qquad (1)$$

$$\varepsilon = 0.21\,\text{A} \times r + 2.07\,\text{V} \qquad (2)$$

Step 2: Solve the pair of simultaneous equations (1) and (2) to find one of the two unknown factors. Equate the right-hand sides as they are both equal to the e.m.f. So they must be equal to each other.

$$0.39\,\text{A} \times r + 1.95\,\text{V} = 0.21\,\text{A} \times r + 2.07\,\text{V}$$

$$0.39\,\text{A} \times r - 0.21\,\text{A} \times r = 2.07\,\text{V} - 1.95\,\text{V} = 0.12\,\text{V}$$

$$(0.39\,\text{A} - 0.21\,\text{A}) \times r = 0.18\,\text{A} \times r = 0.12\,\text{V}$$

$$r = \frac{0.12\,\text{V}}{0.18\,\text{A}} = 0.6666...\,\Omega = 0.67\,\Omega\ (2\ \text{s.f.})$$

Step 3: Substitute r into one of the equations (1) and (2), it doesn't matter which, to find the e.m.f.

$$\varepsilon = 0.39\,\text{A} \times 0.6666...\,\Omega + 1.95\,\text{V} = 0.26\,\text{V} + 1.95\,\text{V} = 2.21\,\text{V} = 2.2\,\text{V}\ (2\ \text{s.f.})$$

Determining the internal resistance of a cell

You should aim to get a range of measurements, allowing you to make use of a straight-line graph shown in Figure 2. You may wish to measure the terminal p.d. V and the current I, or you may have a set of known external resistances R. If you are measuring V and I, the straight-line graph shown in Figure 2 will be easy to obtain. If you are measuring R and V, or R and I, you can use $R = \dfrac{V}{I}$ to obtain data pairs of V and I to be plotted.

Summary questions

1 A 1.5 V battery cell of internal resistance 0.2 Ω is connected to a 2.0 Ω resistor. Calculate:
   a   the current in the circuit   (2 marks)
   b   the p.d. across the terminals of the cell.   (1 mark)

2 A battery is connected to a rheostat (variable resistor). The rheostat is adjusted and the current and terminal p.d. measured. When the current is 1.0 A, the terminal p.d. is 8.7 V. When the current is 1.5 A, the terminal p.d. is 8.5 V. Calculate the e.m.f. and the internal resistance of the battery.   (4 marks)

3 In an experiment to find the internal resistance of a cell, the readings in Table 1 were obtained.

▼ Table 1

External resistance R / Ω	2.00	4.00	6.00	8.00	10.00
Battery terminal p.d. / V	3.86	4.12	4.19	4.26	4.29

Draw an appropriate straight-line graph and use it to obtain the internal resistance r.   (6 marks)

Chapter 3 Practice questions

1 In the network of three resistors shown in Figure 1, each resistor has a resistance of 1.0 Ω.

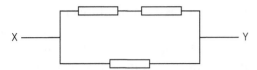

▲ **Figure 1**

What is the overall resistance between the points **X** and **Y**? *(1 mark)*

A 0.67 Ω

B 1.3 Ω

C 3.0 Ω

D 6.0 Ω

2 The circuit in Figure 2 shows a potential divider connected to a battery with e.m.f. 9.0 V and negligible internal resistance.

The resistors have resistances of R_1 = 330 Ω and R_2 = 470 Ω.

What is the p.d. across R_1, measured in V? *(1 mark)*

A 3.7 V

B 5.3 V

C 6.3 V

D 15 V

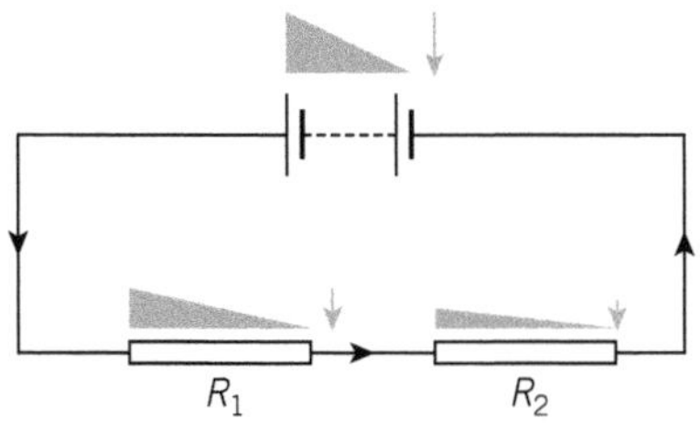

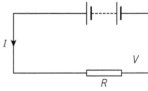

▲ **Figure 2**

3 A metal wire has diameter 1.0 mm and length 60 cm. The metal has conductivity 1.2×10^6 S m^{-1}.

What is the resistance of the wire? *(1 mark)*

A 0.16 Ω

B 0.64 Ω

C 1.6 Ω

D 6.3 Ω

4 A battery of e.m.f. 6.0 V is connected to an external resistor *R* as shown in Figure 3.

The values of current *I* for two different values of *R* are given in Table 1.

▼ **Table 1**

I / A	*R* / Ω
2.4	1.0
1.3	2.0

▲ **Figure 3**

What are the values of e.m.f. and internal resistance of the battery? *(1 mark)*

A ε = 2.6 V, r = 0.16 Ω

B ε = 2.6 V, r = 0.20 Ω

C ε = 2.8 V, r = 0.16 Ω

D ε = 2.8 V, r = 0.20 Ω

5 The tube in an X-ray generator produces an electron beam carrying a current of 5.0 mA across a p.d. of 12 kV onto a metal anode.

a Calculate the number of electrons delivered to the anode each minute. *(2 marks)*

b Calculate the energy delivered to the anode in this time. *(2 marks)*

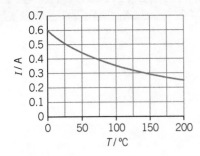

▲ **Figure 4**

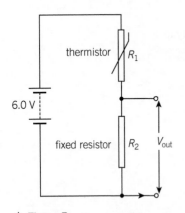

▲ **Figure 5**

6 The graph in Figure 4 shows the current at different temperatures though a metal wire connected to a 6.0 V battery of negligible internal resistance.

The metal wire is now joined in series with the same battery and a fixed resistor of resistance 22 Ω.

Calculate the p.d. across the wire when it has a temperature of 50 °C.

(4 marks)

7 A mains extension cable consists of a coil which measures 25 m long when fully unrolled. The live and neutral conductors in the cable each consist of a bundle of 10 copper wires, with each wire having a mean diameter 0.64 mm.

Copper has a resistivity $\rho = 1.6 \times 10^{-8}\,\Omega\,\text{m}$.

a Show that the combined resistance of the live and neutral conductors in the cable is about $\frac{1}{4}\Omega$. *(2 marks)*

b The cable is used to power a 230 V, 2.0 kW heater. Explain why it is a reasonable approximation to state that the current in the cable $= \left(\dfrac{2000\,\text{W}}{230\,\text{V}}\right)$. *(2 marks)*

c Calculate the power dissipated in the cable when it is used to power this heater and explain why the instructions on the cable recommend that the cable should be fully unrolled in use. *(2 marks)*

8 The circuit shown in Figure 5 is used as a temperature sensor.

The fixed resistor has resistance $R_2 = 10\,\text{k}\Omega$ and the resistance R_1 of the thermistor varies with temperature θ as shown by the data in Table 2.

▼ **Table 2**

$\theta/\,^\circ\text{C}$	0	20	40	60	80	100
$R_1/\,\text{k}\Omega$	33	12	5.1	2.5	1.3	0.82

a Plot a graph of the output voltage V_{out} (y-axis) against temperature θ (x-axis) and use the graph to determine the temperature of the thermistor when the output voltage $V_{\text{out}} = 4.5\,\text{V}$ *(4 marks)*

b Calculate the mean sensitivity of the sensor circuit over the range 50 °C to 60 °C. *(2 marks)*

c State, with an explanation, whether the sensor is better as a thermostat for a bedroom or as a sensor to switching off a kettle. *(2 marks)*

4

TESTING MATERIALS
4.1 Describing materials
Specification references: 3.2 a(iii), 3.2 b(i).

In everyday life, materials are described using a variety of terms; for example, you might describe glass as brittle and describe the material used for toothpaste tubes as tough. In physics such terms have precise meanings and physicists use them to describe the differences in the mechanical properties of materials. This chapter is about describing the mechanical properties of materials. Chapter 5 considers how the microscopic structure of materials affects their properties.

Three classes of materials

The materials you will consider in this course can be placed into three classes: ceramics, metals, and polymers.

- **Ceramics** are hard, stiff, and brittle. Examples of ceramics include pottery and modern engineering ceramics such as silicon carbide.

- **Metals** have a wide range of properties. Some metals are ductile, others are brittle. Pure metals can often be hammered or bent into shape whilst metal alloys are often harder.

- **Polymers** include synthetic materials such as polythene as well as natural materials such as leather. *Glassy polymers* (e.g. Perspex) have properties similar to glass and are brittle and relatively hard. These materials can replace glass for some uses such as spectacle lenses. *Semi-crystalline polymers* are tougher than glassy polymers. PET (polyethylene terephthalate) is a semi-crystalline polymer which is used in 'plastic' bottles and, under the name 'polyester', is used in many textiles.

Key terms

Stiff: A stiff material has a small extension per unit force. The Young modulus indicates the stiffness of a material.

Tough: A tough material does not break by snapping cleanly. Tough materials are resistant to the propagation of cracks and absorb energy when deformed.

Brittle: A brittle material will break by snapping cleanly. It undergoes little or no plastic deformation before fracture.

Hard: A hard material is difficult to dent or scratch.

Ductile: A ductile material can be drawn into wires.

Common misconception: Confusing brittleness and weakness

Brittle does not mean *weak*. Some metals, such as cast iron used in cookware, will fracture cleanly. This is an example of brittle behaviour but these metals are not weak. Glass is brittle but it is not a weak material. The brittleness of glass is not the reason why wine glasses are easy to break. Wine glasses break easily because they are thin.

Revision tip

Make sure that you can recall an example of a metal, a polymer, and a ceramic, the properties of each material and an example of each material in use.

Summary questions

1 Give an example of a polymer used in everyday life. Describe how its mechanical properties make it suitable for the use you have chosen.
(5 marks)

2 Why is it incorrect to say that glass shatters easily because it is brittle?
(2 marks)

3 Explain why transparent semi-crystalline polymers are used to make bottles but not used for spectacle lenses. You may consider the look and feel of the material as well as its mechanical properties in your answer.
(4 marks)

4.2 Stretching wires and springs

Specification references: 3.2 a(i), 3.2 b(i), 3.2 b(ii), 3.2 c(i), 3.2 d(i)

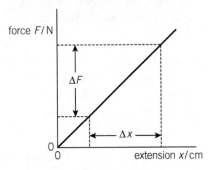

▲ **Figure 1** *A graph showing the relationship F = kx*

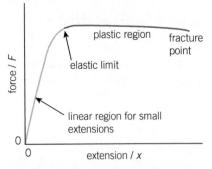

▲ **Figure 2** *The variation of force with extension up to fracture*

If you have ever 'flicked' a rubber band you have performed a simple demonstration of the energy stored in an elastic material when it is deformed (stretched or compressed). A more formal approach to the stretching of materials began with the work of Robert Hooke in the 17th century.

Hooke's law

For small extensions, the force F on the end of a wire or spring is proportional to the extension x.

> **Common misconception: Confusing extension and length**
>
> Hooke's law states that the force is proportional to the *extension* of the specimen not to the length of the specimen.

This proportional relationship can be given as $F = kx$ where the constant of proportionality, k, is known as the spring or force constant. The units of k are $\mathrm{N\,m^{-1}}$. The force constant can be found from the gradient $\Delta F/\Delta x$ of a force–extension graph as shown in Figure 1.

Elastic and plastic deformation

Hooke's law only applies to small extensions or compressions. The graph in Figure 2 shows how force varies with extension beyond the proportional (Hooke's law) section of the graph.

The first part of the graph is the elastic region. When the extension goes beyond the elastic limit the specimen begins to deform plastically. The gradient of the graph decreases, showing that the wire is less stiff in the plastic region.

> **Common misconception: Elastic limit and proportionality**
>
> Although the graph of force against extension is linear for most of the elastic region, for some specimens it curves off a little before plastic deformation begins. The elastic limit does not always coincide with the end of proportional behaviour.

 Practical: Plotting a force–extension graph for a rubber band

- Measure the unstretched length of the band.
- Add a known mass to the bottom of the band (e.g., 100 g).
- Measure the new length of the band.
- Calculate and record the extension (= extended length – original length) and the deforming force (weight).
- Repeat this process with further masses.
- The measurements can be repeated as masses are removed and a graph of force (weight) against extension can be plotted.

Force–extension data for springs and wires can be obtained in a similar manner.

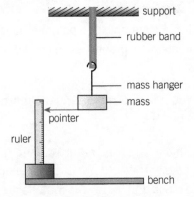

▲ **Figure 3** *Experimental set-up*

Energy stored in a spring

The energy stored in an elastically stretched spring is given by the equation:

$$E = \frac{1}{2}Fx$$

where F is the force extending the spring and x is the extension.

As $F = kx$, you can write:

$$E = \frac{1}{2}kx^2$$

Figure 4 shows that the area under the line of a force–extension graph gives the energy stored.

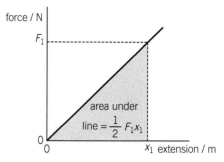

▲ **Figure 4** *Energy stored in a stretched spring* $= \frac{1}{2}kx^2$

Model answers: The energy stored in an extended spring

A spring has an unstretched length of 8.0 cm. The spring extends to a length of 10.2 cm when a 100 g mass (weight 0.98 N) is hung from it. When a second 100 g mass is added the length extends to 12.4 cm.

a Is it reasonable to state that the spring follows Hooke's law over the range of measurements given? Explain your answer.

b Calculate the energy stored in the spring when its length is 12.4 cm.

c Assuming that the spring remains elastic, how much energy will be stored when the spring is stretched to a length of 16.8 cm?

a If the spring follows Hooke's law the load will be proportional to the extension.
The extension for a load of 0.98 N = 10.2 cm – 8.0 cm = 2.2 cm
At a load of 1.96 N the extension = 12.4 cm – 8.0 cm = 4.4 cm
Doubling the load has doubled the extension. Therefore, load is proportional to extension and Hooke's law is followed.

> The candidate has organised the answer carefully. Firstly, Hooke's law is clearly stated. The extensions for the different loads are calculated clearly and correctly and the conclusion is linked back to the original statement of Hooke's law.

b Energy stored $= \frac{1}{2}Fx = \frac{1}{2} \times 1.96\,\text{N}\ 0.044\,\text{m} = 0.043\,\text{J}$

> This is a straightforward calculation but it is still possible to lose marks through not converting cm into m. This candidate has written the units in the working which helps to avoid such errors.

c Energy stored is proportional to extension^2. Doubling the extension will increase the energy stored by a factor of two^2 = four so energy stored = 4 × 0.043 J = 0.172 J (2 s.f.)

> The candidate reached the correct answer through knowledge of the relationship between energy stored and extension. The answer can also be reached by using $E = \frac{1}{2}Fx$ where $F = 3.92\,\text{N}$ and $x = 0.088\,\text{m}$

Revision tip

The value of the force constant is a measure of the stiffness of a particular specimen, not a material. Wires made of the same steel will have different force constants if they have different dimensions.

Key terms

Elastic (deformation): A specimen that has deformed elastically will return to its original dimensions when the deforming force is removed.

Plastic (deformation): A specimen that has deformed plastically will have permanent deformation when the deforming force is removed.

Fracture: An object fractures when it breaks into two or more pieces.

Summary questions

1 An elastic spring has a force constant of $40\,\text{N}\,\text{m}^{-1}$. Calculate the force required to stretch the spring from a length of 12.0 cm to 14.5 cm.

(2 marks)

2 **a** Figure 5 is a graph showing the extension of a spring as masses are added to it. How does the graph show that the spring follows Hooke's law? *(2 marks)*

b Use the graph to calculate the energy stored in the spring at an extension of 0.06 m. *(2 marks)*

c Copy the graph and draw a second line showing the extension of a spring which is half as stiff as the original spring and begins to behave plastically at an extension of 0.06 m *(2 marks)*

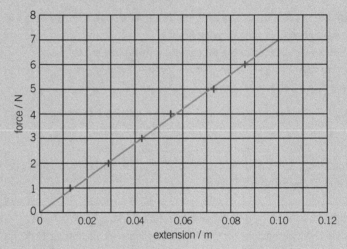

▲ Figure 5

3 The separation between the floor of a car and the ground reduces by about 0.5 cm when the 640 N driver gets into the car. Assume that the suspension of the car consists of a spring for each wheel and that the force constant of each of the springs is the same.

a Calculate the force constant of a single spring. *(2 marks)*

b The floor of the car lowers by a total of 1.5 cm when carrying the driver and three passengers. Calculate the weight of the passengers. *(2 marks)*

4.3 Stress, strain, and the Young modulus

Specification references: 3.2 a (iv), 3.2 b(i), 3.2 b(ii), 3.2 c(ii), 3.2 d(ii).

This topic is about the mechanical properties of materials rather than the properties of particular specimens of materials. For example, you could consider the stiffness of a particular metal (say, stainless steel) rather than the stiffness of a given stainless steel knife or needle. To make a fair comparison between the stiffness of one material and another, physicists use the concepts of stress, strain, and the Young modulus.

Stress

The stress on a specimen can be found from the equation:

$$\text{stress } \sigma \text{ (N m}^{-2} \text{ or Pa)} = \frac{\text{force } F \text{ (N)}}{\text{cross-sectional area } A \text{ (m}^2)}$$

Worked example: Stress

A wire of diameter 0.74 mm fractures under a tensile (stretching) force of 184 N. Calculate the fracture stress.

Step 1: Select the correct equation: $\sigma = \dfrac{F}{A} = \dfrac{F}{\pi r^2}$

Step 2: Substitute and evaluate. Note that the radius in metres = 7.4×10^{-4} m ÷ 2
$$= 3.7 \times 10^{-4} \text{ m}$$

$$\sigma = \frac{184 \text{ N}}{\pi \times (3.7 \times 10^{-4} \text{ m})^2} = 4.3 \times 10^8 \text{ N m}^{-2} \text{ or Pa.}$$

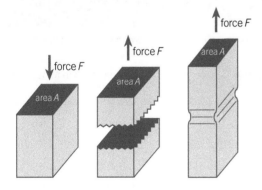

stress is force per unit area | breaking stress is the stress which breaks a material | yield stress is the stress which causes a material to yield

common units of stress:
   MN m^{-2} (meganewton per square metre)
   or MPa (megapascal)

The units of stress are the same as the units of pressure, pascal. One pascal (1 Pa) is 1 newton per square metre.

Useful rule of thumb – a mass of 1 kg weighs about 10 N on the Earth's surface.

▲ **Figure 1** *Force and stress*

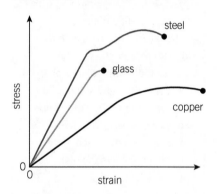

▲ **Figure 2** *Stress–strain curves for steel, glass, and copper*

Strain

The strain of a specimen can be found from the equation:

$$\text{strain } \varepsilon = \frac{\text{extension } x}{\text{original length } L}$$

 Worked example: Strain

A wire of length 2.300 m extends to a length of 2.307 m. Calculate the strain of wire.

Step 1: Select the correct equation: $\varepsilon = \dfrac{x}{L}$

Step 2: Calculate extension: $x = 2.307\,m - 2.300\,m = 0.007\,m$

Step 3: Substitute and evaluate: $\varepsilon = \dfrac{0.007\,m}{2.300\,m} = 0.003043$ (4 s.f.) or 0.3043%

Note that the strain is given to the same number of significant figures as the original data.

Stress–strain graphs

Stress–strain graphs show the behaviour of a material under stress. Brittle materials such as glass show little plastic deformation. Stress–strain graphs of brittle materials are linear for most of their length. Metals such as steel and copper undergo plastic deformation before fracturing.

The Young modulus

The Young modulus E is a measure of the stiffness of a material:

$$E = \frac{\text{stress}}{\text{strain}} = \frac{\sigma}{\varepsilon} = \frac{F/A}{x/L} = \frac{FL}{xA}$$

The Young modulus is often a very large number.

 Worked example: Young modulus

A wire has a diameter of 1.00 mm. When a load of 150 N is applied, the wire extends from a length of 1.800 m to 1.802 mm. Calculate the Young modulus of the wire, giving your answer to a suitable number of significant figures.

Step 1: Arrange the data given in a suitable form.

radius of wire $= 1.00 \times 10^{-3}\,m \div 2 = 5.00 \times 10^{-4}\,m$

original length $= 1.800\,m$

force $= 150\,N$

extension $= 1.802\,m - 1.800\,m = 2 \times 10^{-3}\,m$

Note that the smallest number of significant figures in the original data is three, so the answer should be given to three significant figures.

Step 2: Choose correct equation.

$$E = \frac{F/A}{x/L} = \frac{FL}{xA} = \frac{FL}{x\pi r^2}$$

Step 3: Substitute and evaluate.

$$E = \frac{150\,N \times 1.800\,m}{2 \times 10^{-3}\,m \times \pi \times (500 \times 10^{-4}\,m)^2} = 1.72\ 10^{11}\,N\,m^{-2}\ (172\,GPa)$$

Practical: Determining the Young modulus and fracture stress of a metal

- Figure 3 shows a typical experimental set-up. Although this method is simple, great care is needed with the measurements.
- The uncertainty of the calculated value of the Young modulus can be estimated from the largest source of uncertainty in the measurements.
- The diameter and original length of the wire are measured.
- The extension of the wire is measured as more masses are added. This process can be continued until the wire breaks. This will allow the fracture stress to be calculated.
- Stress and strain values are calculated from the data and a stress (y-axis) against strain (x-axis) graph is drawn.
- The gradient of the linear region of the graph gives the Young modulus of the material.

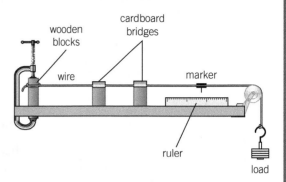

▲ **Figure 3** *Experimental set-up for determining the Young modulus of a wire*

Summary questions

1 Look at the stress–strain curves in Figure 2.
   a Which material has the stiffest region? Give a reason for your choice. *(1 mark)*
   b Which material is the strongest? *(1 mark)*
   c Glass is brittle. How is that demonstrated by the graph? *(1 mark)*
2 A thread of diameter 0.8 mm breaks at a stress of 3.4 GPa. Calculate the maximum load the thread can support. *(2 marks)*

3 A wire of original length 2.0 m is made from a material with a Young modulus of 2.1×10^{11} Pa. The wire is suspended vertically. A load of 52 N is hung from the wire. The wire extends by 1.4 mm. Calculate the diameter of the wire. *(3 marks)*
4 Wire A and wire B are made from the same material. They are suspended vertically and the same load F is hung from each wire. Wire A has diameter d and original length L. Wire B has diameter $3d$ and original length $3L$.
   What is the ratio $\dfrac{\text{extension of wire A}}{\text{extension of wire B}}$? *(2 marks)*

5 The area under the line of a force–extension graph for an elastic material represents the energy stored. Explain why the units for the area under the line of a stress–strain graph for an elastic material suggest that the area represents the energy stored per unit volume. *(2 marks)*
6 A student performs an experiment to determine the Young modulus of a wire using the method shown in Figure 3.
   Initial data: original length of wire = 3.000 m ± 0.002 m, diameter of wire = 0.800 mm ± 0.01 mm
   a Calculate the percentage uncertainty in the diameter. *(1 mark)*
   b Calculate the cross-sectional area of the wire. Include an estimate of the uncertainty, explaining your reasoning. *(3 marks)*
   c When a weight of 49 N was added to the wire, the student measured the extension as 2.0 mm ± 0.5 mm. Calculate an estimate of the Young modulus of the wire material. Include an estimation of the uncertainty in your value, explaining your reasoning. *(4 marks)*

4.4 Choosing materials

Specification references: 3.2 b(i), 3.2 b(iii)

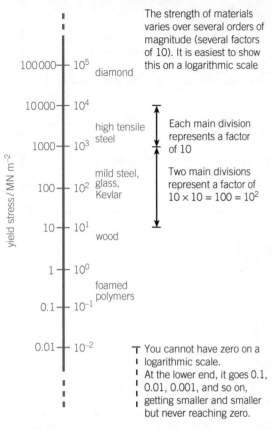

▲ Figure 1 *Logarithmic scale of stress*

Logarithmic charts

Logarithmic scales are used to allow a large range of values to be plotted. Figure 1 shows a chart of yield stress for different materials. A few minutes studying this and ensuring you know how to interpret such charts will be time well spent.

Materials selection charts

When choosing a material for a given situation, many factors are taken into account including cost (financial considerations) and the look of the material (aesthetic considerations). Materials selection charts compare different properties of materials and provide an easy and powerful way of displaying the variation in properties. Figure 2 shows the Young modulus plotted against density ρ (= mass per unit volume, units $kg\,m^{-3}$) for different materials.

Imagine you are designing an aircraft. You want the body to be stiff but not too dense. A chart such as Figure 2 would be a good place to begin your thinking about the materials to choose.

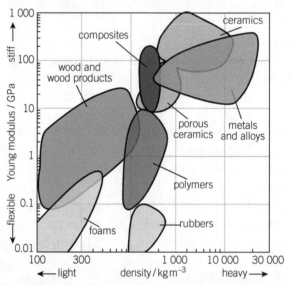

▲ Figure 2 *Young modulus and density values for different classes of materials*

> **Key term**
>
> **Tension:** An object is in tension when two forces act on it in opposite directions to make the object stretch along the line of action of the forces. Forces producing tension are often called tensile forces.

Summary questions

1 Explain how Figure 2 shows that the stiffest polymer is more than 100 times as stiff as the most flexible polymer. *(2 marks)*

2 The density of water is 1000 kg m⁻³. A body will float on a liquid if it is less dense than the liquid. Use Figure 2 to answer the following questions, explaining your reasoning.
   a Is it possible for wood to float on a foam? *(1 mark)*
   b Can any metals float on water and can any woods sink? *(2 marks)*

3 The tensile strength (breaking stress) of a particular grade of steel is 1.65 GPa. Spider silk has a tensile strength of about 1.3 GPa.
   a A 'human spider' requires a steel thread of diameter 0.7 mm to support her weight. What diameter of spider silk would be required? *(3 marks)*
   b The density of steel is about 8000 kg m⁻³. Spider silk has a density of around 1300 kg m⁻³. Show that a spider thread can support about five times the load that a steel thread of the same mass and length can support. *(3 marks)*

LOOKING INSIDE MATERIALS
5.1 Materials under the microscope

Specification reference: 3.2 a (ii)

Chapter 4 considered some of the mechanical properties of materials. This chapter looks at the microscopic structure of materials and uses our knowledge of microscopic structure to explain the macroscopic (large scale) properties such as elasticity and plasticity. This topic concentrates on some methods for estimating the size of atoms and molecules.

Rayleigh's oil drop experiment

Atoms cannot be seen with the naked eye so what evidence is there for their existence?

At the end of the 19th century, Lord Rayleigh performed a simple experiment that still bears his name. He developed a method of measuring the thickness of a film of oil floating on water. If the oil spreads out as far as possible the thickness of the layer will be equal to the length of one molecule.

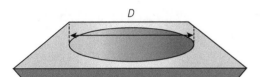

▲ **Figure 1** *Rayleigh's oil drop experiment*

The basic method of the measurement is as follows:

● Measure the diameter d and calculate the radius r of the oil drop.

● Place the drop on still water which has a layer of powder floating on it. The drop will push the powder back as it spreads.

● Measure the diameter of the patch of oil D after it has spread, and use this value to calculate the radius R of the patch.

● volume of the oil patch = volume of oil drop

● Therefore: $\pi R^2 h = \frac{4}{3}\pi r^3$ where h is the height of the oil patch

● Therefore: $h = \frac{4r^3}{3R^2}$

Order of magnitude estimate of the size of an atom

The volume occupied by a single atom of an element can be calculated from the mass of one atom and the density of the element.

$$\text{number of atoms (m}^{-3}) = \frac{\text{density of element (kg m}^{-3})}{\text{mass of atom (kg)}}$$

$$\text{volume of single atom (m}^3) = \frac{1}{\text{number of atoms (m}^{-3})}$$

$$= \frac{\text{mass of atom (kg)}}{\text{density of element (kg m}^{-3})}$$

Revision tip

The largest source of percentage uncertainty in this experiment is the measurement of the diameter of the oil drop. As this measurement determines the uncertainty in radius r, the uncertainty in the value of r^3 is considerable.

Revision tip: Order of magnitude

An order magnitude value is a value to the nearest power of ten.

Revision tip: Order of magnitude

It is useful to remember that the diameter of an atom is of the order of 10^{-10} m.

▲ **Figure 2** *STM image of gold atoms on a graphite surface*

The order of magnitude estimate of the diameter of an atom d can be found by assuming that each atom occupies a cube of length d:

order of magnitude size of atom $d = \sqrt[3]{\text{volume of single atom (m}^3\text{)}}$

$$= \sqrt[3]{\frac{\text{mass of atom (kg)}}{\text{density of element (kgm}^{-3}\text{)}}}$$

Images of atoms

Images from scanning tunnelling microscopes (STM) and atomic force microscopes (ATM) can resolve individual atoms on the surface of materials and allow atomic diameters to be measured.

Figure 2 shows an STM image of gold atoms on a surface of graphite. The matrix of circles shows individual carbon atoms. There are about ten atoms along the front edge which is 1×10^{-9} m in length. This shows an individual atom has a diameter of an order of magnitude of 10^{-10} m.

Summary questions

1. A copper wire has a diameter of 0.75 mm. Make an order of magnitude estimate of the number of copper atoms in a length of 0.75 mm. Order of magnitude diameter of a copper atom = 10^{-10} m. *(2 marks)*

2. The mass of a lead atom is 3.44×10^{-25} kg. The density of lead is 11 300 kg m^{-3}. Calculate an order of magnitude estimate for the diameter of a lead atom. *(2 marks)*

3. **a** An oil drop of diameter d spreads out on water to form an approximately circular patch of diameter D and height h. Use the equations for the volume of a sphere and the volume of a cylinder to show that the height of the oil patch is given by
$h = \dfrac{4r^3}{3R^2}$ *(1 mark)*

   b A student performs the oil drop experiment (Figure 1). She measures the diameter of the drop d as 1.0 mm and the diameter of the oil patch D as 30 cm. Use these values to calculate an order magnitude estimate for the height of the oil patch. State the two major sources of uncertainty in the experiment and explain why the results of this experiment should only be stated to the nearest order of magnitude. *(6 marks)*

5.2 Modelling material behaviour

Specification references: 3.2 a (iii), 3.2 b (i), 3.2 b (iv)

Metal structure and ductility

- Metals are crystalline – individual particles are arranged in a regular pattern over distances many times the spacing between the particles.
- Malleability and ductility are consequences of plastic behaviour which is explained by the movement of dislocations within the crystalline structure.
- Dislocations are mismatches in the regular rows of atoms – missing atoms in an otherwise orderly arrangement.

Figure 1 shows how a mobile dislocation moving through the metal structure allows layers to move one atom at a time. This reduces the energy needed to deform the metal and allows metals such as gold to be hammered into shape.

Atoms in gold are in a regular array: a crystal lattice. To shape the metal, one layer must be made to slide over another.

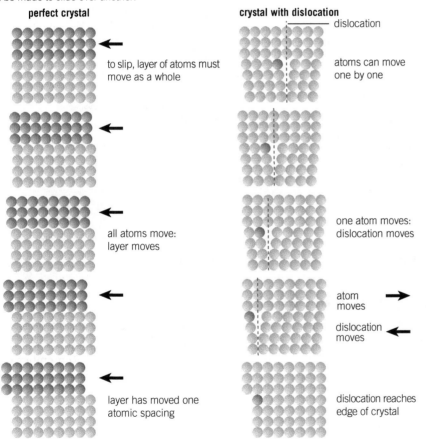

Revision tip

Spend a little time studying Figure 1 to visualise what is happening. The single darker atom in the crystal with a dislocation is the atom which is about to move.

in both examples a layer has slipped by one atomic spacing

Wrong model:

Making all the atoms slip together needs considerable energy.
This model predicts metals to be 1000 times as strong as they actually are.

Better model:

One atom slipping at a time needs much less energy.

The dislocation model predicts the strength of metals much better.

▲ **Figure 1** *Slipping of particles in metals*

Alloying

Metal alloys tend to be less ductile than pure metals. Alloys are formed by the addition of other metallic elements (or non-metals, such as carbon in steels) that usually have different sized atoms. These 'pin' the dislocations in the metals making movement of the layers more difficult.

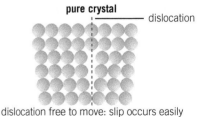

dislocation free to move: slip occurs easily move as a whole

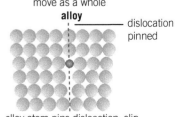

alloy atom pins dislocation: slip is more difficult

▲ **Figure 2** *Particles in metals and metal alloys*

▲ **Figure 3** *Polycrystalline structure of brass (an alloy of copper and zinc) showing grain boundaries*

Amorphous, crystalline, and polycrystalline materials

When a liquid cools, a solid forms. The internal structure of the solid can be crystalline (like a metal) or amorphous (disordered). Many solids are neither purely crystalline nor purely amorphous. These are 'polycrystalline'. These consist of grains arranged in a random fashion but with regular structure within each grain.

Fracture in brittle materials

Tiny cracks in the structure of a material lead to stress concentrations. As one bond breaks, the stress is transferred to the next, allowing cracks to propagate through a specimen until it fractures. In this manner, tiny cracks and scratches can considerably weaken specimens. This has great importance in engineering.

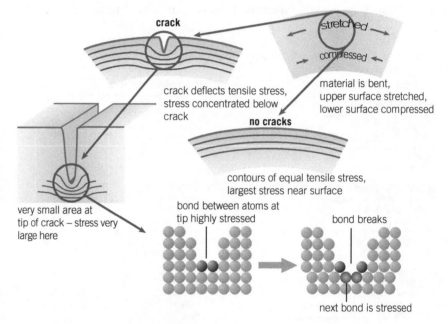

▲ **Figure 4** *Cracks propagate through materials under stress*

Summary questions

1   Describe the differences between a crystalline and a polycrystalline material.
    (2 marks)

2   Explain why a scratch on the surface of a glass rod can make it easier to break.   *(3 marks)*

3   Explain why bricks can be used safely in buildings even though brick is a brittle material of low tensile strength.*(3 marks)*

Toughness in metals

Toughness is a measure of the energy required to extend cracks through a material. When a stress is applied to a crack in a metal the material deforms around the crack. This widens the crack, reducing the stress. Remember that toughness is not the same as strength. In the same way, brittleness is not the same as weakness.

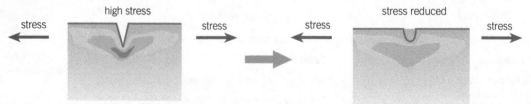

Metals resist cracking because they are ductile. Under stress, cracks are broadened and blunted – they do not propagate.

▲ **Figure 5** *Stopping cracks in metals*

5.3 Microscopic structures and macroscopic properties

Specification references: 3.2 a (iii)

'Microscopic structure' means structure that is too small to see with the unaided eye. 'Macroscopic' implies properties that are detectable without using sophisticated equipment. So the ordered pattern of atoms in a crystalline metal is a description of microscopic structure whereas the toughness (or otherwise) of the metal is an example of a macroscopic property.

Bonding in ceramics and in metals

The macroscopic properties of a material are affected by the bonding between the particles in the material.

There are three types of bonds between atoms: covalent, ionic, and metallic. Unlike metallic bonds, the bonds in ceramics and ionic compounds are directional. This means that the atoms are locked in place, making ceramics hard and brittle.

Ceramics have rigid structures

Covalent structures, for example, silica, diamond, and carborundum

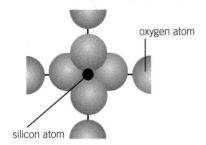

oxygen atom

silicon atom

Atoms share electrons with neighbouring atoms to form covalent bonds. These bonds are directional – they lock atoms in place, like scaffolding.

The bonds are strong – silica is stiff. The atoms cannot slip – silica is hard and brittle.

Metals have non-directional bonds

Metallic structures, for example, gold

negative electron 'glue'

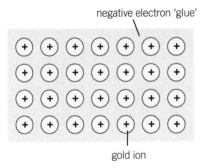

gold ion

Atoms in metals are ionised. The free electrons move between the ions. The negative charge of the electrons 'glues' the ions together, but the ions can easily change places.

The bonds are strong – metals are stiff.

The ions can slip – metals are ductile and tough.

▲ **Figure 1** *Microscopic diagram of ceramics and metals*

Elastic behaviour in metals and polymers

Elasticity is an example of a macroscopic property that can be explained with reference to the microscopic structure of the material. Metals are typically elastic up to strains of about 0.1%. Up to this point the extension is explained by the increasing spacing between the positive ions in the metal. When the tensile force is removed the metal returns to its original length as the spacing between the ions returns to the original value. This is shown in Figure 2.

> **Revision tip**
> Remember that metallic bonds and covalent bonds are both strong but covalent bonds are also directional.

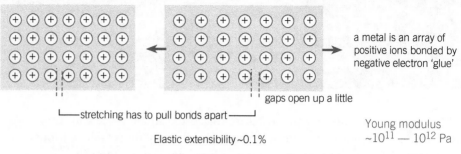

a metal is an array of positive ions bonded by negative electron 'glue'

gaps open up a little

└─────stretching has to pull bonds apart─────┘

Elastic extensibility ~0.1%

Young modulus ~10^{11} — 10^{12} Pa

▲ **Figure 2** *Stretching a metal pulls bonds apart*

Polymers such as polythene are long-chained molecules that can extend elastically up to strains of around 1%. This behaviour is explained by the bonds rotating under the action of a tensile force, increasing the length of the specimen. Polymers can 'untangle'. Polythene is 'floppy' because of bond rotation but the bonds themselves are strong and are difficult to break. (See Figure 3.) Up to about 1% strains, the chains tangle up once again when the deforming force is removed. This is shown macroscopically by the specimen returning to its original dimensions.

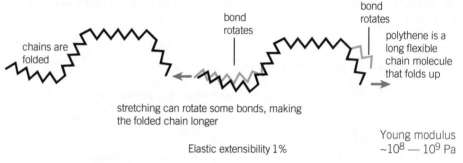

bond rotates

bond rotates

chains are folded

polythene is a long flexible chain molecule that folds up

stretching can rotate some bonds, making the folded chain longer

Elastic extensibility 1%

Young modulus ~10^8 — 10^9 Pa

▲ **Figure 3** *Stretching polythene rotates bonds*

Designing polymers

Polymers can be stiff if the rotation of the chains of molecules is difficult. Adding cross-linkages produces a stiffer material.

Polystyrene has benzene rings sticking out sideways, which make chain rotations difficult.

Young modulus ~10^9 — 10^{10} Pa

Bakelite has extensively cross-linked chains. The cross-links stop the chains from unfolding.

Young modulus ~10^{10} Pa

▲ **Figure 4** *Reducing chain rotation in polystyrene and Bakelite*

For example, when natural rubber is heated with sulfur, cross-linkages between polymer chains are formed by the sulfur atoms, stiffening the material.

Summary questions

1 There are three types of strong bond between atoms: metallic, ionic, and covalent. Which type of bonding is found in polymers? Which type of bonding is non-directional?   (*2 marks*)

2 Describe metallic bonding and use your description to explain elasticity in metals.   (*4 marks*)

3 A piece of rubber 6 cm long cut from a rubber band extends elastically to a length of 8 cm when supporting a small load. Bonds between atoms typically break when the distance between atoms is increased by 1%. Show that the extension of the rubber cannot be simply due to the stretching of the bonds between atoms and suggest an alternative explanation.   (*2 marks*)

Chapter 4 and 5 Practice questions

1 A wire has a breaking stress of z Pa. What is the breaking stress of a wire made from the same material which is twice as long and of half the diameter of the initial wire?

   A $\dfrac{z}{4}$ **B** $\dfrac{z}{2}$ **C** z **D** $2z$ *(1 mark)*

2 Which of the following terms does not apply to a ceramic material?
   A brittle   **B** hard   **C** strong   **D** tough   *(1 mark)*

3 Copper has a density of $8960\,\text{kg m}^{-3}$. The mass of a copper atom is $1.068 \times 10^{-25}\,\text{kg}$.

   a Estimate, by calculation, the diameter of a copper atom. Show your working and analysis clearly.   *(3 marks)*

   b When a dislocation moves through a crystalline material such as copper the planes of atoms move across each other by one atomic spacing. Use your answer to **a** to calculate the number of dislocations that have occurred when a sample of copper is permanently deformed by 2 mm.   *(2 marks)*

4 The energy stored in a stretched wire is given by the equation $E = \frac{1}{2}Fx$ where F is the tensile force on the wire and x is the extension.

   a Consider a wire of length L and cross-sectional area A. Use the equation $E = \frac{1}{2}Fx$ to show that the energy stored per unit volume is given by $\frac{1}{2}\,stress \times strain$.   *(2 marks)*

   b Show that the units J m^{-3} are equivalent to Pa.   *(1 mark)*

   c A wire of original length 1.2 m and diameter 1.5 mm is extended elastically by a force of 250 N. The Young modulus E of the wire is $1.8 \times 10^{11}\,\text{Pa}$.

      Calculate the energy stored per m^3 in the stretched wire.   *(3 marks)*

5 Figure 1 shows a graph of force against extension for a wire of original length 2.0 m and diameter 0.4 mm.

   a Calculate the energy stored when the wire is extended by 1.5 mm.   *(2 marks)*

   b Use data from the graph to find the Young modulus of the material.   *(2 marks)*

   c The yield stress of the wire is $3.7 \times 10^8\,\text{N m}^{-2}$. Calculate the force required to make the wire yield.   *(2 marks)*

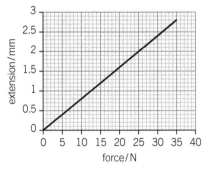

▲ **Figure 1**

6 Figure 2 shows a representation of the microscopic structure of pure iron and a steel alloy. Describe and explain the effect alloying has on the mechanical properties of the alloy. You should explain any technical terms you use in your answer.   *(6 marks)*

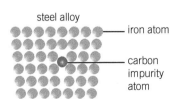

▲ **Figure 2**

7 The microscopic structure of polythene has long chain molecules with bonds that can rotate easily. Polystyrene also has long chain molecules but these have side rings branching from them, making rotation more difficult. Describe and explain the differences you would expect in macroscopic properties of these materials. *(4 marks)*

8 Here are some data about a cable used to support a lift in a building:

Length of cable: 75 m

Weight of lift: 4200 N

Maximum passenger load: 5200 N

Young modulus of the steel: 2.0×10^{11} N m^{-2}

Yield stress of the steel: 5.8×10^8 N m^{-2}

a What is meant by the term *yield stress*? *(1 mark)*

b Calculate the extension of the cable when the steel begins to yield. *(3 marks)*

c Three students are discussing whether the diameter of the cable would need to be changed if the same lift was to be used in a building requiring a cable length of 150 m. Paul suggests that the cable would have to have a diameter increased by a factor of $\sqrt{2}$, Ameena suggests that the cross-sectional area would not need to be changed and Jack suggests that they are both wrong and that the answer lies somewhere in between.

Who is correct? Explain your reasoning and suggest the reason for Paul's suggestion of a diameter increase of a factor of $\sqrt{2}$. *(6 marks)*

9 Here are some data about a steel cable and a nylon cable:

Young modulus of steel: 2.0×10^{11} N m^{-2}

Young modulus of nylon: 7.0×10^7 N m^{-2}

Cross-sectional area of steel: 1×10^{-5} m^2

Cross-sectional area of nylon: 5×10^{-4} m^2

Length of each cable = 15.0 m

a Calculate the extension of each cable when a force of 1500 N is applied. *(2 marks)*

b Calculate the energy stored in each cable when a force of 1500 N is applied. *(2 marks)*

c Suggest and explain why steel cables are used for supporting suspension bridges and why nylon ropes can be used as climbing ropes. *(4 marks)*

10 This question is about estimating the length of an oil molecule. A drop of oil of diameter 0.5 mm spreads into a disc of average diameter 0.20 m.

a Calculate the height of the disc of oil. *(2 marks)*

b State why your value for the height of the disc gives an estimate of the maximum length of an oil molecule. *(1 mark)*

c A low-power microscope was used to measure the diameter of the oil drop. The uncertainty in the reading was estimated at ±0.1 mm. The uncertainty in the diameter of the disc of oil was ±0.04 m as the disc was not a perfect circle. Show that the maximum calculated value for the height of the disc is more than seven times that of the lowest calculated value. *(3 marks)*

11 The diameter of a typical human hair is about 5×10^{-5} m. A hair is found to break at a tensile force of 0.58 N.

a Calculate the breaking stress of the hair. *(2 marks)*

b How many hairs would it take to support the weight of a 75 kg person? *(2 marks)*

6
WAVE BEHAVIOUR
6.1 Superposition of waves
Specification references: 4.1 a (i), 4.1 b(i), 4.1 c(i), 4.1 d(i), 4.1 d(iii), 4.1 d(v)

Superposition

When two water waves pass through each other you will notice, if you look carefully, that the height of the wave becomes bigger as the two wave crests overlap. This is an example of superposition. The principle of superposition is incredibly simple but has great explanatory power in a wide range of contexts from describing how musical instruments work to explaining the shimmering iridescence of a beetle to understanding the nature of atoms.

Describing waves

Practical: Measuring frequency using an oscilloscope

- An oscilloscope displays potential difference (y-axis) against time (x-axis).
- The time base of the oscilloscope shows the time interval represented by one centimetre on the screen. This can be changed.
- When a stable frequency source (such as a frequency generator) is connected to the signal generator, a display similar to that shown in Figure 1 can be obtained. A value for the time period of the oscillation can be determined by measuring the peak-to-peak distance x and multiplying this value in centimetres by the time base setting.

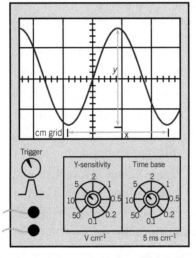

▲ **Figure 1** *Using an oscilloscope*

- Frequency is obtained from $f = \dfrac{1}{T}$. The frequency of the signal in Figure 1 is 59 Hz. Check that you agree with this value.
- A microphone can be connected to the oscilloscope to measure the frequency of live sounds. However, these signals are much less stable.

Phase, phase difference, and phasors

- Two waves doing the same thing at the same time have no phase difference – they are in phase.
- Two waves doing exactly opposite things at the same time are in antiphase.

The position of a wave in its cycle can be represented by a phasor.

A phasor arrow turns through 360° (2 radians) for one cycle of the wave, so the number of rotations the phasor makes per second is the same value as the frequency of the wave.

Figure 2 shows two waves, A and B. You can see the phasors for the waves rotating anticlockwise through one complete cycle and that wave B is out of phase with wave A. The superposition of waves A and B is shown in wave C. Notice that

Synoptic link

You will meet phasors again in Topic 7.2, Quantum behaviour and probability. You will look at wave motion in more detail throughout Chapter 11, Oscillations and SHM.

the length of the phasor arrow for C is greater than that for A or B. This is because the amplitude of the two waves superposed is larger than the amplitude of either A or B. The combined displacement of waves A and B is found by adding the rotating arrows tip-to-tail, as shown in the Figure 2.

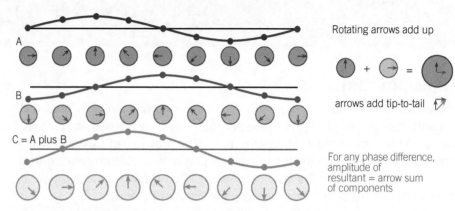

Rotating arrows add up

arrows add tip-to-tail

For any phase difference, amplitude of resultant = arrow sum of components

▲ **Figure 2** *Oscillations with a phase difference of a quarter of a cycle*

Standing waves

Progressive (or travelling) waves move through a medium. Standing (or stationary) waves appear to remain in one position. Standing waves are formed by the superposition of waves travelling in opposite directions and are easily observed on a stretched string.

When a string is plucked, waves:

● move along the string in opposite directions

● reflect at the ends of the string

● superpose as they pass through one another.

● Where waves meet in phase a point of maximum oscillation is formed. This is an antinode.

● Where waves of equal amplitude meet in antiphase the amplitude of the superposition is zero. This is a node.

Standing waves are also produced when sound waves superpose and when electromagnetic waves superpose.

▲ **Figure 3** *Nodes (N) and antinodes (A) on a standing wave on a string for* $\lambda = 2L$, $\lambda = L$, *and* $\lambda = \frac{2}{3}L$

Revision tip

The wavelength of a standing wave is the same as the wavelength of the progressive waves that are superposing and forming the wave.

Common misconception: Standing waves and progressive waves

Don't forget that a standing wave is formed from two (or more) progressive waves passing through one another. When a standing wave forms on string, progressive waves are constantly moving along the string. The Worked example below calculates the velocity of such waves, using the equation: $v = f\lambda$

🖩 Worked example: Velocity of waves along a string

A guitar string is 0.610 m long. It oscillates with frequency of 196 Hz. The standing wave formed on the string has a node at both ends and a single antinode in the middle of the string.

a What is the wavelength of the standing wave on the string?

b Calculate the velocity of the wave along the string.

a The wavelength of the standing wave is 1.22 m as there is half a wavelength between adjacent nodes – the top wave in Figure 3 shows the shape of the wave described in the question.

b **Step 1:** Identify the values you are given: $\lambda = 1.22$ m, $f = 196$ Hz

  Step 2: Substitute and evaluate: $v = 1.22$ m × 196 Hz = 240 m s^{-1} (3 s.f.)

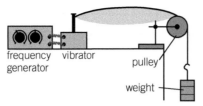

▲ **Figure 4** *Set-up for observing standing waves on a spring*

Practical: Standing waves on a rubber cord

- The rubber cord is stretched to about twice its original length (100% strain).
- The signal generator is set at 10 Hz and its frequency is gradually increased.
- The lowest frequency standing wave has a wavelength of twice the length of the string. This is the fundamental frequency, f_0.
- The next standing wave is formed at twice the fundamental frequency, $2f_0$.
- As the frequency is set at integer multiples of the fundamental frequency, $3f_0$, $4f_0$ and so on, standing waves of shorter wavelength are observed.

Standing waves in air

Standing waves can be formed in air columns:

- A sound (pressure) wave travels along the tube.
- The wave reflects at the end of the tube.
- Waves travelling in different directions along the tube superpose.

Waves can be reflected from open ends and closed ends of tubes. A tube with two open ends produces a different set of standing waves from a tube with one closed end. These are illustrated in Figure 5.

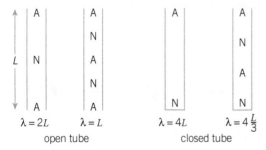

▲ **Figure 5** *Positions of nodes (N) and antinodes (A) in open and closed tubes*

Patterns of standing waves can also be observed when a source of sound is placed in front of a reflecting surface.

Practical: Determining the speed of sound in air using a tube

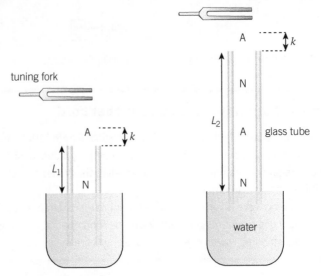

▲ **Figure 6** *Resonance tube experiment*

- A stable frequency source (a signal generator or a tuning fork) is held above the tube.
- L_1, the shortest length of tube to produce a loud sound is determined.
- $L_1 + k = \dfrac{\lambda}{4}$ where k is an end correction.
- The tube is gradually pulled out of the water until, at L_2 the sound reaches a second maximum amplitude.
- $L_2 + k = \dfrac{3\lambda}{4}$ which gives $L_2 - L_1 = \dfrac{\lambda}{2}$
- As the frequency of the source is known, the velocity of sound in air can be found by using the equation:

$$v = f\lambda = f \times 2\,(L_2 - L_1)$$

Summary questions

1 A wave has a time period of 0.25 s. How many rotations does the phasor representing the wave make in one second? *(2 marks)*

2 From memory, describe how a standing wave is formed on a vibrating string. *(5 marks)*

3 In an experiment to measure the speed of sound in air a tuning fork of frequency 440 Hz produced a loud sound when held above a tube of length $L_1 = 0.19$ m. The tube was raised further out of the water and a second loud sound was detected at a tube length $L_2 = 0.58$ m. Use this data to calculate the speed of sound in air. *(2 marks)*

4 a A flute can be considered as a tube open at both ends. Calculate the frequency of the lowest note emitted from a flute of effective length 0.28 m when the speed of sound in air is 340 m s^{-1}. *(3 marks)*

   b During a performance, the air in the flute warms up. This increases the speed of sound in the tube. State and explain the effect, if any, this will have on the pitch (frequency) of the note emitted for any given length of tube. *(3 marks)*

6.2 Light, waves, and refraction

Specification references: 4.1 a (iii), 4.1 b (i), 4.1 c (ii), 4.1 d (ii)

Visible light is an example of electromagnetic radiation. In a vacuum, electromagnetic radiation travels (or 'propagates') at $299\,792\,458\,\text{m s}^{-1}$. In this course, this value is rounded to $3.00 \times 10^8\,\text{m s}^{-1}$. The speed of light in air is very slightly lower because of interactions between light and the electrons in the air. Light travels considerably slower in glass because it interacts with more electrons per metre than in air.

Refractive index

The (absolute) refractive index of a medium is given by:

$$\text{refractive index } n = \frac{\text{speed of light in a vacuum}}{\text{peed of light in medium}} = \frac{c_{\text{vacuum}}}{c_{\text{medium}}}$$

If the light is travelling from one medium to another the equation becomes:

$$n = \frac{c_{\text{1st medium}}}{c_{\text{2st medium}}}$$

When the refractive index of a material is given, the figure is for the ratio for light travelling from a vacuum or air (first medium) into the material (second medium).

> ### Common misconception: Speed and wavelength
>
> All wavelengths of electromagnetic radiation propagate at the same speed in a vacuum. This is also true for air to a good approximation. However, different wavelengths experience different changes to speed when entering materials such as glass. This is why a prism splits white light into a spectrum – the violet light is slowed down more than the red light.

> ### Worked example: Speed of light in the lens of a human eye
>
> **The refractive index of the material of the lens of a human eye is about 1.4. The speed of light in air is $3.00 \times 10^8\,\text{m s}^{-1}$. Calculate the speed of light in the eye lens.**
>
> **Step 1:** Select and rearrange the appropriate equation.
>
> $$n = \frac{c_{\text{1st medium}}}{c_{\text{2st medium}}} \; \therefore c_{\text{2st medium}} = \frac{c_{\text{1st medium}}}{n}$$
>
> **Step 2:** Substitute values and evaluate.
>
> $$c_{\text{2st medium}} = \frac{3.00 \times 10^8\,\text{m s}^{-1}}{1.4} = 2.1 \times 10^8\,\text{m s}^{-1}\,(2\text{ s.f.})$$

Snell's law

The refractive index n of a material is also given by the equation:

$$n = \frac{\sin i}{\sin r}$$

where i is the angle of incidence and r is the angle of refraction. This relationship is known as Snell's law. Note that the angles of incidence and refraction are measured from the normal line, an imaginary line at right angles to the boundary between the two materials.

From the two definitions of refractive index this gives:

$$\frac{\sin i}{\sin r} = \frac{c_{\text{1st medium}}}{c_{\text{2st medium}}}$$

> ### Key term
>
> **Refractive index:** The refractive index of a transparent material is the ratio of the speed of light in a vacuum to the speed of light in the material.

> ### Revision tip
>
> 'Medium' is a term for the material that a wave is travelling through. One of the characteristics of electromagnetic waves is that they don't require a medium – they can travel through a vacuum. The plural of 'medium' is 'media'.

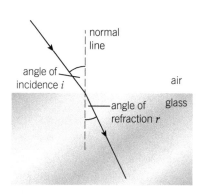

▲ **Figure 1** *Ray representation of refraction at a plane boundary*

Synoptic link

You have met the concept of wave-fronts in Topic 1.1, Bending light with lenses.

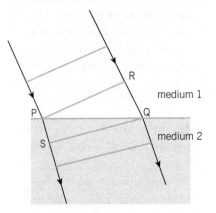

▲ **Figure 3** *Wave-fronts changing direction at a boundary*

Summary questions

1 Calculate the angle of refraction in flint glass ($n = 1.6$) for an angle of incidence of 65°.
(2 marks)

2 The speed of light in air is $3.00 \times 10^8 \, \text{m s}^{-1}$. The speed of light in Pyrex is $2.04 \times 10^8 \, \text{m s}^{-1}$. Calculate the angle of refraction in a Pyrex block for an angle of incidence of 27°.
(3 marks)

3 The refractive index of air is 1.0003. What is the difference between the speed of light in a vacuum and the speed of light in air? (precise value of speed of light in vacuum = 299 792 458 m s^{-1})
(2 marks)

 Practical: Determining the refractive index for a transparent block

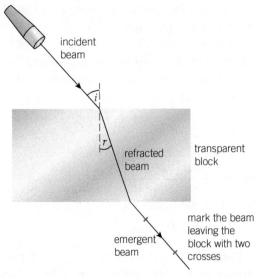

▲ **Figure 2** *Determining the refractive index of a transparent block*

- A narrow beam of light is directed at the transparent block at a known value of *i*.
- The path of the emergent beam is marked with two crosses. This allows the path of the refracted beam (in the block) to be constructed when the block is removed. The angle *r* is measured between the normal line and the constructed refracted beam.
- This process is repeated for a number of values of *i*.
- A graph of sin *i* (*y*-axis) against sin *r* (*x*-axis) is plotted. The gradient of the line gives the refractive index of the material of the transparent block.
- Uncertainties in your values for *i* and *r* will lead to an uncertainty in the gradient of the line and therefore in the value of the refractive index calculated from the graph.

Explaining refraction using the wave model of light

The model of light as a succession of wave-fronts can be used to explain refraction. When light enters a medium 'straight on' the wave-fronts are parallel to the boundary between one medium and the other. The wave-fronts travelling through the medium of high refractive index will travel more slowly so the wave-fronts behind catch up.

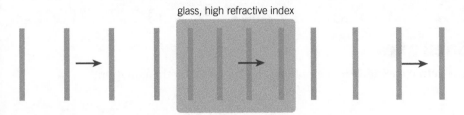

▲ **Figure 4** *Wave-front representation of light travelling from air to glass*

When light changes medium at an angle to the normal the wave-fronts are 'kinked' at the boundary because of the different speeds in the two media. This is shown in Figure 3. The waves are moving more slowly in medium 2 so in the time the wave-front travels from R to Q in medium 1 it travels from P to S in medium 2. The change of direction of the wave-front is a consequence of the change of speed of the wave-fronts as they move from one medium to another.

6.3 Path difference and phase difference

Specification references: 4.1 b(i), 4.1 d(iii)

Superposition and interference

When waves superpose, the displacements of the two (or more) superposing waves combine. When waves meet in phase, the amplitude of the superposition is a maximum value. When waves meet in antiphase, the amplitude of the superposition is a minimum value. The minimum value is zero when the amplitudes of the superposing waves are equal. If you walk in front of two speakers playing the same note you will hear a series of maximum and minimum amplitudes. There are places where the sound from the speakers combines to produce a louder sound and places where the sound from the speakers combines to produce a much quieter sound. This pattern of maxima and minima is often called an *interference pattern*: maxima are produced where there is *constructive interference*, minima are produced where there is *destructive interference*. The two (or more) superposing sources must be coherent to produce a stable interference pattern.

coherent waves with constant phase difference

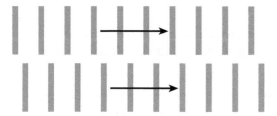

incoherent wave bursts with changing phase difference

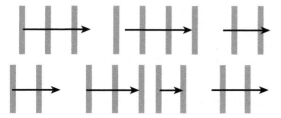

▲ **Figure 1** *Coherence*

Path difference

Figure 2 shows a microphone placed at a position where the waves from the two speakers combine in phase. The path difference is two wavelengths so the waves meet at the microphone at the same point in their cycles. You can think of the phasor arrow associated with a wave from speaker 2 making exactly two more revolutions than the phasor arrow associated with waves from speaker 1.

- Waves meet in phase when the path difference = $n\lambda$ where n is an integer.

- Waves meet in antiphase when the path difference = $\left(n + \frac{1}{2}\right)\lambda$.

> **Key term**
>
> **Coherence:** Sources of waves are coherent if they emit waves with a constant phase difference and have the same frequency.

> **Key term**
>
> **Interference:** Interference arises from the superposition of waves. An interference pattern of maxima and minima is produced when waves from two or more coherent sources overlap, or if waves from a single source are divided and then reunited.

> **Key term**
>
> **Path difference:** When waves travel from one point to another by two or more routes, the difference in the distance travelled is called the path difference. This is often given in wavelength terms, for example, 'a path difference of 7λ'.

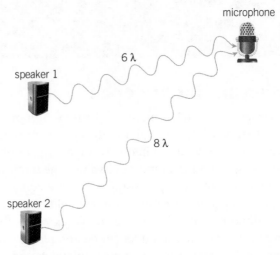

▲ Figure 2 *An arrangement for waves meeting in phase*

Common misconception: Out of phase and antiphase

Antiphase is not the same as 'out of phase'. Two waves are in phase if they meet at the same point in their cycles. Two waves are in antiphase if they meet at opposite points in their cycles (180° or π radians).

The idea of path difference can be used to calculate the wavelength of the signals producing an interference pattern. This can be observed using microwaves.

 ## Practical: Measuring the wavelength of microwaves

- A metal reflector M, microwave transmitter T and receiver R are positioned as shown in Figure 3.
- Waves from the transmitter reach the receiver along paths TR and TMR. The path difference is given by TMR – TR.

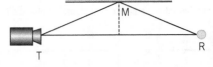

▲ Figure 3 *Measuring the wavelength of microwaves*

- As the metal reflector is moved towards line TR, a series of maxima and minima are detected.
- The difference in path differences (think about this) between adjacent maxima = wavelength, λ.

 ## Worked example: Measuring the wavelength of microwaves

An experiment is performed using the method shown in Figure 3. A maximum is detected when the path difference $TM_1R - TR = 0.57$ m.

As the metal reflector is moved towards line TR, the detected signal falls to minimum, rises to a maximum, falls to a second minimum and then rises to a second maximum. The final path difference, TM_2R is found to be 0.51 m.

a Calculate the difference in path differences $(TM_1R - TR) - (TM_2R - TR)$ between the original position of the mirror and the final position.
b Determine the wavelength of the microwave source.
a Difference = 0.57 m – 0.51 m = 0.06 m
b Change in path difference = 2λ = 0.06 m, wavelength λ = 0.03 m

Summary questions

1 A speaker produces a note of frequency 500 Hz. The speed of sound in air is 340 m s⁻¹. Calculate the wavelength of the sound from the speaker.
(2 marks)

2 Use ideas of path difference, phase difference, and coherence to explain how two sources of sound can combine to produce silence. *(3 marks)*

3 A signal generator produces a signal of frequency 850 Hz. The signal drives two loudspeakers in phase, setting up a stable interference pattern in front of the speakers. The speed of sound in air is 340 m s⁻¹.
A microphone is placed at distance of 1.8 m from one speaker and 2.0 m from the other speaker.
a Use calculations to explain why the microphone detects a minimum sound amplitude at this position. *(3 marks)*
b Suggest why the amplitude of the sound is not zero at this position. *(1 mark)*

6.4 Interference and diffraction of light

Specification references: 4.1 a(ii). 4.1 a(iv), 4.1 a(v), 4.1 b(i), 4.1 c(iii), 4.1 d(iii), 4.1 d(iv)

Diffraction

- All waves diffract.
- Diffraction does not change the wavelength, speed, or frequency of the waves.
- The amount of diffraction depends on the width of the gap compared to the wavelength of the diffracting waves.

Young's double slit experiment

- When light of wavelength λ is passed through a pair of narrow slits with separation d, a superposition pattern of bright fringes is observed on a distant screen.
- Maxima (bright fringes) are formed where waves from the two slits meet in phase.
- Maxima are found at angles of $\theta_1 \ldots \theta_n$ as given by the equation:

$$n\lambda = d\sin\theta_n$$

where n, an integer, is the order of the maximum.

- When $n = 1$ the path difference between waves striking the screen is λ. When $n = 2$ the path difference is 2λ. The nth order maximum is produced by a path difference between the waves of $n\lambda$.

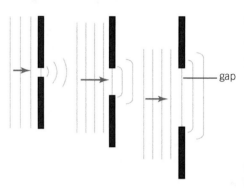

▲ **Figure 1** Diffraction

 Worked example: Two-slit diffraction pattern

Light of wavelength 580 nm is incident at right angles on two narrow slits of separation 0.40 mm. Calculate the angle between the central maximum and the third order maximum.

Step 1: Select the appropriate equation.

$n\lambda = d\sin\theta_n$ which rearranges to give: $\sin\theta_n = \dfrac{n\lambda}{d}$

Step 2: Convert data to metres, substitute, and evaluate.

$\sin\theta_n = \dfrac{3 \times 5.8 \times 10^{-7}\,\text{m}}{4.0 \times 10^{-4}\,\text{m}} = 4.35 \times 10^{-3}$

$\theta_3 = 0.25°$

Don't be surprised that two-slit diffraction produces maxima at very small angles. This is because the slit separation is large compared to the wavelength of light.

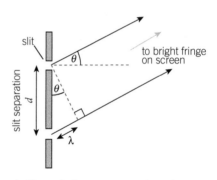

▲ **Figure 2** Ray representation of one wavelength path difference

The two-slit experiment in practice

The Worked example shows that the angular separation between maxima (bright fringes) is small. Producing a measurable fringe separation requires a large distance between the slits and the screen. Figure 4 shows the geometry of rays meeting at a distant screen.

From Figure 4, using the small angle approximation that $\sin\theta \approx \tan\theta$ gives:

$$\sin\theta = \frac{x}{L} = \frac{\lambda}{d} \therefore \lambda = \frac{xd}{L}$$

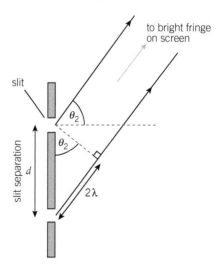

▲ **Figure 3** Ray representation of two wavelength path difference

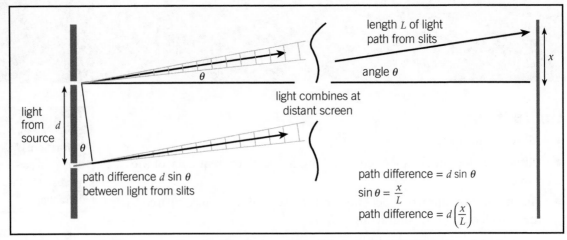

Approximations – angle θ very small; paths effectively parallel; distance L equal to slit–screen distance. Error less than 1 in 1000

▲ **Figure 4** *Geometry*

The diffraction grating

- The diffraction grating is a multiple-slit version of the two-slit system.
- The equation $n\lambda = d\sin\theta_n$ also holds for gratings.
- The fringe pattern from a grating is brighter as more light passes through.
- The pattern from a grating is sharper than the pattern produced by a two-slit system.
- The separation between the 'slits' of a grating is far smaller than the two-slit separation used in A level experiments. This leads to a greater angular separation between fringes.
- Gratings can spread white light into a spectrum because each wavelength of light produces a maximum at a different angle.

Practical: Determining the wavelength of light using two-slit apparatus or a diffraction grating

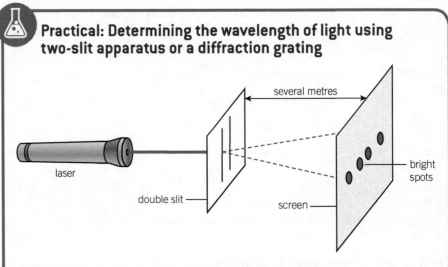

▲ **Figure 5** *Basic set-up for determining the wavelength of light*

- The key measurements are: slit separation (or line spacing), slit–screen distance, and fringe separation.
- If a two-slit apparatus is used, the greatest source of uncertainty is the slit separation.
- You may choose to measure the length on the screen of a number of fringes to reduce the error in the measurement of fringe separation. This method is used in the question below.

Model answer: Young's double slit experiment

A laser beam is shone through a pair of slits of separation 0.30 mm onto a screen 2.2 m from the slits.

The distance between four bright fringes on the screen is 15 mm. Calculate the wavelength of the light from the laser.

There are three gaps between four fringes, so the fringe separation $= \dfrac{15}{3}$ mm $= 5.0$ mm

> The candidate has made the working very clear so the examiner can see each stage of the calculation.

Convert all measurements to metres:

slit separation $d = 3.0 \times 10^{-4}$ m, fringe separation $x = 5.0 \times 10^{-3}$ m, slit–screen distance $L = 2.2$ m

Calculation:

$$\lambda = \frac{xd}{L} = \frac{5.0 \times 10^{-3}\,\text{m} \times 3.0 \times 10^{-4}\,\text{m}}{2.2\,\text{m}}$$
$$= 6.8 \times 10^{-7}\,\text{m} \ (2 \text{ s.f.})$$

> It is always good practice to write out all the values you are using in the correct units before attempting the calculation. This will help you avoid making simple arithmetical errors.

Single-slit diffraction

Interference effects would not be observed from double slits or diffraction gratings if light did not diffract when passing through each individual slit.

Single slit

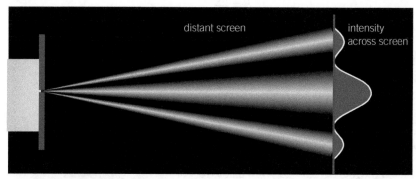

distant screen   intensity across screen

▲ **Figure 6** *Single slit diffraction*

A slit of width b will produce a diffraction *minimum* at an angle θ where $\lambda = b \sin \theta$

The wavelength of visible light is of the order of 10^{-7} m so diffraction effects are only observed when light passes through very narrow slits.

Summary questions

1 Explain why diffraction effects are easily observed with sound waves but less easily observed in visible light. *(2 marks)*

2 The angle between the central maximum and the first order maximum in a two-slit experiment is found to be 0.10°. The slit separation is 0.40 mm. Calculate the wavelength of light used in the experiment. *(2 marks)*

3 A sodium lamp emits light at wavelengths of 589.0 nm and 589.6 nm. A beam of light from the lamp passes through a diffraction grating of 300 lines per mm. Show that the separation between the second-order maximum of the two wavelengths on a screen 3.500 m from the grating is more than 1 mm. *(3 marks)*

Revision tip

The small value for h means that the energy of individual photons is tiny on a human scale.

Key term

Electronvolt: The joule is not a convenient unit to use when considering the energies of photons or sub-atomic particles. The electronvolt (eV) is used as an alternative.

One electronvolt (eV) is the kinetic energy transferred when an electron passes through a potential difference of one volt.
$1\,eV = 1.6 \times 10^{-19}\,J$

The work of Thomas Young and others showed that light has wave-like properties. For example, superposition effects cannot be explained using the idea of light behaving as discrete particles. However, new experimental findings at the beginning of the 20th century led to the wave model of light being questioned by, amongst others, Albert Einstein and Max Planck.

Quanta

Electromagnetic radiation is emitted and absorbed as quanta or packets of energy. These packets are called photons.

The energy of a photon is given by the equation:

energy E (J) = Planck constant h (J s) frequency × (Hz)

The Planck constant $h = 6.6 \times 10^{-34}\,J\,s$

As $c = f\lambda$, the energy of a photon can be linked to wavelength:

$$E = \frac{hc}{\lambda}$$

 Worked example: Photon energy in electronvolts

Calculate the energy of a photon of frequency 1.3×10^{15} Hz. Give your answer in electronvolts.

Step 1: Select the correct equation: $E = hf$

Step 2: Substitute values and calculate the energy of the photon in joules.

$E = 6.6 \times 10^{-34}\,J\,s\ 1.3 \times 10^{15}\,Hz = 8.58 \times 10^{-19}\,J$

Note that this intermediate value has not been rounded.

Step 3: Convert the value in J to eV.

$$\text{Energy (eV)} = \frac{8.58 \times 10^{-19}\,J}{1.6 \times 10^{-19}\,J\,eV^{-1}} = 5.4\,eV\ (2\ s.f.)$$

Key term

Intensity: The intensity of a wave is the energy per unit time carried by the wave and incident at right angles per unit area of surface. The unit of intensity is $W\,m^{-2}$. For light, the intensity can be thought of as the brightness of a light source.

The photoelectric effect and Einstein's equation

- Electrons are ejected when light of a sufficiently high frequency strikes a metal surface. Such electrons are often called photoelectrons.

- The kinetic energy of the photoelectrons is not affected by the intensity of the light striking the surface.

- There is no measurable delay between the light striking the metal surface and the emission of the photoelectrons.

- A more intense light produces more photoelectrons.

- Below the threshold frequency, f_0, no photoelectrons are emitted no matter how bright the light source.

Einstein pictured light as interacting with matter as particles called photons. Individual photons interact with individual electrons in the metal surface. Einstein's equation states that the maximum kinetic energy of an ejected electron is equal to the energy of the photon interacting with the electron in the surface minus the work function of the metal.

$$E_{k(max)} = hf - \phi$$

The graph in Figure 1 shows that the work function $\phi = hf_0$

🖩 Worked example: Calculating the work function of a metal

Electromagnetic radiation of wavelength 340 nm strikes a metal surface, releasing photoelectrons of maximum kinetic energy 1.8×10^{-19} J. Calculate the work function ϕ of the metal.

Step 1: Select the correct equation and rearrange to make ϕ the subject.

$$E_{k(max)} = hf - \phi$$

$$\therefore \phi = hf - E_{k(max)} = \frac{hc}{\lambda} - E_{k(max)}$$

Step 2: Substitute and evaluate.

$$\phi = \frac{6.6 \times 10^{-34}\,\text{J s} \times 3.0 \times 10^8\,\text{m s}^{-1}}{340 \times 10^{-9}\,\text{m}} - 1.8 \times 10^{-19}\,\text{J} = 4.0 \times 10^{-19}\,\text{J (2 s.f.)}$$

Determining the Plank constant using the photoelectric effect

The gradient of the graph in Figure 2 gives the value of the Planck constant.

Line spectra

- Electrons in atoms gain and lose energy by changing energy levels.
- Atoms release photons when an electron falls from a higher energy level to a lower energy level. The energy of the released photon is equal to the difference in energy between the two energy levels.
- Atoms of each element have their own set of energy levels and so emit photons of specific energies – light of different wavelengths. Each element has its own characteristic line spectrum, the specific wavelengths of light emitted as electrons fall between energy levels in atoms of that element.

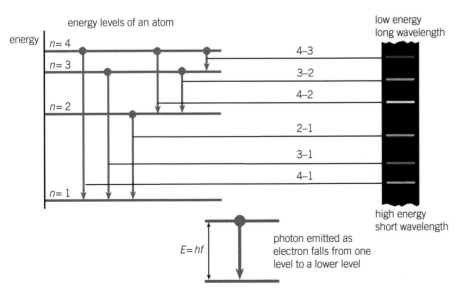

▲ **Figure 3** Spectral lines and energy levels

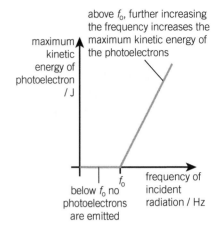

▲ **Figure 1** Graph showing the relationship between the maximum kinetic energy of the photoelectrons and the frequency of incident light

---

Key terms

Threshold frequency: The minimum frequency of light that will eject an electron from a given surface.

Work function: The work function ϕ is the minimum energy required to eject photoelectrons from a given surface.

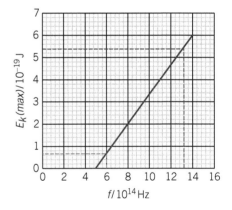

▲ **Figure 2** Graph showing the variation in maximum kinetic energy with frequency of incident radiation

---

Maths skill: The photoelectric effect and the Planck constant

The equation $E_{k(max)} = hf - \phi$ is of the form $y = mx + c$, identifying h as the gradient of the graph of $E_{k(max)}$ against f.

Revision tip

Atoms absorb light of the same frequencies as the light they emit. When a photon is absorbed, its energy promotes an electron from a lower energy level to a higher energy level.

Light emitting diodes (LEDs)

LEDs are semiconducting devices that allow current to flow in one direction only. As an electron crosses from one side of the diode to the other it falls to a lower energy level and a photon is emitted.

 Practical: Determining the Planck constant using LEDs

- The 'striking p.d.' of an LED is the potential difference across the diode when it just begins to glow.
- A number of LEDs are selected which emit light of different, known frequencies.
- The striking p.d.s of the LEDs are measured. This should be carried out in a darkened room or by observing the LED through a tube to cut out background light. This allows the observer to detect the p.d. at which the LED first begins to glow.
- The energy of each photon released = charge on an electron × striking p.d. In symbols, energy, $E = e \times V$
- The Planck constant is found from the gradient of the graph of photon energy (y-axis) against frequency (x-axis).

Sources of uncertainty:

- Each LED can emit photons over a small range of frequencies.
- Measuring the striking p.d. requires the observer to judge the point at which he or she first detects a glow from the LED. This can vary between observers.

Summary questions

1 Calculate the energy of a photon of frequency 7.0×10^{14} Hz. Give your answers in J and eV. *(3 marks)*

2 Two energy levels of the hydrogen atom have an energy difference of 10.2 eV. Calculate the frequency of the photon emitted when an electron falls from the higher energy level to the lower energy level. *(2 marks)*

3 An LED emits light at a rate of 12 mW. The light emitted has a wavelength of 590 nm. Calculate the number of photons emitted per second. *(3 marks)*

4 The work function of a metal is 2.8 eV. The metal surface is illuminated with electromagnetic radiation of wavelength 310 nm. Calculate the maximum kinetic energy of the photoelectrons emitted from the surface of the metal. *(2 marks)*

5 Table 1 shows the maximum kinetic energy of electrons ejected from a metal surface for two frequencies of incident radiation.

▼ **Table 1**

Frequency of light / Hz	Maximum kinetic energy / J
6.90×10^{14}	5.54×10^{-20}
6.40×10^{14}	2.24×10^{-20}

a Use the data in Table 1 to calculate a value for the Planck constant. *(3 marks)*

b Use your answer to **a** and the data in Table 1 to calculate **i** the work function of the metal **ii** the threshold frequency of the metal. *(4 marks)*

7.2 Quantum behaviour and probability

Specification references: 4.1 a (vii), 4.1 b(i)

The rules for quantum behaviour

Quantum objects such as photons have one rule of behaviour: explore all possible paths. This simple rule helps explain why light produces interference patterns (which are usually explained using wave-like behaviour) and also explains particle-like behaviour.

The rules to explain the behaviour of photons are:

- A photon is emitted by a source and is detected at a certain place and time.
- The photon can be imagined to take every possible path from the source to where it is detected at a given place and time. The longer the path, the longer the trip time of the photon.
- A phasor arrow is associated with each path. The phasor arrow is thought of as rotating with frequency $f = \dfrac{E}{h}$ for a time equal to the time it takes the photon to travel the length of the path, that is, the trip time.
- The angle at which the phasor ends up (on detection) can be determined for each path.
- The phasor arrows are added, tip-to-tail, for each path from source to detector. This produces the resultant phasor.

> **Synoptic link**
>
> You have met phasors in Topic 6.1, Superposition of waves, and Topic 6.4, Interference and diffraction of light.

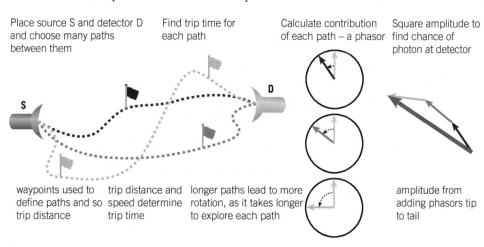

Place source S and detector D and choose many paths between them

Find trip time for each path

Calculate contribution of each path – a phasor

Square amplitude to find chance of photon at detector

waypoints used to define paths and so trip distance

trip distance and speed determine trip time

longer paths lead to more rotation, as it takes longer to explore each path

amplitude from adding phasors tip to tail

Repeating for more paths produces more accurate calculations. With limited time, choose wisely.

▲ **Figure 1** *Carrying out quantum calculations*

Phasor amplitude, probability, and intensity of light

The length of the resultant phasor arrow at a particular location is a measure of the probability of a photon arriving at that point. A longer arrow indicates a larger amplitude and therefore a higher probability of arrival.

Consider these two statements:

1 The intensity of light at a point is proportional to the probability of arrival of a photon at that point.

2 The intensity of light is proportional to the square of the length of the resultant phasor arrow at that point.

The statements lead to the relationship:

probability of arrival of a photon ∝ square of the length of the resultant phasor arrow

> **Revision tip**
>
> Figure 1 covers just about all the ideas covered in this topic so make sure that you spend some time studying it and that you understand the process it describes.

> **Key terms**
>
> **Probability:** In this context, the 'probability' is used to mean how likely it is that a photon will arrive at a particular place during a given time interval.
>
> **Intensity:** You have already met this term. In this context, intensity means the rate at which energy arrives at a point on a screen.

Figure 2 shows how the double-slit experiment can be interpreted in photon terms. Importantly, the phasor description does not indicate definitely where a photon will appear on the screen but instead gives a probability of a photon appearing on one part of the screen compared to another. This probabilistic nature of light is not observed in real life because of the vast numbers of photons that make up interference patterns.

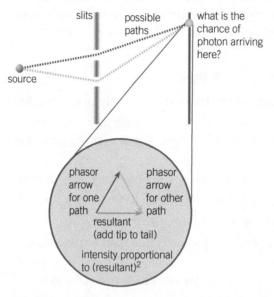

▲ **Figure 2** *Double-slit photon experiment*

 Worked example: Phasor arrows and probability

In an arrangement similar to Figure 2, the resultant phasor amplitude at one point (point A) on the screen is found to be 1.5 units in length. At another point (point B) on the screen the resultant phasor amplitude is 6.0 units in length. Calculate the probability of arrival of a photon at point B compared to point A.

Step 1: State what you know: probability of arrival of a photon at $B \propto 6.0^2$

probability of arrival of a photon at $A \propto 1.5^2$

Step 2: Use a constant to change the proportional relationships into equations:

probability of arrival of a photon at $B = k \times 6.0^2 = k \times 36.0$

probability of arrival of a photon at $A = k \times 1.5^2 = k \times 2.25$

Step 3: Divide the two equations: $= \dfrac{\text{probability of arrival of a photon at B}}{\text{probability of arrival of a photon at A}}$

$= \dfrac{k \times 36.0}{k \times 2.25} = 16$

A photon is 16 times more likely to arrive at B than at A. If a steady stream of photons passes through the slits, the intensity at B will be 16 times that at A.

Summary questions

1 Calculate the number of rotations per second for the phasor associated with a photon of energy 2.0 eV. (*3 marks*)

2 A photon is 3.2 times more likely to strike a screen at point A than at point B.
Calculate the ratio: $\dfrac{\text{length of resultant phasor arrow at A}}{\text{length of resultant phasor arrow at B}}$ (*1 mark*)

3 Figure 3 shows possible photon paths from a source to a detector.

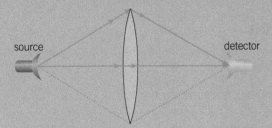

▲ **Figure 3** *Refraction with a lens*

a The phasor arrows for photons travelling from the source to the detector through the centre of the lens rotate the same number of times on their path as for photons travelling through the top of the lens, even though the distances travelled are different. Use the phasor model to explain how this is the case. (*3 marks*)

b Explain why the intensity is a maximum at the detector. (*2 marks*)

7.3 Electron diffraction

Specification references: 4.1 a (viii), 4.1 c(v)

Electron diffraction

A thin layer of atoms can act as a diffraction grating. The two-dimensional array of atoms in the layer produces a diffraction pattern of concentric circles on a fluorescent screen when a beam of electrons passes through the layer and strikes the screen. This is evidence that electrons show wave-like behaviour. Electrons diffract through narrow slits in the same manner as photons of light.

De Broglie's equation

This equation describes the wavelength associated with a matter particle, such as an electron.

$$\lambda = \frac{h}{p} \text{ where } p, \text{ momentum} = mv$$

 Worked example: Calculating the de Broglie wavelength

An electron has a velocity of $2.8 \times 10^6\,\text{m s}^{-1}$. The mass of an electron is $9.1 \times 10^{-31}\,\text{kg}$. Calculate the de Broglie wavelength.

Step 1: Choose the correct equation: $\lambda = \frac{h}{p} = \frac{h}{mv}$

Step 2: Substitute and evaluate.

$$\lambda = \frac{6.6 \times 10^{-34}\,\text{J s}}{9.1 \times 10^{-31}\,\text{kg} \times 2.8 \times 10^6\,\text{m s}^{-1}} = 2.6 \times 10^{-10}\,\text{m (2 s.f.)}$$

Common misconception: It's not just electrons that diffract

Although most examples using the de Broglie equation consider the diffraction of electrons, there is nothing special about electrons. The de Broglie equation is universal – it applies to all particles. Particles of greater momentum have shorter de Broglie wavelengths and so the wave-like behaviour is more difficult to detect. Nonetheless, molecules containing hundreds of atoms have been shown to diffract.

Unlike photons, electrons have mass and do not travel at a fixed speed in a given medium. However, as with the model of light, an electron can be modelled by exploring all possible paths between two points and by using the phasor representation to track the phase change along each path. Phasors for photons and electrons superpose in the same way. Once again, the probability of detection of an electron is calculated from the square of the amplitude of the resultant phasor.

In Topic 7.2, Quantum behaviour and probability, the photon phasor was pictured as rotating with a frequency $f = \frac{E}{h}$. In the model of electron waves, the phasor arrow is pictured making one turn for each distance $\frac{h}{p}$, the de Broglie wavelength.

Synoptic link

You will meet momentum in more detail in Topic 9.1, Conservation of momentum.

Summary questions

1 The mass of an electron is 9.1×10^{-31} kg.

   a Calculate the de Broglie wavelength for an electron with velocity $= 2.2 \times 10^6$ m s^{-1}. *(2 marks)*

   b Calculate the velocity of an electron with a de Broglie wavelength of 9.0×10^{-10} m. *(2 marks)*

2 Show that the units of $\dfrac{h}{p}$ are equivalent to metres (m). *(2 marks)*

3 A student writes the following in her notes for this topic of the course: *"When a beam of electrons passes through a diffraction grating we cannot predict where they will hit the fluorescent screen and emit light because it is all just probability."*
   Explain how the pattern of light on the fluorescent screen can be predicted. In your answer, use ideas about rotation of phasors and the relationship between the amplitude of the resultant phasor arrow and probability. *(6 marks)*

1 A phasor representing a wave motion rotates at a frequency of 80 Hz. Calculate the time period of the wave. *(2 marks)*

2 A standing wave is formed on a wire of length 0.6 m. The wavelength of the standing wave is 1.2 m.

  a Show the standing wave on a fully-labelled diagram. *(3 marks)*

  b The frequency of the standing wave is 220 Hz. Calculate the speed of the wave along the wire. *(1 mark)*

  c The speed of the wave in the wire is proportional to the square root of the tension in the wire. Calculate the frequency of the wave of wavelength 1.2 m when the tension in the wire is doubled. *(1 mark)*

3 a A student performs an experiment to find the refractive index of a block of Perspex. She uses the method shown in Topic 6.2 Figure 2. She states that the uncertainty in the angle of incidence is small compared to the uncertainty in the angle of refraction. Suggest and explain why this might be the case. *(2 marks)*

  b Table 1 gives the student's results. Plot a graph of $\sin i$ (*y*-axis) versus $\sin r$ (*x*-axis). Include uncertainty bars on your graph. *(3 marks)*

▼ **Table 1**

$\sin i$	$\sin r \pm 0.03$
0.34	0.25
0.50	0.33
0.77	0.55
0.87	0.59

  c Use the graph to calculate an estimate for the refractive index of the material. Give an estimate of the uncertainty in your final answer. *(3 marks)*

  d The speed of light in air $= 3.0 \times 10^8\,\mathrm{m\,s^{-1}}$. Calculate the speed of light in the transparent block. *(1 mark)*

4 This question is about measuring the wavelength of microwaves using the apparatus shown in Figure 1. This comprises a microwave transmitter T, a receiver R, and a reflector, M. The reflector is originally positioned to give a maximum signal at the receiver.

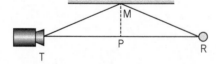

▲ **Figure 1**

  a The reflecting surface is moved further away from the path TR, increasing the distance MP. The amplitude of the signal detected is observed to fall and then rise again as the distance MP is increased. Explain these observations using ideas of path difference and phase difference. *(6 marks)*

  b The distance TR = 1.60 m. A maximum is detected when MP = 0.21 m. The signal reduces to a minimum and then rises to a maximum once more when MP = 0.24 m. Calculate the wavelength of the microwaves. *(3 marks)*

  c A student suggests that the uncertainties in measuring distance MP could be reduced by moving the reflector through a number of maxima and minima rather than just one. Explain the student's reasoning and suggest a difficulty with the idea. *(3 marks)*

5 A laser produces light of wavelength 590 nm. The light is incident normally on a grating which has 600 lines per mm. An interference pattern is formed on a screen 2.5 m from the grating.

   a Calculate the spacing between lines on the grating.   (*1 mark*)

   b Calculate the angle between the central maximum and the first-order maximum.   (*2 marks*)

   c Calculate the number of orders of maxima which can be produced by this equipment.   (*3 marks*)

6 A double-slit experiment is set up using a laser. The two slits are separated by 0.50 mm. The spacing between bright fringes on a screen is measured as 4.0 mm. The screen is 2.8 m from the slits. Calculate the wavelength of light used.   (*2 marks*)

7 a Ultraviolet radiation of wavelength 470 nm is incident on a metal surface. Photoelectrons are ejected with a maximum energy of 0.3×10^{-19} J. Calculate the work function of the metal.   (*2 marks*)

   b Calculate the longest wavelength that will emit photoelectrons from the surface.   (*2 marks*)

8 Light of wavelength 490 mm is normally incident on a diffraction grating of 600 lines per mm. A metal surface is placed at an angle of 17° to the original beam, as shown in Figure 2. The work function of the metal surface is 3.7×10^{-19} J.

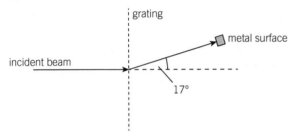

▲ **Figure 2**

   a Explain, using calculations where appropriate, why photoelectrons of maximum kinetic energy 3.4×10^{-20} J are emitted when the metal surface is positioned as shown in the diagram.   (*4 marks*)

   b Explain how you would expect the energy and rate of emission of photoelectrons to change as the angle increases up to 36°. Use calculations where appropriate.   (*5 marks*)

   c Explain why this experiment shows that neither a simple wave model nor a simple particle model can fully describe the properties of light.   (*2 marks*)

9 a Show that, for a body of mass m and velocity v, kinetic energy $E_k = \dfrac{p^2}{2m}$ where p is the momentum of the body.   (*1 mark*)

   b An electron is accelerated through a p.d. of 500 V. Calculate the de Broglie wavelength of the accelerated particle. (mass of electron = 9.1×10^{-31} kg)   (*3 marks*)

   c A beam of electrons accelerated through 500 V passes through a graphene sheet of interatomic spacing about 1.4×10^{-10} m. Explain whether a diffraction pattern could be observed on a sensitive screen placed behind the graphene sheet.   (*3 marks*)

   d Use the phasor model to describe how an interference pattern can be formed when electrons pass through two slits. Include ideas of superposition and probability in your answer.   (*4 marks*)

8.1 Graphs of motion

Specification references: 4.2a(vii), 4.2b(i), 4.2b(ii), 4.2d(i)

Synoptic link

The relationship between graphs of functions, their gradients, and the areas under them occur in many areas of Physics A level, including radioactive decay and discharge of capacitors (Chapter 10, Growth and decay), simple harmonic motion (Chapter 11, Oscillations and SHM and Chapter 12, The gravitational field), gravitational field and potential (Chapter 13, Our place in the Universe), induced e.m.f. and magnetic flux (Chapter 16, Electromagnetism) and electric field and potential (Chapter 17, The electric field).

Displacement–time graphs

The velocity at any point in a displacement–time graph can be found by calculating the gradient. If the graph is a curve, a tangent must be drawn at that point.

 Worked example: Finding velocity from a displacement–time graph

The construction on Figure 1 shows that the velocity at time $t = 0.20\,s$ is:

$$v = \frac{0.22\,m - 1.40\,m}{0.60\,s - 0.02\,s} = -2.0\,m\,s^{-1}.$$

Use Figure 1 to find the average velocity between $t = 0.40\,s$ and $t = 0.50\,s$.

Step 1: Read the changes in displacement and time from the graph.

$$\Delta s = final\ s - initial\ s = 0 - 0.42\,m = -0.42\,m$$
$$\Delta t = final\ t - initial\ t = 0.50\,s - 0.40\,s = 0.10\,s$$

Step 2: average velocity $= \dfrac{\text{change in displacement, }\Delta s}{\text{time taken, }\Delta t} = \dfrac{-0.42\,m}{0.10\,s} = -4.2\,m\,s^{-1}$ (2 s.f.)

(The minus sign is because the moving object is approaching $s = 0$, not moving away from it.)

Velocity–time graphs

The area between the velocity–time graph and two different times on the t-axis is the displacement between those two times.

The v–t graph given is often a series of straight-line sections, so finding the area is done by dividing it into simpler shapes.

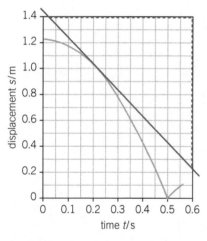

▲ **Figure 1** *Calculating velocity from a displacement–time graph*

 Worked example: Finding displacement from a velocity–time graph

Use Figure 2 to find the distance travelled in the first 3.5 s. of travel.

Step 1: Divide the area under the first 3.5 s into a rectangle and a triangle.

The rectangle is between the origin (0, 0) and (3.5 s, 2.0 m s⁻¹) and the triangle 'sits on top' of it, with base from (0, 2.0 m s⁻¹) to (3.5 s, 2.0 m s⁻¹) and apex (3.5 s, 6.2 m s⁻¹).

Step 2: Calculate the area of each shape and add them.

area of rectangle $= 2.0\,m\,s^{-1} \times 3.5\,s = 7.0\,m$

area of triangle $= \dfrac{1}{2} \times 3.5\,s \times (6.2\,m\,s^{-1} - 2.0\,m\,s^{-1}) = 1.75\,s \times 4.2\,m\,s^{-1} = 7.35\,m$

total area = distance travelled $= 7.0\,m + 7.35\,m = 14.35\,m = 14\,m$ (2 s.f.)

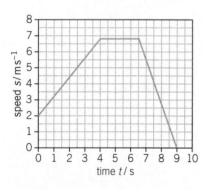

▲ **Figure 2** *Using a speed–time graph to find distance travelled*

The gradient of the velocity–time graph at any time t is the acceleration at that time.

Worked example: Finding acceleration from a velocity-time graph

Use Figure 2 to find the acceleration during the last 2.5 s of travel.

Step 1: The graph is straight during this time, so the acceleration is constant. The gradient is negative, so the acceleration is negative (it is decelerating).

Step 2: Substitute the velocity changes and time into the definition of acceleration.

$$\text{acceleration} = \frac{\text{change in velocity}}{\text{time}} = \frac{\text{final velocity} - \text{initial velocity}}{\text{time}}$$

$$= \frac{0 - 6.8\,\text{m s}^{-1}}{2.5\,\text{s}} = -2.72\,\text{m s}^{-2}$$

$$= -2.7\,\text{m s}^{-2}\ (2\ \text{s.f.})\ \text{where the negative sign indicates deceleration.}$$

Investigating motion

A trolley running down a ramp (Figure 3) can be investigated using light gates and computer/data logger to determine the velocity of the passing trolley. This will allow measurements of velocity at different displacements along the ramp, enabling readings of displacement, velocity, and time from release to be obtained. The changes in a variety of different physical quantities treated in Chapters 8 and 9 can be monitored and analysed. Motion can also be investigated using computer analysis of video recordings.

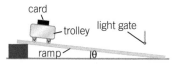

▲ **Figure 3** *Trolley on a ramp*

Summary questions

1 A car, driving along a straight road, travels at a constant speed for 10 seconds, accelerates uniformly for 5 seconds and then decelerates uniformly to rest for 10 seconds. Using the same time axis, sketch displacement–time and speed–time graphs for this trip.   *(6 marks)*

2 Table 1 shows the velocity–time data that describes a simple journey. Use an appropriate graph to calculate the total distance moved.
                                                                            (4 marks)

▼ **Table 1**

t / s	0	1	2	3	4	5	6	7	8
$v / \text{m s}^{-1}$	0	2	4	6	9	12	8	4	0

3 Table 2 contains displacement–time measurements for a falling object.

▼ **Table 2**

t / s	0.0	0.10	0.20	0.30	0.40	0.50	0.60
s / cm	0.0	4.8	19.6	44.2	78.3	122.8	17.5

Plot an appropriate s–t graph, find the velocities at two suitable times and use these values to find the acceleration due to gravity. *(6 marks)*

Revision tip

Displacement and velocity are vector quantities, where changes in direction are important, whereas distance and speed are scalars (Topic 8.2, Vectors). The graphs are often referred to as 'displacement–time' and 'velocity–time' graphs, where it is understood that the motion is in a straight line in each case.

Key terms

Displacement: Displacement is the distance moved in a given direction.

Velocity: Velocity is the rate of change of displacement. If displacement s changes by an amount Δs in a time Δt, then the mean velocity v in that time interval is $v = \dfrac{\Delta s}{\Delta t}$.

Key term

Acceleration:
$$\text{acceleration } a = \frac{\text{change in velocity}}{\text{time taken for that change}} = \frac{\Delta v}{\Delta t}$$

8.2 Vectors

Specification references: 4.2a(i), 4.2b(i), 4.2c(i), 4.2c(ii)

Key terms

Scalar quantities: Scalar quantities have no direction, only magnitude (size).

Vector quantities: Vector quantities have direction as well as magnitude.

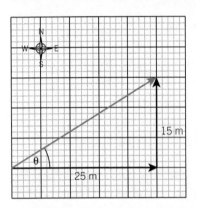

▲ **Figure 1** Adding displacements

Revision tip

Even when you use Pythagoras' theorem and trigonometry, you should always sketch the vector diagram with a clearly labelled angle. This will clearly indicate the vector direction.

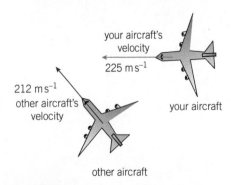

▲ **Figure 3** Will they collide [1]?

Vector quantities and scalar quantities

Distance travelled and speed are scalar quantities. Their vector equivalents are displacement and velocity. Acceleration is also a vector.

Adding vectors

Two or more vector quantities are added by drawing them tip-to-tail finding the resultant vector from the start to the end of the chain.

This can be done by a scale drawing, as in Figure 1 or by using Pythagoras' theorem and trigonometry: by either method, the resultant displacement in Figure 1 is 29 m in a direction N 59° E (2 s.f.).

> ### 🖩 Worked example: Calculating displacement and mean velocity
>
> **A car drives 500 m due west, then 2.0 km due south. The total trip took 5 minutes. Calculate the mean velocity.**
>
> **Step 1:** Sketch and label the vector addition diagram, converting distances to metres (Figure 2).
>
> **Step 2:** Measure or calculate the magnitude of the displacement s.
>
> $$s^2 = (500\,m)^2 + (2000\,m)^2$$
> $$= 250\,000\,m^2 + 4\,000\,000\,m^2$$
> $$= 4\,250\,000\,m^2$$
>
>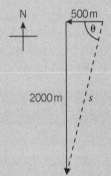
>
> ▲ **Figure 2** Adding vectors
>
> so $s = \sqrt{4\,250\,000}\,m^2 = 2061\,m = 2100\,m$ (2 s.f.)
>
> **Step 3:** $\tan\theta = \dfrac{2000\,m}{500\,m} = 4.0$ so $\theta = \arctan(4.0) = 75.96° = 76°$ (2.s.f)
>
> so the displacement is 2100 m in a direction W 76° S
>
> (Note that the magnitude of the displacement is NOT the same as the distance travelled, which is 2000 m + 500 m = 2500 m.)
>
> You could write this direction as a bearing, measured clockwise from north.
>
> This is $180° + (90° - 76°) = 194°$
>
> **Step 4:** Use the displacement s to calculate the mean velocity v, using the time Δt in seconds.
>
> mean velocity $v = \dfrac{\text{displacement, } s}{\text{time taken, } \Delta t} = \dfrac{2061\,m}{(5 \times 60)\,s} = 6.87\,m\,s^{-1} = 6.9\,m\,s^{-1}$ in the same direction as the displacement, that is, W 76° S (bearing 194°).

Subtracting vectors

If two objects **A** and **B** are moving at velocities v_A and v_B then the velocity of **B** relative to **A** is found by subtracting v_A from v_B. This is done by adding $(-v_B)$ to v_A. This is illustrated in Figures 3–5 showing two aircraft which may be going to collide. All velocities are measured relative to the ground.

In this case, object **B** is the aircraft travelling at 212 m s^{-1} and object **A** is 'your' aircraft: the velocity of **B** relative to **A** is the velocity **B** seems to have when viewed from **A**. As Figure 5 shows, the resultant relative velocity (red) is not in the direction of your aircraft, so the two will not collide.

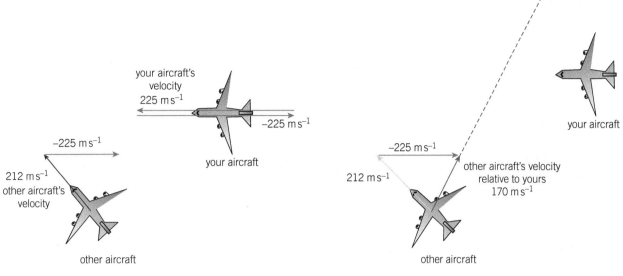

▲ **Figure 4** *Will they collide [2]?* ▲ **Figure 5** *Will they collide [3]?*

Components of a vector

Any vector can be resolved into two components, usually at right angles to each other. This is true for displacement or for velocity; in Chapter 12 you will apply it for acceleration and forces also.

In Figure 6, the two components are horizontal and vertical, which is common. The horizontal component, $s_H = s \cos \theta$ and the vertical component, $s_V = s \sin \theta$.

> 🖩 **Worked example: Calculating components of displacement.**
>
> In Figure 6, the total displacement $s = 2.4$ m at an angle θ of 28° to the horizontal. Calculate the horizontal and vertical components of displacement.
>
> **Step 1:** Horizontal component $s_H = s \cos \theta = 2.4$ m $\times \cos (28°) = 2.4$ m $\times 0.8829 \ldots$
> $= 2.1$ m (2 s.f.)
>
> **Step 2:** Vertical component $s_V = s \sin \theta = 2.4$ m $\times \sin (28°) = 2.4$ m $\times 0.4694 \ldots$
> $= 1.1$ m (2 s.f.)

Summary questions

1 A boat sails 25 km due north and then 30 km due east. Calculate the displacement of the boat. *(3 marks)*

2 Aircraft X is flying due north at 250 m s^{-1} relative to the ground. Aircraft Y is flying due east at 150 m s^{-1} relative to the ground. Calculate the velocity of aircraft X relative to aircraft Y. *(3 marks)*

3 A boat is sailing in a direction S 50° W at 12 m s^{-1} relative to the land. A passenger is walking on the ship's deck at 5 m s^{-1} heading due north. By taking components in suitable directions, find the velocity of the passenger relative to the land. *(7 marks)*

> **Key term**
>
> **Relative velocity:** The relative velocity of an object B relative to another object A is the velocity B appears to have when viewed from A.

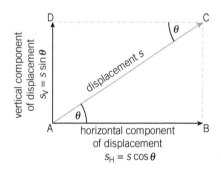

▲ **Figure 6** *Components of displacement*

> **Key terms**
>
> **Components and resolution:** Any vector can be treated as the sum of two other vectors in convenient directions, e.g., horizontally and vertically, or N–S and E–W. Splitting up the vector in this way is called **resolution**, and the two new vectors, which add to give the original, are called **components** of the vector in the chosen directions.

> **Revision tip**
>
> Be careful with the angles: in Figure 6, θ is between the vector and the horizontal. You may be given the angle between the vector and the vertical which is $90° - \theta$.

8.3 Modelling motion

Iterative models

In an iterative model, motion is treated by dividing the time into a number of identical intervals Δt. Changes in displacement Δs during each interval are calculated using the velocity at the end of the previous interval: new s = previous s + Δs = previous s + (previous v)Δt. Changes in velocity Δv during each interval are calculated using new v = previous v + Δv = previous v + $a\Delta t$.

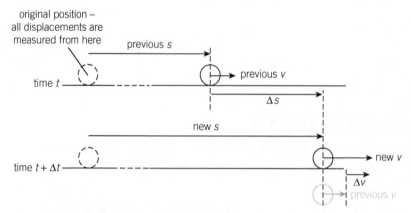

▲ **Figure 1** *An iterative model*

In AS Physics, the acceleration will always be constant but you will see in Chapter 11 that the process works just as well if the acceleration changes.

> ### 🖩 Worked example: Constant acceleration
>
> **The data in Table 1 show the first steps in an iterative model for an object falling from rest.**
>
> ▼ **Table 1**
>
> | t/s | v/m s^{-1} | s/m |
> |---|---|---|
> | 0.05 | 0 | 0 |
> | 0.10 | 0.50 | 0 |
> | 0.15 | 1.00 | 0.025 |
> | 0.20 | 1.50 | 0.075 |
> | 0.25 | 2.00 | 0.150 |
> | 0.30 | 2.50 | |
>
> **a** Explain how the velocity data show that the acceleration is uniform, and calculate the value of acceleration.
> **b** Calculate the displacement at time $t = 0.30$ s.
>
> > **a** For each equal interval of time Δt (0.05 s), the velocity goes up by the same amount Δv (0.50 m s^{-1})
> >
> > so acceleration $a = \dfrac{\Delta v}{\Delta t} = \dfrac{0.50 \, \text{m s}^{-2}}{0.05 \, \text{s}} = 10 \, \text{m s}^{-2}$
> >
> > **b** (displacement at $t = 0.30$ s) = (displacement at $t = 0.25$ s) + (velocity at $t = 0.25$ s) $\times \Delta t$
> >
> > $= 0.150 \, \text{m} + (2.00 \, \text{m s}^{-1}) \times 0.05 \, \text{s} = 0.150 \, \text{m} + 0.100 \, \text{m} = 0.250 \, \text{m}$

Advantages and disadvantages of iterative models

The Worked example above shows how iterative models work, but Topic 8.4, Speeding up and slowing down, will show that equations can be used very quickly to give the correct answers for the case of uniform acceleration.

However, iterative models can be used in the case of very complex models with many variables, and these may not be solved in any other way.

If you look at the displacement column in Table 1, you will see that the values are not realistic: although the object is accelerating from rest, after 0.10 s it seems not to have moved at all. This is because the iterative model uses the previous value of velocity to calculate displacement, whereas the velocity is increasing all the time. This problem can be reduced by using a much smaller time interval, e.g., $\Delta t = 0.001$ s instead of 0.05 s. This would normally be done using a computer.

Graphical models

The iterative model above finds new values of v by adding Δv to the previous value of v. As velocity is a vector, this can involve vector addition if Δv is not in the same direction as v.

Figure 2 shows an example where the initial velocity v (black) is horizontal, but each Δv is vertical. This is a projectile (treated in Topic 9.4, Projectiles) where the resultant velocity (dark grey) of each addition becomes the initial velocity of the next interval. As gravity provides a constant downwards acceleration, each Δv is the same as the previous one.

In this example, note that each 'step' in the model takes the same horizontal space of two large squares. This is because gravity acts vertically, not horizontally, so the horizontal component of velocity does not change.

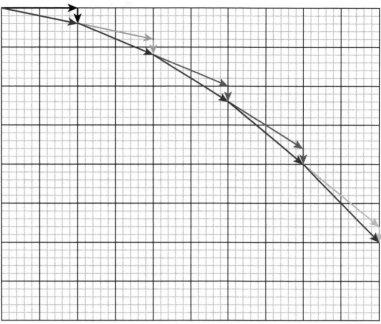

▲ **Figure 2** *Graphical model for a projectile*

Investigating terminal velocity

In this investigation, you will be dealing with a case where the resistive forces are great enough to equal the weight of the falling object during the time it takes to fall. One possible situation is that of falling marbles or ball bearings in a thick liquid such as wallpaper paste. Another situation is that of the paper case used in baking cup-cakes falling though air.

You will need to measure and control the variables in the experiment. The terminal velocity can be measured by timing the fall over a measured distance provided that the object is no longer accelerating. You may wish to vary the weight or the cross-sectional area of the falling object.

> **Key term**
>
> **Terminal velocity:** When an object is accelerated though a medium, resistive forces increase as the object speeds up. At some point the force accelerating the object will be equal to the resistive force, and the object will no longer accelerate. It will be travelling at its terminal velocity.

Summary questions

1. In the Worked example, for an object falling in a school lab, the time interval Δt was 0.05 s. Suggest why a time interval of 5 s was not chosen. *(1 mark)*

2. For the Worked example, suggest one advantage and one disadvantage of choosing a time interval $\Delta t = 0.5$ ms. *(2 marks)*

3. The graphical model illustrated in Figure 2 has a constant horizontal component, which is the velocity at which it was originally thrown. Describe and explain how the model would look different if it was not a thrown object but a rocket launched horizontally. *(3 marks)*

8.4 Speeding up and slowing down

Specification references: 4.2c(iii), 4.2d(ii)

Kinematic (*suvat*) equations

The equations that you will need in the examinations are:

$$v = u + at \qquad s = ut + \frac{1}{2}at^2 \qquad v^2 = u^2 + 2as$$

where s is the displacement, u is the initial velocity, v is the final velocity, a the acceleration, and t the time taken.

These equations apply for motion in a straight line over a time t where the acceleration is constant.

 Worked example: The height of a cliff

A stone is dropped from a cliff and takes 3.2 s to reach the bottom. Calculate the height of the cliff. The acceleration due to gravity, $g = 9.8\,\text{m s}^{-2}$.

Step 1: Write down the variables.

$a = g = 9.8\,\text{m s}^{-2}, t = 3.2\,\text{s}, s = ?$, and $u = 0$ (easy to miss that one)

Step 2: Choose the equation with a, t, s, and u.

$$s = ut + \frac{1}{2}at^2$$

Step 3: Substitute in the values and work out s.

$$s = ut + \frac{1}{2}at^2 = 0 \times 3.2\,\text{s} + \frac{1}{2} \times 9.8\,\text{m s}^{-2} \times (3.2\,\text{s})^2$$

$$= 0 + 4.9\,\text{m s}^{-2} \times 10.24\,\text{s}^2 = 50.176\,\text{m} = 50\,\text{m (2 s.f.)}$$

Worked example: How high will the stone go?

A stone is thrown vertically into the air at a speed of $15\,\text{m s}^{-1}$. How high will it rise? $g = 9.8\,\text{m s}^{-2}$.

Step 1: Write down the variables, including the directions. Choose to make upwards positive.

$a = g = -9.8\,\text{m s}^{-2}$ (because gravity acts downwards), $s = ?$, $u = 15\,\text{m s}^{-1}$, and $v = 0$ (Did you spot that value?)

Step 2: Choose the equation with a, s, u, and v.

$$v^2 = u^2 + 2as$$

Step 3: Substitute in the values and work out s.

$$v^2 = u^2 + 2as \Rightarrow 0^2 = (15\,\text{m s}^{-1})^2 + 2 \times (-9.8\,\text{m s}^{-2}) \times s$$

$$0 = 225\,\text{m}^2\,\text{s}^{-2} - 19.6\,\text{m s}^{-2} \times s$$

$$19.6\,\text{m s}^{-2} \times s = 225\,\text{m}^2\,\text{s}^{-2} \Rightarrow s = \frac{225\,\text{m}^2\,\text{s}^{-2}}{19.6\,\text{m s}^{-2}} = 11.479\ldots\,\text{m} = 11\,\text{m (2 s.f.)}$$

Measuring the acceleration due to gravity

There are many ways to measure the acceleration of gravity, but all will involve an object falling freely. The object should be dense and compact to minimise air resistance.

Figure 1 shows one possible method. This relies on timing the fall over a known distance.

The distance s needs to be measured carefully, and systematic errors such as measuring to or from the wrong positions should be avoided.

The experiment is quick to do once set up, so you may wish to repeat readings to determine the uncertainty in the times obtained. You may also wish to obtain the time of fall for different values of s, which will allow you to plot an appropriate straight-line graph to find g.

Applying the equations to two-dimensional motion

In Topic 8.2, Vectors, you saw that vector quantities can be resolved into two components. This allows you to analyse more complex motion, as in this example (see also Topic 9.4, Projectiles).

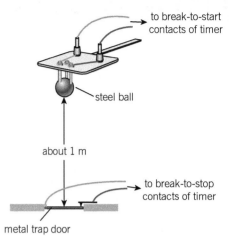

▲ **Figure 1** *Timing free fall to measure g*

 ### Worked example: The range of a thrown ball

A ball is thrown horizontally at a speed of 12 m s^{-1} at a height of 1.8 m above the ground. Ignoring air resistance, calculate the horizontal distance it travels before hitting the ground.

Step 1: Consider the vertical components of the *suvat* vectors. The sub-script v shows these are vertical components.

$s_v = 1.8\,\text{m}, u_v = 0, v_v = ?, a_v = g = 9.8\,\text{m s}^{-2}, t = ?$

Step 2: Choose the equation to give the time of fall t and solve to find t.

v_v is not needed and can be ignored, so use $s_v = u_v t + \frac{1}{2} a_v t^2$.

$1.8\,\text{m} = 0 \times t + \frac{1}{2} \times (9.8\,\text{m s}^{-2}) \times t^2 = (4.9\,\text{m s}^{-2}) \times t^2$

$t^2 = \dfrac{1.8\,\text{m}}{4.9\,\text{m s}^{-2}} = 0.3673...\text{s}^2$ so $t = \sqrt{0.3673...\text{s}^2} = 0.6061\,\text{s}$

Step 3: Consider the horizontal components (sub-script h) of the *suvat* vectors.

$s_h = ?, u_h = 12\,\text{m s}^{-1}$ and $v_h = 12\,\text{m s}^{-1}$ also as $a_h = 0$ (gravity has no horizontal effect), $t = 0.6061\,\text{s}$

Step 4: Calculate s_h

$s_h = u_h t + \frac{1}{2} a_h t^2 = u_h t + 0 = 12\,\text{m s}^{-1} \times 0.6061\,\text{s} = 7.273\,\text{m} = 7.3\,\text{m}$ (2 s.f.)

Summary questions

1 A car accelerates from an initial velocity of 4.6 m s^{-1} with an acceleration of 1.2 m s^{-2} for 3.5 seconds. Calculate its final velocity.
(2 marks)

2 A ball is thrown vertically upwards at a velocity of 12 m s^{-1}. Calculate the height above the thrower when its vertical velocity has dropped to 2.5 m s^{-1}.
(3 marks)

3 A stone is thrown vertically upwards and reaches its maximum height 2.5 s later. Calculate its speed when it has dropped to 1.5 m above the point from which it was thrown.
(4 marks)

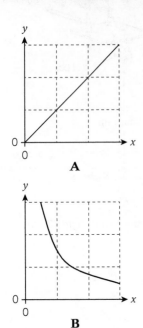

A

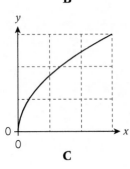

B

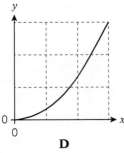

C

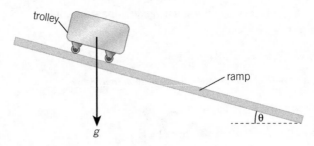

D

▲ Figure 1

Questions 1, 2 and 3 are about the graphs **A** to **D** in Figure **1**.

The graphs in Figure 1 all describe the motion of an object moving from rest with constant acceleration.

Which graph **A**, **B**, **C**, or **D** best represents the relationship between the variables x and y in each of the following cases?

1 y is the displacement of the object

   x is the time for which it has been moving. *(1 mark)*

2 y is the velocity of the object

   x is the time for which it has been moving. *(1 mark)*

3 y is the velocity of the object

   x is the displacement of the object. *(1 mark)*

4 A trolley which runs with negligible friction is placed on a ramp inclined at an angle θ as shown in Figure 2.

▲ Figure 2

What is the acceleration of the trolley down the slope? *(1 mark)*

A $g \times \sin \theta$ **C** $g \times \cos \theta$

B $g \div \sin \theta$ **D** $g \div \cos \theta$

5 In this question, you should ignore any effect of air resistance.

   a A stone is thrown vertically downwards into a well which is 25 m deep. It takes 1.3 s to reach the bottom. Calculate the initial velocity of the stone. *(2 marks)*

   b A ball is thrown vertically and gains a height of 34 m. Calculate the velocity of the ball as it leaves the thrower's hand. *(2 marks)*

6 The displacement when moving from town **A** to town **B** is 200 km east, 300 km south.

   a On a day with no wind, a plane flies from **A** to **B** in a time of 35 minutes. Assuming that the speed is constant during the flight, calculate the velocity of the plane, in both magnitude in m s^{-1} and direction, relative to the ground. *(3 marks)*

   b On a different day, the plane needs to fly due south from **A**. It flies at a constant speed of 150 m s^{-1} relative to the air, but the wind is blowing due west (from east to west) at 25 m s^{-1}. Calculate the direction in which the plane should fly to obtain a resultant velocity due south. *(3 marks)*

7 Plot a displacement–time graph using the data in Table 1, and use the graph to determine:

   a the velocities at times $t = 0.40$ s and $t = 0.60$ s *(6 marks)*

   b the mean acceleration between these two times. *(2 marks)*

▼ Table 1

time t / s	0	0.1	0.2	0.3	0.4	0.5	0.6	0.7	0.8
displacement s / m	1.2	1.4	1.6	1.8	2.1	2.5	3.0	3.6	4.3

8 When a light object like a balloon falls through air, air resistance reduces its acceleration and this effect increases as the velocity v increases. Lizzy constructs an iterative model for this using the equation:

$a_{new} = a_{previous} - k \times v_{previous}$ where k is a constant

together with the usual modelling equations

$v_{new} = v_{previous} + a_{previous} \times \Delta t$ and $s_{new} = s_{previous} + v_{previous} \times \Delta t$

In her model, she uses $k = 1.5 \, s^{-1}$ and $\Delta t = 0.1 \, s$. All downwards values are positive.

a Copy Table 2 below showing the first two 'steps' of the model and fill in the missing values in the bottom row, working to two significant figures.

▼ Table 2

t/s	$a/m\,s^{-2}$	$v/m\,s^{-1}$	s/m
0	9.8	0	0
0.1	9.8	0.98	0.0
0.2			

(2 marks)

b When the model is continued for several more steps, the graph shown in Figure 3 is obtained.

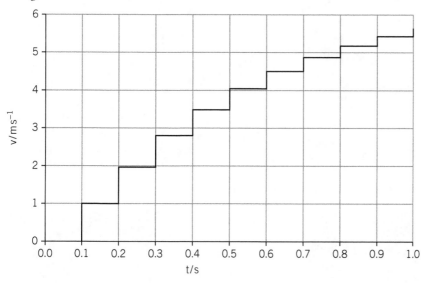

▲ Figure 3

i Describe how this graph differs from the v–t graph to be expected from a falling object. (2 marks)

ii Suggest how the iterative model could be changed to give a more realistic graph. (1 mark)

9

MOMENTUM, FORCE, AND ENERGY
9.1 Conservation of momentum
Specification references: 4.2a(ix), 4.2b(i), 4.2c(iv), 4.2 c(vi)

Conservation of momentum

In any interaction, momentum is conserved. If you calculate the total momentum of interacting bodies before they interact, that value is the same after the interaction.

▲ **Figure 1** *A collision on a snooker table*

▲ **Figure 2** *A cannon being fired*

On the snooker table, the white ball hits a stationary yellow ball. Some of the white ball's momentum is transferred to the yellow ball, and some remains in the white ball, which moves slowly in a different direction after impact.

In the cannon, there is no momentum before firing, but the cannon ball has momentum afterwards: this means the cannon recoils with equal and opposite momentum, so the two momentums add to give a zero sum.

Worked example: Finding velocity after a 'sticky' impact

A block A of soft clay of mass 2.0 kg strikes a similar stationary block B of mass 3.0 kg at a speed of 4.2 m s^{-1}. After the impact, the two blocks stick together. Calculate the velocity of the combined block after impact.

Step 1: Calculate the total momentum of the two blocks before impact.

$p_A = m_A v_A = 2.0\,\text{kg} \times 4.2\,\text{m s}^{-1} = 8.4\,\text{kg m s}^{-1}$ and $p_B = 0$ (it is not moving) so total $p = 8.4\,\text{kg m s}^{-1}$

Step 2: Equate this to the total momentum after the impact.

$8.4\,\text{kg m s}^{-1} = p_{(A+B)} = m_{(A+B)} v_{(A+B)} = (2.0\,\text{kg} + 3.0\,\text{kg}) \times v_{(A+B)} = 5.0\,\text{kg} \times v_{(A+B)}$

Step 3: Calculate $v_{(A+B)}$, the velocity of the joined blocks.

$v_{(A+B)} = \dfrac{8.4\,\text{kg m s}^{-1}}{5.0\,\text{kg}} = 1.68\,\text{m s}^{-1} = 1.7\,\text{m s}^{-1}$ (2 s.f.).

Velocity and momentum are vectors: the direction in which the joined blocks move is the same as the direction in which block A was moving before impact, as both the magnitude and the direction of the momentum are conserved.

Note in this Worked example that no mention is made of frictional forces. Even if friction is present, at the very instant of sticking the combined block will have the calculated velocity even if it then starts to slow down.

Summary questions

1 Calculate the momentum of:
   a a 2500 kg van travelling at 12 m s^{-1} *(1 mark)*
   b a bullet of mass 9.5 g travelling at 230 m s^{-1}. *(2 marks)*

2 A 12 g bullet travelling at 210 m s^{-1} embeds itself in a stationary wooden block of mass 0.50 kg which is free to move. Calculate:
   a the momentum transferred to the gun during the firing of the bullet *(1 mark)*
   b the velocity of the bullet–block combination immediately after impact. *(2 marks)*

3 A ball of mass 4.5 kg, travelling at 25 m s^{-1}, collides with a stationary ball of mass 6.3 kg. The 4.5 kg ball rebounds at 1.6 m s^{-1}. Calculate the velocity of the 6.3 kg ball after the collision, assuming that no external forces act on either ball. *(4 marks)*

▲ **Figure 1** *The statue of Newton in his Cambridge college (Trinity)*

Revision tip

As $W = mg$, $g = \dfrac{W}{m}$ is the gravitational force per unit of mass so it can be given the units N kg^{-1}. You may see the Earth's gravitational field strength written as $g = 9.81 \text{ N kg}^{-1}$ rather than as $g = 9.81 \text{ m s}^{-2}$.

Key terms

Weight: Weight W is the gravitational force acting on any object in a gravitational field g: it is given by $W = mg$.

Mass: mass m is the amount of matter in an object.

Newton's first and second laws

Every body with mass has inertia. It will continue moving with the same velocity unless an external force acts on it, and this includes a velocity of 0 (a stationary body). This is Newton's first law. A constant mass and a constant velocity means that each object has a constant momentum, if no external force acts on it.

Newton's second law relates the external force to the rate of change of momentum it produces: where the force is in N and the momentum in kg m s^{-1}:

$$F = \frac{\Delta p}{\Delta t} = \frac{\Delta(mv)}{\Delta t}$$

Where the mass is constant this can be simplified to: $F = m\dfrac{\Delta v}{\Delta t} = ma$

Key terms

Inertia: Inertia is the tendency of an object to continue in its present state of motion, either stationary or else moving with a constant non-zero velocity.

Newton's first law of motion: A stationary object will remain stationary, and a moving object will continue moving with the same momentum, unless an external force is acting on it.

Newton's second law of motion: When an external force acts on an object, it produces a momentum change according to

F = rate of change of momentum = $\dfrac{\Delta p}{\Delta t} = ma$ if there is no change in mass.

🖩 Worked example: Using momentum change to find force

A cricket ball of mass 160 g, moving at 37 m s⁻¹, is struck by the cricket bat and moves back along its original path at 35 m s⁻¹. The bat is in contact with the ball for 1.2 ms. Calculate the force acting on the ball during the strike.

Step 1: Calculate the momentum before (p_1) and after (p_2) striking, taking the initial direction of the ball to be positive.

$p_1 = mv_1 = 0.16 \text{ kg} \times 37 \text{ m s}^{-1} = 5.92 \text{ kg m s}^{-1}$ and $p_2 = mv_2 = $
$0.16 \text{ kg} \times (-35 \text{ m s}^{-1}) = -5.60 \text{ kg m s}^{-1}$

Step 2: Calculate the momentum change Δp and the time Δt for that change.

$\Delta p = p_2 - p_1 = -5.60 \text{ kg m s}^{-1} - 5.92 \text{ kg m s}^{-1} = -11.52 \text{ m}$ and
$\Delta t = 1.2 \text{ ms} = 1.2 \times 10^{-3} \text{ s}$

Step 3: $F = \dfrac{\Delta p}{\Delta t} = \dfrac{-11.52 \text{ kg m s}^{-1}}{1.2 \times 10^{-3} \text{ s}} = -9600 \text{ kg m s}^{-2} = -9600 \text{ N}$

(The minus sign is because the force is in the opposite direction to that of the approaching ball.)

Mass and weight

Although everyday speech treats these two words as meaning the same thing, they are quite different. Weight is a force and mass is a property of the object being discussed.

Impulse and momentum change

As $F = \dfrac{\Delta p}{\Delta t}$: $\Delta p = F\Delta t$ or momentum change = impulse

where the impulse is the product of the force and the time for which it acts. If the force is changing, as in Figure 2, then the impulse, and the momentum change, is given by the area under the curve.

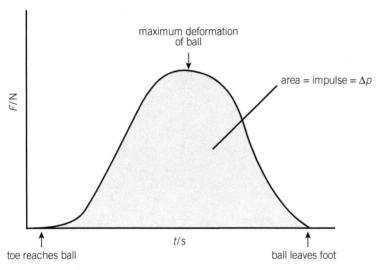

maximum deformation of ball

area = impulse = Δp

F / N

t / s

toe reaches ball

ball leaves foot

▲ **Figure 2** *Kicking a football*

> **Revision tip**
> Because $\Delta p = F\Delta t$ the units of both sides of the equation must be the same: $kg\,m\,s^{-1} = N \times s = N\,s$. This means that the units of momentum can be written either as $kg\,m\,s^{-1}$ or as $N\,s$.

> **Key term**
> **Impulse:** Impulse is the product $F\Delta t$ summed over the whole action of a force on an object resulting in a momentum change Δp which is equal to the impulse.

> ### Worked example: Weight, impulse, and momentum change
> A stone of mass 2.5 kg is dropped and falls for 0.24 s. Calculate the impulse on the stone and hence its velocity after the 0.24 s.
>
> **Step 1:** Calculate the constant force acting on the stone during the fall.
>
> This force is the weight of the stone, $W = mg = 2.5\,kg \times 9.81\,N\,kg^{-1} = 24.5\ldots N$
>
> **Step 2:** Calculate the impulse.
>
> impulse $= F\Delta t = 24.5\ldots N \times 0.24\,s = 5.8\ldots N\,s$
>
> **Step 3:** Equate the impulse to the momentum gained and calculate v.
>
> $p = mv = 5.8\ldots N\,s$
>
> $v = \dfrac{p}{t} = \dfrac{5.8\ldots N\,s}{2.5\,kg} = 2.3544\,m\,s^{-1} = 2.4\,m\,s^{-1}$ (2 s.f.)
>
> (Of course, it is quicker to use $v = u + at$ where $a = g$ and $u = 0$, but the question did ask for the impulse to be calculated first and used to find the velocity.)

Newton's third law

If two bodies **A** and **B** interact, **A** exerts a force on **B** and **B** exerts a force on **A**. These two forces are often described as an interaction pair. One example is shown in Figure 3.

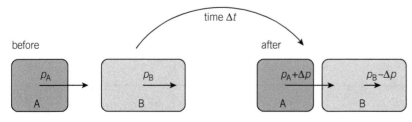

time Δt

before

after

p_A

p_B

$p_A + \Delta p$

$p_B - \Delta p$

A   B   A   B

▲ **Figure 3** *An interaction between two bodies*

Revision tip

It is easy to confuse Newton's first and third laws. In cases of equilibrium, equal and opposite forces will be acting on one object. For Newton's third law, the forces in the interaction pair always act on different objects.

Key term

Newton's third law: When an object A exerts a force F upon an object B, then the object B exerts a force $(-F)$ on object A.

The total momentum is unchanged, so the momentum gained by **A** is the same as the momentum lost by **B**. This means the impulse $F\Delta t$ exerted on **A** by **B** is the same as that exerted on **B** by **A**, but in the opposite direction: one is a gain of momentum, and the other a loss. The time Δt is the same for both bodies so the forces must be equal and opposite. This is Newton's third law.

▦ Worked example: Identifying interaction pairs

In Figure 4, two forces are labelled. Do these illustrate Newton's third law?

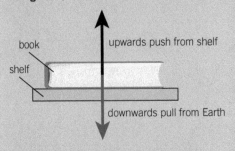

▲ **Figure 4** *Forces on a book on a shelf*

Step 1: Identify the interaction(s) present.

> There are two different interactions here: a gravitational interaction is pulling the book downwards, while physical contact with the shelf is pushing the book upwards.

Step 2: Identify the 'Newton III' interaction pairs for each interaction.

> The gravitational force is between the book and the Earth: the Earth pulls the book downwards, and the book pulls the Earth upwards with a force identical in size and opposite in direction.

The physical contact with the shelf results in the shelf pushing the book upwards, while the book pushes the shelf downwards.

The two forces shown in Figure 4 do *not* illustrate Newton's third law: they illustrate Newton's first law. The book is stationary on the shelf because the resultant of the two forces acting on it is zero.

Summary questions

1. **a** A cricket ball of mass 160 g, moving at 28 m s^{-1} is caught by a cricketer. Calculate the momentum change experienced by the ball. *(2 marks)*
   b If the cricketer catches the ball with his hands kept still, the ball stops in 0.025 s. Calculate the mean decelerating force acting on the ball. *(2 marks)*

2. Explain why, in Question 2, it would be better to catch the ball by 'giving way' and moving the hands back in the direction the ball was travelling. *(2 marks)*

3. A spacecraft of mass 820 kg is powered by an ion drive, which ejects xenon ions out of the engine at a rate of 5.5×10^{21} ions s^{-1}. The speed of the ions, relative to the spacecraft, is 30 km s^{-1}. Each ion has a mass of 2.2×10^{-25} kg. Calculate the thrust provided by the engine and the time it would take to accelerate the spacecraft from rest to a speed of 500 m s^{-1}. *(6 marks)*

9.3 Conservation of energy

Specification references: 4.2a(v), 4.2b(i), 4.2c(vii), 4.2c(viii), 4.2 c(ix)

Synoptic link

Energy and its conservation provide a linking theme throughout Physics. You have met it in electrical potential energy and p.d. (Topic 3.1, Current, p.d., and electrical power), elastic potential energy (Topic 4.2, Stretching wires and springs), and photon energies (Topic 7.1, Quantum behaviour) and will feature in the Year 2 course in energy stored in capacitors (Topic 10.3, Capacitors in circuits), in oscillating systems (Topic 11.4, Resonance) and in gravitational fields (Topic 12.3, Gravitational potential in a uniform field, and Topic 12.4, Gravitational potential in a radial field) and electric fields (Topic 17.1, Uniform electric fields and Topic 17.3, Charged spheres). In Chapter 18 (Topic 18.2, Accelerating charges and electron scattering) Einstein's famous $E = mc^2$ relates mass to energy and the energy levels of atoms are met while Topic 19.4, Fission and fusion, deals with energy released in nuclear fission and nuclear fusion.

Force and work

When a force moves its point of application, it does work, which is an energy transfer. The energy transfer by a constant force F moved by a displacement Δs is given by $\Delta E = F\Delta s$ provided that the force and displacement are in the same direction. (The case when they are at an angle to each other is dealt with in Topic 9.5, Work and power.)

Worked example: Work done against friction

A brass block of mass 1.6 kg is pushed at a steady speed across a flat table top. The frictional force opposing the block's motion is one-fifth of its weight. Calculate the work done in moving the block a distance of 75 cm.

Step 1: Calculate the weight of the block.

$$W = mg = 1.6\,\text{kg} \times 9.81\,\text{N kg}^{-1} = 15.696\,\text{N}$$

Step 2: Use the information given to calculate the frictional force F.

$$F = \frac{W}{5} = \frac{15.696\,\text{N}}{5} = 3.1392\,\text{N}$$

Step 3: Calculate the work done, remembering to convert the displacement into metres.

$$\Delta E = F\Delta s = 3.1392\,\text{N} \times 0.75\,\text{m} = 2.3544\,\text{J} = 2.4\,\text{J (2 s.f.)}$$

Kinetic energy and gravitational potential energy

When a force does work by accelerating an object, the work done is stored by the moving object as kinetic energy. When a force does work by lifting an object at a constant speed, the work done is stored by the moving object as gravitational potential energy. The energy transfer by a constant force F moved by a displacement Δs is given by $\Delta E = F\Delta s$ provided that the force and displacement are in the same direction. (The case when they are at an angle to each other is dealt with in Topic 9.5, Work and power.)

Revision tip

Work is sometimes given the symbol W, but because weight (W) is often a force involved in calculations, it is safer to use ΔE, as here, to avoid confusion.

Key term

Work: Work is the energy transfer when a force moves its point of application and is given by $\Delta E = F\Delta s$ where Δs is the displacement in the direction in which the force acts. The equation to use when F and Δs are at an angle θ to each other is given in Topic 9.5, Work and power.

Key terms

Kinetic energy: Kinetic energy E_k is the energy possessed by a body by virtue of its motion and is given by $E_k = \frac{1}{2}mv^2$.

Gravitational potential energy: Gravitational potential energy E_{grav} is the energy possessed by a body due to its position in a gravitational field. The gravitational potential energy difference between two points in a uniform gravitational field is given by $\Delta E_{grav} = mg\Delta h$ where Δh is the vertical separation between the two points.

Worked example: How high will it rise?

A stone of mass 0.26 kg is thrown vertically with an initial speed of 21 m s^{-1}. How high will it rise if air resistance is ignored?

Step 1: Calculate the initial kinetic energy of the stone.

$$E_k = \frac{1}{2}mv^2 = 0.5 \times 0.26 \text{ kg} \times (21 \text{ m s}^{-1})^2 = 0.13 \text{ kg} \times 441 \text{ m}^2\text{s}^{-2} = 57.33 \text{ J}$$

Step 2: Equate the initial kinetic energy to the gravitational potential energy gained when the stone stops moving.

no energy losses, so $E_{grav} = E_k = 57.33$ J

Step 3: Use the gravitational potential energy equation to find the height h risen by the stone.

$$E_{grav} = mgh \Rightarrow h = \frac{E_{grav}}{mg} = \frac{57.33 \text{ J}}{0.26 \text{ kg} \times 9.81 \text{ N kg}^{-1}} = 22.477 \text{ m} = 22 \text{ m (2 s.f.)}$$

Summary questions

1 A constant force of 16 N pushes a box at steady speed for 30 cm. Calculate the work done. *(2 marks)*

2 Calculate the kinetic energy of a 1200 kg car moving at 17 m s^{-1}. *(1 mark)*

3 Calculate the gravitational potential energy gained when a 600 g object is lifted 75 cm vertically. *(1 mark)*

4 A rock of mass 2400 kg falls from a cliff 84 m high. Calculate its speed when it hits the ground below, stating any assumption made. *(4 marks)*

5 In the Angel Falls in Venezuela, water drops uninterrupted through a height of 807 m. Assuming that all of the gravitational potential energy change experienced by the falling water results in an increase in the internal energy of the water, calculate the temperature rise experienced by the water in this fall. (An increase in internal energy of 4190 J per kg of water will result in a temperature rise of 1 °C.) *(6 marks)*

9.4 Projectiles

Specification references: 4.2a(ii), 4.2a(iii)

Components of forces act independently

When resolving forces into components at right angles to each other, it is important to remember that perpendicular forces are independent and have no effect upon each other. This fact does not depend on the chosen directions. In Figure 1 the two effects of the components of weight $mg\cos\theta$ and $mg\sin\theta$ can be analysed separately.

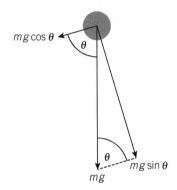

▲ **Figure 1** *Components of weight*

Horizontal and vertical components

A projectile is a body which has been thrown at an angle to the horizontal. Once it has started moving, the only force acting is its weight, which acts vertically downwards. To analyse the motion of projectiles, it is usual to resolve the initial velocity of the projectile into horizontal and vertical components.

The horizontal and vertical components of initial velocity, $u_h = u\cos\theta$ and $u_v = u\sin\theta$ can be used separately with the *suvat* equations met in Topic 8.4, Speeding up and slowing down. Two simplifying factors make this possible:

- the time t for the motion of an projectile is the same for horizontal and vertical motion
- gravity acts downwards only, so a projectile has a vertical acceleration but no horizontal acceleration: $a_v = g$ but $a_h = 0$.

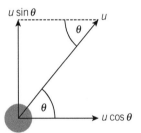

▲ **Figure 2** *Resolving the initial velocity of a projectile*

 Worked example: Finding the velocity of a projectile during its flight

A ball is thrown with an initial velocity of 26 m s⁻¹ at an angle of 52° to the horizontal. Calculate its velocity 0.34 s after it is thrown. Air resistance can be ignored.

Step 1: Calculate the horizontal and vertical components of the initial velocity of the ball.

$$u_h = u\cos\theta = 26\,\text{m s}^{-1} \times \cos(52°) = 16.01\,\text{m s}^{-1}$$

$$u_v = u\sin\theta = 26\,\text{m s}^{-1} \times \sin(52°) = 20.49\,\text{m s}^{-1}$$

Step 2: State the horizontal velocity v_h after $t = 0.34\,\text{s}$

No calculation is necessary. g has no horizontal component, so $a_h = 0$.

$$v_h = u_h = 16.01\,\text{m s}^{-1}$$

Synoptic link

This topic links with Topic 8.2, Vectors, and Topic 8.3, Modelling motion, to explain the motion of objects where the accelerating force and the velocity of the moving object are not in the same direction. This leads into later study of motion in gravitational fields (Topic 12.1, Circular motion) and magnetic fields (Topic 17.2, Deflecting charged beams).

Revision tips

Make sure that all the variables for the horizontal and vertical directions, except for time, are clearly labelled to show which is horizontal and which is vertical. Here suffixes, e.g., u_v and u_h, have been used.

A projectile landing at the same height as that which it started from has $s_v = 0$.

At the highest point of the trajectory, the projectile has a vertical component of velocity $v_v = 0$.

Step 3: Use the *suvat* equations to find the vertical velocity v_v after $t = 0.34$ s.

$s_v = ?, u_v = 20.49 \text{ m s}^{-1}, v_v = ?, a_v = -g = -9.81 \text{ m s}^{-2}, t = 0.34$ s

Note the directions chosen here: upwards (e.g., v_v) is positive, while a_v acting downwards, is negative.

Eliminate the unwanted variable, which is s_v. This shows that you need the equation $v = u + at$.

$v_v = u_v + a_v t = 20.49 \text{ m s}^{-1} + (-9.81 \text{ m s}^{-2}) \times 0.34 \text{ s} = 20.49 \text{ m s}^{-1} - 3.35 \text{ m s}^{-1}$
$= 17.14 \text{ m s}^{-1}$

Step 4: Add the two components v_h and v_v to find the magnitude and direction of the final velocity v at 0.34 s as shown in Figure 3.

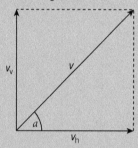

▲ **Figure 3** *Velocity after 0.34 s*

$v = \sqrt{(v_h)^2 + (v_h)^2} = \sqrt{(16.01 \text{ms}^{-1})^2 + (17.14 \text{ms}^{-1})^2} = \sqrt{(256.3 \text{m}^2 \text{s}^{-2}) + (293.8 \text{m}^2 \text{s}^{-2})}$

$= \sqrt{(256.3 \text{m}^2 \text{s}^{-2} + 293.8 \text{m}^2 \text{s}^{-2})} = \sqrt{550.1 \text{m}^2 \text{s}^{-2}} = 23.45 \text{ms}^{-1}$ (2 s.f.)

The angle a is given by $\tan a \dfrac{v_v}{v_h} = \dfrac{17.14 \text{ m s}^{-1}}{16.01 \text{ m s}^{-1}} = 1.071$

so $a = \arctan(1.071) = 46.95° = 47°$ (2 s.f.)

The velocity v after 0.34 s is 23 m s^{-1} in an upwards direction at 47°.

Summary questions

1 A cannon fires a cannonball at 120 m s^{-1} at an angle of 37° to the horizontal. Calculate the horizontal and vertical components of this initial velocity. *(3 marks)*

2 For the cannonball fired in Question 1, find the time taken to reach its maximum height, the value of that maximum height and the horizontal range of the projectile. State the assumption you must make to do these calculations. *(6 marks)*

3 A stone is thrown out to sea from the top of a cliff. It is thrown upwards at an angle of 65° to the horizontal with an initial speed of 30 m s^{-1}. The stone hits the sea 6.5 s later. Calculate:
   a the height of the cliff above sea level *(2 marks)*
   b its horizontal distance from the thrower when it hits the water. *(2 marks)*

9.5 Work and power

Specification references: 4.2a(iv), 4.2a(vi), 4.2b(i), 4.2c(x)

Displacement, force, and work

Displacement and force are both vector quantities, where the direction in which they 'point' is important. Work, as an energy transfer, is a scalar quantity, and has no direction.

> ### Revision tip
> Displacement and velocity are vector quantities, where changes in direction are important, whereas distance and speed are scalars (Topic 8.2, Vectors). The graphs are often referred to as 'displacement-time' and 'velocity-time' graphs, where it is understood that the motion is in a straight line in each case.

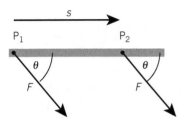

▲ **Figure 1** Force and work

> ### 🖩 Worked example: Calculating work done
>
> In Figure 1, the angle $\theta = 49°$. Calculate the work done in moving from P_1 to P_2, a distance of 73 cm, if $F = 1.3$ kN.
>
> **Step 1:** Convert the values to m and to N.
>
> $s = 0.73$ m and $F = 1300$ N
>
> **Step 2:** Calculate the work done.
>
> $W = Fs \cos \theta = 1300$ N $\times 0.73$ m $\times \cos(49°) = 622.6$ J $= 620$ J (2 s.f.)

Power

Power has been met in electrical circuits in Topic 3.1, Current, p.d., and electrical power. In this section, power is used to measure the rate of energy transfer when a force moves its point of application.

When a constant force moves at a constant velocity for a time t, then the power is:

$$P = \frac{W}{t} = \frac{Fs \cos \theta}{t} = Fv \cos \theta$$

Often, the force and displacement are in the same direction, when $\cos \theta = \cos(0°) = 1$ so $P = Fv$.

Synoptic link

Power, as the rate of doing work or of transfer of energy, links to Topic 9.3, Conservation of energy, and to all of the AS and A level sections listed there.

Key term

Work: Work is an energy transfer occurring when a force moves its point of application in its own direction. The work done is equal to the component of the force in the direction of the displacement of the point of application multiplied by that displacement, $W = Fs \cos \theta$.

Key term

Power: Power is the rate at which work is done *or* the rate at which energy is transferred.

Worked example: Calculating power in a moving car

A car drives at a steady speed of $24\,\text{m s}^{-1}$. The engine provides a constant driving force of $1400\,\text{N}$. Calculate the power delivered and explain the forces present in the situation.

Step 1: Use the equation $P = Fv$

$$P = Fv = 1400\,\text{N} \times 24\,\text{m s}^{-1} = 33\,600\,\text{W} = 34\,000\,\text{W (2 s.f.)}$$

Step 2: Use Newton's first law to explain the forces.

As the velocity of the car is not changing, the resultant force on the car must be zero. The car provides a $1400\,\text{N}$ force in the direction in which the car is travelling: an equal force must be opposing this, and this force is caused by resistive forces – a combination of air resistance and frictional forces acting on the rotating axles of the car.

Summary questions

1 A force of $250\,\text{N}$ pushes an object a distance of $82\,\text{cm}$. The object moves at an angle of $38°$ to the direction of the force. Calculate the work done in this motion. *(2 marks)*

2 A car travels at a steady speed of $39\,\text{m s}^{-1}$ along a straight, horizontal road under the action of a constant driving force of $2700\,\text{N}$. Calculate the power in kW dissipated against resistive force. *(2 marks)*

3 A parachutist, falls at her terminal velocity for a distance of $300\,\text{m}$ in $5.6\,\text{s}$ before opening her parachute, after which she takes a further $26\,\text{s}$ to drop the remaining $150\,\text{m}$ to the ground. Calculate the ratio $\dfrac{P_1}{P_2}$ where P_1 is the power dissipated against air resistance with the parachute closed and P_2 is the power dissipated against air resistance with the parachute open. Hint: together with all her kit, she weighs the same whether the parachute is open or closed. *(5 marks)*

4 A car of mass $1300\,\text{kg}$ accelerates up a long, straight hill of constant gradient $16°$ to the horizontal at a rate of $0.95\,\text{m s}^{-2}$, starting at rest. Calculate:
   a the gain in kinetic energy after $6.8\,\text{s}$ of travel *(2 marks)*
   b the gain in gravitational potential energy after $6.8\,\text{s}$ of travel. *(3 marks)*

5 The energy supplied by the car engine in the $6.8\,\text{s}$ to produce driving force in Question 2 is $220\,\text{kJ}$. Calculate:
   a the mean power dissipated against resistive forces *(3 marks)*
   b the mean resistive force. *(2 marks)*

1 A gun of mass 0.680 kg fires a bullet of mass 9.5 g. The bullet leaves the gun horizontally at a speed of 160 m s^{-1}. The bullet is accompanied by 12.5 g of exhaust gases travelling in the same directions with mean speed 96 m s^{-1}.

What is the recoil speed of the gun? (*1 mark*)

A 0.47 m s^{-1} C 2.2 m s^{-1}

B 1.8 m s^{-1} D 4.0 m s^{-1}

2 A spacecraft of mass 16 000 kg is moving away from the Earth at 1100 m s^{-1}. To accelerate, its rockets eject 24 kg of gas each second at a speed of 3000 m s^{-1} relative to the space probe. What is the increase in velocity of the space probe after a 40-second burst from the rockets?

A 4.5 m s^{-1} C 180 m s^{-1}

B 66 m s^{-1} D 1200 m s^{-1} (*1 mark*)

3 A car of mass 880 kg accelerates from 10 m s^{-1} to 30 m s^{-1} over a horizontal distance of 80 m. The mean driving force over this distance is 5000 N. What is the work done against friction, expressed to two significant figures?

A 44 000 J   C 350 000 J

B 48 000 J   D 400 000 J   (*1 mark*)

4 A ball is thrown at an angle of 36° to the horizontal at a speed of 12 m s^{-1}. The table shows possible values of the vertical and horizontal components of the initial velocity of the ball.

Which row is correct? (*1 mark*)

	vertical component of velocity / m s^{-1}	horizontal component of velocity / m s^{-1}
A	4.0	8.0
B	6.0	6.0
C	7.1	9.7
D	9.7	7.1

5 A ball of mass 0.28 kg bounces off a wall. It strikes the wall at a speed of 14 m s^{-1} and leaves it at a speed of 8.0 m s^{-1}.

a Calculate the impulse acting on the ball during the collision. (*3 marks*)

b The duration of the impact is 0.32 s. Calculate the mean force acting on the wall. (*2 marks*)

6 When a stationary football is kicked, the force on the ball varies with time as shown in Figure 1.

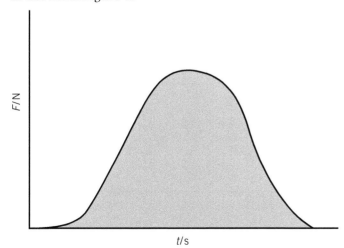

▲ Figure 1

The ball is in contact with the foot for a total time of 0.64 s, and the maximum force acting on the ball is 30 N.

   a Estimate the mean force acting on the ball. *(1 mark)*

   b Use your answer to **a** to calculate the velocity with which the football leaves the foot. (mass of football = 0.42 kg) *(2 marks)*

7 A lorry of mass 2100 kg drives up a straight road on a hill at a constant speed of 15 m s⁻¹. The road makes a constant angle of 18° with the horizontal.

   a Calculate the rate of increase of gravitational potential energy in kW. *(3 marks)*

   b The mean frictional force acting on the lorry is 42 000 N. Calculate the efficiency of energy transfer into gravitational potential energy. *(2 marks)*.

   c The lorry's engine suddenly stops. Calculate the time it takes to come to rest, assuming that the average frictional force during this time is 20 000 N. *(4 marks)*

8 This question is about the motion of a projectile as shown in Figure 2.

Table 1 shows the coordinates of the object measured from the point from which it was thrown.

▼ **Table 1**

t / s	0	1	2	3	4	5
x / m	0	31.5	63	94.5	126	157.5
y / m	0	20	29	29	20	0

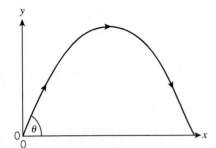

▲ **Figure 2**

   a Estimate the maximum height reached by the projectile. *(1 mark)*

   b Estimate the angle θ at which the object was projected. Make your working clear, and explain why the value obtained is likely to be an underestimate. *(3 marks)*

   c Give one reason, with justification, why the data indicates that there is no significant air resistance acting on the object *(2 marks)*.

   d On a copy of the graph, sketch the original trajectory and also the trajectory to be expected if the object experienced significant air resistance. Label the second curve 'air resistance'. *(3 marks)*

10
GROWTH AND DECAY
10.1 Radioactive decay and half-life
Specification reference: 5.1.1a(iv), 5.1.1 b(ii), 5.1.1. b(iv) 5.1.1c(i), 5.1.1 c(ii) 5.1.1 d(iv)

In the early years of the 20th century, an understanding developed that atoms are not always stable. Unstable atoms break down, or decay, emitting three distinct types of radiation: alpha particles (α), beta particles (β), and gamma rays (γ).

Radioactive decay and randomness

Radioactive decay is an example of a random process.

- Each unstable nucleus in a sample has a fixed probability of decaying in a given time.

- The number of nuclei decaying in a given time can be predicted from the probability of the decay of the individual nuclei.

- The decay of an individual nucleus cannot be predicted.

The decay constant and activity

The unit of activity is the becquerel, Bq. $1\,\text{Bq} = 1\ \text{decay s}^{-1}$

Activity A = probability of one nucleus decaying in one second × number of nuclei $N = \lambda N$

Half-life

As activity A is proportional to number of nuclei N, half-life can also be defined as the time taken for the activity of a sample to fall to half its original value.

Half-life

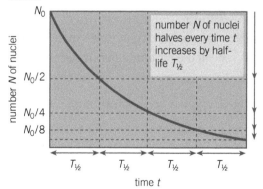

▲ **Figure 1** *Graph showing first four half-lives of a sample*

- In one half-life, the activity is reduced by a factor of 2.

- In two half-lives, the activity is reduced by a factor of $2^2 = 4$.

- In L half-lives, the activity is reduced by a factor of 2^L.

- After L half-lives, activity $A = \dfrac{\text{original activity } A_0}{2^L}$

Synoptic link

You will meet the characteristics of particles released in radioactive decay in more detail in Topic 19.1, Ionising radiation.

Key term

Randomness: A random process is one in which an event occurs entirely by chance. It is a change or event with one or more outcomes, including no change, that can occur with a certain probability in a given time interval.

Key term

Probability: In this context, probability is the chance of an event occurring in unit time.

Key terms

Decay constant: The decay constant λ is the probability that a nucleus will decay in a given time interval. The time interval is usually 1 s, giving units for λ of s^{-1}.

Activity: The activity A of a source is the number of nuclei decaying per second.

Key term

Half-life $T_{\frac{1}{2}}$: The half-life of a radioactive source is the time required for half the nuclei in a sample to decay.

Worked example: Activity and half-life

At the start of a measurement, a radioactive source has an activity of 4700 Bq. The half-life of the radioactive element in the source is 80 s. Calculate the activity after 304 s have passed.

Step 1: Calculate the number of half-lives.

$$\frac{304\,\text{s}}{80\,\text{s}} = 3.80 \text{ half-lives}$$

Step 2: Substitute and evaluate.

$$A = \frac{\text{original activity } A_0}{2^L}$$

$$= \frac{4700\,\text{Bq}}{2^{3.80}} = 337\,\text{Bq} \ (3 \text{ s.f.})$$

Common misconceptions: Activity and count rate

The activity is the number of nuclei in a sample that decay in one second. The count rate is the number of decays the measuring system detects in one second. Both values are measured in Bq.

Count rate is proportional to activity. For example, if the activity falls by 10% so will the count rate.

Finding the half-life from a graph

Draw a horizontal line from a given number of nuclei and find the time value at the point the horizontal line meets the curve. Repeat this for half your original choice of number of nuclei. The half-life is the difference between the two time values.

Practical: Determining the half-life of protactinium

- Protactinium-234 is a radioactive isotope that emits beta particles which can be detected with suitable apparatus.
- Before measuring the activity of the source, the background count is measured.
- When the protactinium source is in position, the detection apparatus records the counts every 10 seconds for a period of about 3 minutes.
- The count rate is found by dividing the counts in each 10 second period by 10.
- The corrected count rate is found by subtracting the background count rate from the measured count rate.
- A graph of corrected count rate (y-axis) against time (x-axis) can be drawn and the half-life determined. You will consider a different method of analysing the results in Topic 10.2, Another way of looking at radioactive decay.

Exponential decay

- An exponential decay is one in which the rate of decay of a quantity is proportional to the value of the quantity.
- For quantity x, rate of change $= \dfrac{\Delta x}{\Delta t}$ where Δt is a time interval.
- For exponential decay: $\dfrac{\Delta x}{\Delta t} \propto -x$ or $\dfrac{\Delta x}{\Delta t} = -kx$ where k is a constant. The negative sign indicates that the value of the quantity x is decreasing over time.

Exponential decay of nuclei

The number of nuclei decaying in a small time interval is given by $\Delta N = -\lambda N \Delta t$

Therefore, $\dfrac{\Delta N}{\Delta t} = -\lambda N$

An iterative model of radioactive decay

An iteration is a repeat of a mathematical operation. An iterative model is one in which a mathematical operation is repeated over a number of cycles. The equation $\dfrac{\Delta N}{\Delta t} = -\lambda N$ can be used to make such a model.

Consider a radioactive source of 10^3 nuclei with a decay constant of $0.6\,\text{s}^{-1}$.

- In the first second, number decaying $= \lambda N \Delta t = 10^3 \times 0.6\,\text{s}^{-1} \times 1\,\text{s} = 600$
- At the beginning of the 2nd second, number remaining $= N - \Delta N = 400$
- In the 2nd second, number decaying $= 400 \times 0.6\,\text{s}^{-1} \times 1\,\text{s} = 240$
- At the beginning of the 3rd second, number remaining $= 400 - 240 = 160$

The process can be repeated as often as desired. The model is a simplification as it assumes that the decay rate is constant over each 1 s time interval Δt whereas the rate of decay will fall throughout the time interval. The model can be improved by reducing the length of the time interval between iterations. Figure 2 shows graphs plotted from the original model with a time interval of 1 s between iterations and with a time interval of 0.25 s between iterations. Notice that the improved model shows a slower decay.

(a)

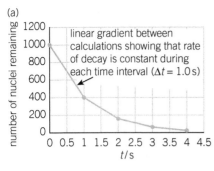

(b)

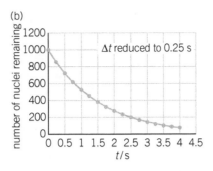

▲ **Figure 2** *Graphs showing results of iterative calculations based on the source described in the text. Graph (a) shows results for Δt = 1 s. Graph (b) shows results for Δt = 0.25 s*

Summary questions

1 A radioactive sample has a half-life of 4 hours. What percentage of the radioactive nuclei in the sample will remain after one day (24 hours)? *(3 marks)*

2 The activity of a sample falls from 1000 Bq to 125 Bq in 1 hour. Calculate the half-life of the radioactive nuclei in the sample. *(2 marks)*

3 The decay constant of carbon-14 is $3.8 \times 10^{-12}\,\text{s}^{-1}$. A typical adult will have about 6×10^{14} of carbon-14 atoms in his or her body. Calculate the activity resulting from these atoms. *(2 marks)*

4 a The graph in Figure 3 shows how the count rate from a source varies over time. Use the graph to determine the half-life of the source. *(1 mark)*

   b The source originally contained about 103 radioactive nuclei. Estimate by calculation the decay constant of the source. *(2 marks)*

5 At time = 0 s, a radioactive source contains 24 000 unstable nuclei with decay constant = $0.4\,\text{s}^{-1}$.

   a Copy and complete Table 1 by performing iterative calculations with $\Delta t = 0.5\,\text{s}$. *(3 marks)*

Time elapsed / s	Number of nuclei N	Number decaying $\Delta N = \lambda N \Delta t$	Number remaining = $N - \Delta N$
0.0	24 000	0.4 × 24000 × 0.5 = 4800	24000 − 4800 = 19 200
0.5	19 200	3840	15 360
1.0	15 360		
1.5			
2.0			

   b Plot a graph of your results. *(3 marks)*

   c Use the graph to estimate the half-life of the source. *(2 marks)*

   d The accepted value for the half-life of the source is 1.7 s. Compare this to the value you obtained from the graph and explain any difference. *(2 marks)*

corrected count rate/s^{-1}

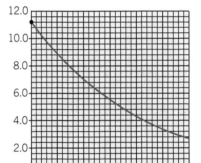

▲ **Figure 3** *A radioactive decay curve*

10.2 Another way of looking at radioactive decay

Specification reference: 5.1.1 a (iv), 5.1.1 b(v), 5.1.1 c(i)

A differential equation and its solution

- In Topic 10.1, you used the equation $\frac{\Delta N}{\Delta t} = -\lambda N$ to model radioactivity.
- $\frac{dN}{dt}$, the differential of N with respect to time, is the limit of the ratio $\frac{\Delta N}{\Delta t}$ as Δt tends to zero.
- $\frac{dN}{dt} = -\lambda N$ is a differential equation. This means it is an equation involving the rate of change of a quantity, in this case the rate of change of number of nuclei.
- The solution to the equation $\frac{dN}{dt} = -\lambda N$ is $N = N_0 e^{-\lambda t}$
- As activity $A \propto N$, you can also write $A = A_0 e^{-\lambda t}$

$A = A_0 e^{-\lambda t}$ and half-life

Taking natural logarithms of both sides of the equation $A = A_0 e^{-\lambda t}$ gives:

$$\ln A = \ln A_0 - \lambda t$$

which gives:

$$\ln \frac{A}{A_0} = -\lambda t$$

When the activity falls to half its original value $\frac{A}{A_0} = \frac{1}{2}$. This happens after a time interval of one half life, $T_{1/2}$.

Thus,

$$\ln \frac{1}{2} = -\lambda T_{1/2}$$

So,

$$T_{1/2} = \frac{\ln 2}{\lambda} \text{ or } \lambda = \frac{\ln 2}{T_{1/2}}$$

> **Revision tip**
>
> Make sure that you are confident about using all the equations in this topic and that you know how to use your calculator to find the natural logarithm (ln) of a number.

Model answer: Half-life, the decay constant and activity

Potassium-44 has a half-life of 22.1 minutes. A sample containing potassium-44 has an activity of 2.25 kBq.

a Calculate the activity of the sample after 70 minutes.

b Calculate the time for the activity to fall to 0.6 kBq.

a The decay constant of potassium $= \frac{\ln 2}{22.1} = 0.0314 \text{ min}^{-1}$

> The units of the decay constant are usually given as s^{-1}. You can use different units if this makes the arithmetic easier but you must make sure that the units used are consistent. This student has decided to use minutes and minutes^{-1}.

Activity $A = A_0 e^{-\lambda t}$ so activity after 70 minutes $= 2.25 \text{ kBq} \times e^{-0.0314 \times 70} = 0.250 \text{ kBq (3 s.f.)}$

b $\ln A = \ln A_0 - \lambda t$

$\ln 0.6 = \ln 2.25 - 0.0314 \text{ min}^{-1} t$

$\ln \frac{0.6}{2.25} = -0.0314 \text{ min}^{-1} t$

$t = \frac{-1.32}{-0.0314 \text{ min}^{-1}} = 42.1 \text{ minutes}$

> Notice that the student has not converted kBq into Bq as the units of kBq have been used throughout the calculation. It is very good practice to include the units in all steps of the calculation to check that you are being consistent.

Decay graphs

You met graphs of activity against time and number of nuclei against time in Topic 10.1, Radioactive decay and half-life. A graph of the natural logarithm of activity ($\ln A$) against time (t) has the equation $\ln A = \ln A_0 - \lambda t$. The gradient of graph is $-\lambda$. This is another graphical way of finding the half-life of a source because $T_{\frac{1}{2}} = \dfrac{\ln 2}{\lambda}$.

🖩 Worked example: Activity

Figure 1 shows how the natural log of the activity of a sample varies with time.

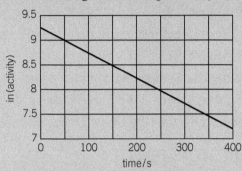

▲ **Figure 1** *Graph of ln activity versus time*

a Use the graph to find the decay constant of the sample.

b Find the half-life of the sample.

a $\lambda = -\text{gradient} = 0.0052\ \text{s}^{-1}$

b $T_{\frac{1}{2}} = \dfrac{\ln 2}{\lambda} = \dfrac{00.693}{0.0052\ \text{s}^{-1}} = 130\ \text{s}$ (2 s.f.)

Common misconception: Decay constant

The gradient of a graph of $\ln A$ against time t gives the negative of the decay constant. The decay constant itself is *not* negative.

Summary questions

1 The decay constant of krypton-87 is $1.5 \times 10^{-4}\ \text{s}^{-1}$. Calculate the half-life of krypton-87. *(2 marks)*

2 The half-life of polonium-218 is 3.1 minutes. A sample containing polonium-218 has an initial activity of $1.7 \times 10^3\ \text{Bq}$. Calculate its activity after a time interval of 45 seconds. *(2 marks)*

3 The activity of a sample falls from $9.0 \times 10^5\ \text{Bq}$ to $9.0 \times 10^4\ \text{Bq}$ in 76 minutes. Calculate the half-life of the sample. *(3 marks)*

4 Bismuth-210 has a half-life of 5.00 days. A source containing bismuth-210 is placed near a detector which measures a corrected count-rate of 1.7 kBq.

   a Estimate (by calculation) the corrected count rate 4.00 days before the measurement. *(2 marks)*

   b Chemical analysis suggests that approximately 2×10^{11} bismuth-210 atoms were present at the time of the 1.7 kBq measurement. Explain, using relevant calculations, how this shows that the activity of the sample was about 200 times the measured count rate. Suggest a reason for this difference. *(4 marks)*

10.3 Capacitors in circuits

Specification reference: 5.1.1a(i), 5.1.1 a(ii), 5.1.1 b(vi), 5.1.1c (v)

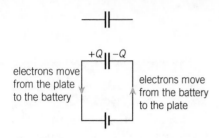

▲ Figure 1 *Capacitor symbol (top) and charging a capacitor*

The gradient of the graph of charge against p.d. gives the capacitance

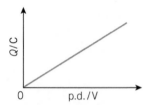

▲ Figure 2 *Relationship between p.d. and charge Q for a capacitor*

Capacitors

Capacitors are electrical components that store charge. The fundamental design of the capacitor is simple: a pair of electrical conductors or 'plates' separated by a thin layer of insulating material. When a p.d. is applied across the plates, negative charge flows onto one plate, giving it a negative charge and an equal negative charge flows from the other plate resulting in that plate becoming positively charged.

Figure 2 shows the proportional relationship between the charge on a capacitor and the p.d. across its plates.

- Capacitance C is the charge separated per volt: $C = \dfrac{Q}{V}$
- The capacitance is the gradient of the graph of charge against p.d. (Figure 2).
- The unit of capacitance is the farad, F, where $F = C\,V^{-1}$.

Energy stored on a capacitor

- The energy stored on a capacitor is given by the equation energy $E = \dfrac{1}{2} QV$ where Q is the charge on the capacitor and V is the potential difference across the capacitor.
- As $Q = CV$ the relationship between the capacitance and energy stored is also given by:

$$E = \frac{1}{2} CV^2 \text{ and } E = \frac{1}{2} \frac{Q^2}{C}$$

- The energy stored on a capacitor is the area under the graph of potential difference across the capacitor plotted against the charge.

 Worked example: Energy stored on a capacitor

A 220 µF capacitor has a potential difference of 1.30 V across it. Calculate the energy stored on the capacitor.

Step 1: Choose the correct equation: $E = \dfrac{1}{2} CV^2$

Step 2: Substitute and evaluate: $E = \dfrac{1}{2} \times 220 \times 10^{-6}\,F \times 1.30^2\,V^2 = 1.86 \times 10^{-4}\,J$ (3 s.f.)

Summary questions

1 Table 1 shows the energy stored, p.d., and charge for a number of different capacitors. Copy and complete the table. *(3 marks)*

▼ Table 1

Capacitance / F	Potential difference / V	Charge / C	Energy / J
4700×10^{-6}	9.50		
4.70×10^{-4}			0.0180
6.90×10^{-4}		3.20×10^{-3}	

2 A camera flash uses a 185 µF capacitor which stores 9.47 J when fully charged. Calculate the potential difference across the capacitor. *(2 marks)*

3 The p.d. across a capacitor falls from 6.0 V to 1.5 V. Calculate the ratio:
$\dfrac{\text{energy stored at 1.5 V}}{\text{energy stored at 6.0 V}}$ *(2 marks)*

10.4 Modelling capacitors

Specification reference: 5.1.1a(iii), 5.1.1b(i), 5.1.1c(iii), 5.1.1c(iv), 5.1.1c(v), 5.1.1d(iii)

Capacitor discharge

This topic considers how the charge on a capacitor changes over time.

Practical: Investigating the discharge of a capacitor

- The capacitor in the circuit shown in Figure 1 is charged by connecting the switch to A.
- Begin timing as the switch is connected to B, allowing the capacitor to discharge through the resistor. Take measurements of the p.d. across the capacitor at suitable time intervals. This data can be analysed to produce graphs of the variation of:
  - p.d. across the capacitor with time
  - charge on the capacitor with time
  - current in the circuit with time.

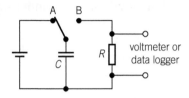

▲ **Figure 1** *Circuit for observing the change in potential difference across a capacitor as it discharges*

The graph in Figure 2 shows the variation of p.d. across a capacitor with time during a discharge. It resembles the graph of count rate against time for a radioactive sample in Topic 10.1, Radioactive decay and half-life. Discharge of a capacitor is another example of exponential decay.

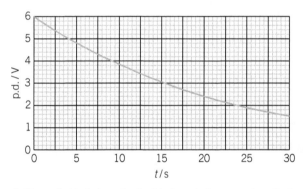

▲ **Figure 2** *Variation of p.d. with time during capacitor discharge*

- As $Q = CV$ and C is a constant, the graph of the variation of charge on a discharging capacitor with time is also an exponential decay.
- As current through the resistor is proportional to the p.d. across the resistor, the current in the discharge circuit will also show exponential decay.

Modelling capacitor discharge

You can model the discharge of a capacitor in the simple circuit shown in Figure 3 using the same technique you used in modelling radioactive decay.

▲ **Figure 3** *A simple circuit for capacitor discharge*

Assume that the current I remains steady over a short time interval Δt.

The charge leaving the capacitor over this time interval,

$$\Delta Q = -I\Delta t = -\frac{V}{R}\,\Delta t = -\frac{Q}{RC}\,\Delta t$$

The negative sign indicates that the charge on the capacitor is decreasing over time.

Rearranging $\Delta Q = -\dfrac{Q}{RC}\,\Delta t$ gives: $\dfrac{\Delta Q}{\Delta t} = -\dfrac{Q}{RC}$

This is another example of an exponential relationship. The equation can be solved iteratively in the manner shown in the flow chart in Figure 4.

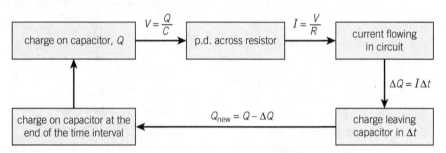

▲ **Figure 4** *Flowchart for iterative calculation of the changing charge on a discharging capacitor*

- $\dfrac{dQ}{dt}$, the differential of Q with respect to time, is the limit of the ratio $\dfrac{\Delta Q}{\Delta t}$ as Δt tends to zero.

- The solution to the equation $\dfrac{dQ}{dt} = -\dfrac{Q}{RC}$ is $Q = Q_0 e^{-\frac{t}{RC}}$

- Similarly, the p.d. across a discharging capacitor is given by: $V = V_0 e^{-\frac{t}{RC}}$

- Similarly, the current in the circuit is given by: $I = I_0 e^{-\frac{t}{RC}}$

> ▣ **Worked example: Capacitor discharge**
>
> **A 2200 µF capacitor discharges through a 9.0 kΩ resistor. The initial p.d. across the capacitor is 9.0 V. Calculate the time taken for the p.d. to fall to 4.5 V.**
>
> **Step 1:** Choose the correct equation: $V = V_0 e^{-\frac{t}{RC}}$
>
> **Step 2:** Take natural logarithms of both sides: $\ln V = \ln V_0 - \dfrac{t}{RC}$
>
> **Step 3:** Rearrange the equation: $\ln V - \ln V_0 = -\dfrac{t}{RC}$ $\therefore \ln\dfrac{V}{V_0} = -\dfrac{t}{RC}$
>
> **Step 4:** Substitute and evaluate: $\ln\dfrac{4.5}{9.0} = -\dfrac{t}{9.0 \times 10^3\,\Omega \times 2200 \times 10^{-6}\,\text{F}}$
>
> which gives $t = 14\,\text{s}$ (2 s.f.)

Time constant $\tau = RC$

- After RC seconds of discharge, the charge on a capacitor will have fallen to e^{-1} of its original value. The time interval RC is called the time constant, symbol τ.

- e^{-1} is about 0.37. A useful approximation is that the charge on a capacitor falls to about 37% of its original value during RC seconds.

- Similarly, the p.d. across the capacitor and the current in the discharge circuit fall to 37% of their original values during RC seconds.

- After 2τ ($2RC$) seconds, the charge (and p.d. and current) will have fallen to e^{-2} of their original values. This is about 14% of the original values.

Charging a capacitor

Figure 5 shows a capacitor charging circuit.

The p.d. across the capacitor, V_C is given by:

$$V_C = V_0 - V_0 e^{-\frac{t}{RC}} = V_0(1 - e^{-\frac{t}{RC}})$$

where V_0 is the supply p.d.

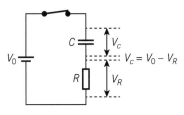

As the p.d. across a capacitor is proportional to its charge:

$$Q = Q_0(1 - e^{-\frac{t}{RC}})$$

where $Q_0 = CV_0$

▲ **Figure 5** *Capacitor circuit*

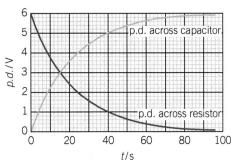

The variation in p.d. across a capacitor and resistor in the circuit of Figure 5 during charging is shown in Figure 6. The e.m.f. of the cell is 6.0 V.

▲ **Figure 6** *Charging curve of a capacitor*

Worked example: Charging a capacitor

A 2200 μF capacitor is charged in a circuit similar to Figure 5. The cell has e.m.f. $V_0 = 1.5$ V and negligible internal resistance. The resistor has value $R = 9.0$ kΩ. Calculate the p.d. across the capacitor after 10 s.

Step 1: Choose the correct equation: $V_C = V_0(1 - e^{-\frac{t}{RC}})$

Step 2: Substitute and evaluate: $V_C = 1.5\,V\left(1 - e^{-\frac{10\,s}{9.0 \times 10^3\,\Omega \times 2200 \times 10^{-6}\,F}}\right) = 0.59\,V$

Summary questions

1   A 470 μF capacitor has an initial p.d. of 6.0 V across its plates. It
    discharges through a 4500 Ω resistor. Calculate:
    a   the initial charge on the capacitor   *(2 marks)*
    b   the time constant τ of the capacitor–resistor pair   *(2 marks)*
    c   the charge on the capacitor after 3τ.   *(2 marks)*

2   A 4700 μF capacitor has an initial charge of 0.021 C. It is discharged
    through a 2000 Ω resistor. Calculate:
    a   the initial p.d. across the capacitor   *(2 marks)*
    b   the charge on the capacitor after 3.0 s of discharge.   *(2 marks)*

3   Show that the units of RC can be expressed as the unit of
    time, s.   *(2 marks)*

4   A 220 μF capacitor is connected in a circuit similar to Figure 5.
    The cell has e.m.f. $V_0 = 3.0$ V and negligible internal resistance.
    The resistor has a resistance of 11 kΩ. Calculate the time it
    takes to charge the capacitor to 2.0 V.   *(3 marks)*

5   A capacitor–resistor pair have a time constant τ of 3.0 s.
    At the start of a discharge the energy stored on the capacitor = E.
    What is the energy stored on the capacitor after 6.0 s of discharge?
                                                               (3 marks)

Practical: Investigating the charging of a capacitor

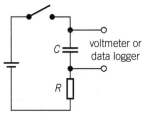

▲ **Figure 7** *Charging a capacitor*

- Figure 7 shows a circuit that can be used to investigate how the p.d. across a capacitor changes with time as it is charged.
- Measurements of p.d. are taken at regular time intervals after the switch has been closed. A data logger will allow readings to be taken at short intervals of time.

1 The mass of one mole (6.0×10^{23} atoms) of polonium-210 is 210 g. One microgram (1×10^{-6} g) of polonium-210 has an activity of 167 MBq.

   a Calculate the number of atoms in 1 microgram of polonium-210.

           (1 mark)

   b Calculate the decay constant of polonium-210   *(2 marks)*

   c Calculate the half-life of polonium-210. Give your answer in days.

           (2 marks).

2 The decay constant of radioisotope A is 1×10^{-4} s^{-1}.

   a Explain what this tells you about the decay nuclei of this radioisotope.

           (3 marks)

   b A second radioisotope, B, has a decay constant of 2×10^{-4} s^{-1}.

      At time $t = 0$ s, activity of A = activity of B.

      i Compare the number of atoms of both isotopes.   *(1 mark)*

      ii At what time will the activities be equal?   *(2 marks)*

3 The activity of a radioisotope falls to $\frac{1}{16}$ of its original value after 20 hours. Calculate the half-life of the isotope.   *(2 marks)*

4 A radioisotope has a half-life of 12.5 hours. A sample has an initial activity of 100 kBq.

   a Calculate the activity of the sample after one hour.   *(3 marks)*

   b Calculate the time for the activity of a sample of the isotope to fall to 10% of its original value.   *(2 marks)*

5 Here are some data about the circuit shown in Figure 1.

   p.d. of cell = 4.5 V, load resistance $R = 4.2$ kΩ capacitance $C = 2200$ µF

   a State the p.d. across the capacitor when the switch is in position A.

           (1 mark)

   b Calculate the energy stored on the capacitor when the switch is in position A.   *(1 mark)*

   c Calculate the time constant for the circuit. Assume the voltmeter has a very high resistance.   *(1 mark)*

   d The switch is moved to position B. Show that it will take about 13 s for the energy stored on the capacitor to fall to 25% of its original value.   *(3 marks)*

   e Calculate how long it will take for the energy stored to fall to 25% of its original value.   *(3 marks)*

   f A student sets up the circuit and finds that it takes longer than 13 s for the p.d. to fall to 25% of its original value. He suggests that this may be because the resistance of the voltmeter was lower than assumed. Comment on his suggestion, explaining your reasoning.   *(3 marks)*

6 The radioisotope potassium-40 can be used to find the age of a rock sample. The half-life of potassium-40 is 1.25×10^9 years. It decays into argon, a stable isotope. It is assumed that all the argon in a sample of rock is produced through the decay of potassium.

   a How long will it take for the ratio of argon atoms to potassium atoms to reach 1 : 1?   *(1 mark)*

   b The ratio of argon to potassium in a sample is 2.5 : 1. Calculate the age of the rock (the time over which potassium has been decaying into argon).   *(2 marks)*

7 An uncharged 4700 µF capacitor is charged by a 4.5 V battery in series with a 22 kΩ resistor. Calculate the charge on the capacitor after 75.0 s.   *(3 marks)*

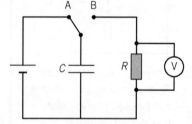

▲ **Figure 1** *Circuit for charging and discharging a capacitor*

Describing oscillations

An oscillation is a back-and-forth movement about a fixed point, the equilibrium position. The amplitude of an oscillation is the maximum displacement from the equilibrium position. Examples of oscillations include a child on a swing and a mass suspended on a vertical spring. The sound of a violin is produced by an oscillating string and the sound of a bagpipe is produced by oscillating reeds.

Simple harmonic oscillation

- Simple harmonic oscillators are oscillators in which the acceleration of the oscillator is proportional to the negative of the displacement (from the equilibrium position): $a \propto -x$

- Simple harmonic oscillators are isochronous; the period of oscillation is independent of amplitude. For example, for small angles of displacement, the time period of a simple pendulum is independent of the amplitude of oscillations. This makes pendulums useful as timekeepers.

- The displacement of a simple harmonic oscillator varies sinusoidally over time.

Simple harmonic motion and circular motion

Figure 2 shows particle P which is moving at a constant speed around a circle of radius A. P* is the projection of P onto the line RS.

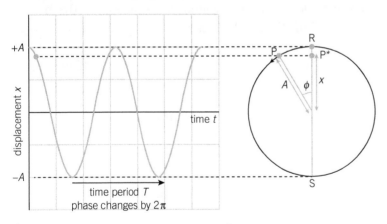

▲ **Figure 2** *Circular motion projected onto a line*

At the instant shown in Figure 2, $x = A \cos \phi$.

Key Terms

Time period: The period of an oscillation T is the time taken for one cycle of the oscillation.

Frequency: The frequency of an oscillation f is the number of cycles in one second. The unit of frequency is the hertz, Hz.

$$\text{frequency} = \frac{1}{\text{time period}},$$

$$f = \frac{1}{T} \text{ or } T = \frac{1}{f}$$

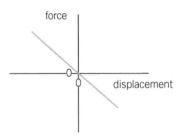

▲ **Figure 1** *The force on a simple harmonic oscillator is proportional to −displacement, so $a \propto -x$*

Maths skill: Angular frequency

Angular frequency ω is given by $\omega = 2\pi f = \dfrac{2\pi}{T}$ where f is the frequency of the simple harmonic oscillator and T is the time period. The units of angular frequency are rad s⁻¹.

Revision tip
The factor of 2π in the equations should remind you to check the settings on your calculator and make sure that it is radian mode.

If point P is at R when $t = 0$, after t seconds P* will be at displacement x as shown in the figure where:

$$x = A \cos 2\pi ft = A \cos \omega t$$

If $x = 0$ when $t = 0$, the equation describing the variation of displacement is:

$$x = A \sin 2\pi ft = A \sin \omega t$$

 Worked example: Simple pendulum

A pendulum oscillates in simple harmonic motion. The time period of the pendulum is 0.50 s. The amplitude of the oscillation is 0.040 m. Calculate the position of the end of the pendulum 0.60 s from its maximum displacement.

Step 1: Choose the correct equation. You can use the equation

$x = A \cos 2\pi ft = A \cos \dfrac{2\pi t}{T}$ because the timing is from the position of

maximum displacement ($x = A$ when $t = 0\,\text{s}$).

Step 2: $x = 0.040\,\text{m} \times \cos\left(2\pi \times \dfrac{0.60\,\text{s}}{0.5\,\text{s}}\right) = 0.012\,\text{m}$

Acceleration of a simple harmonic oscillator

$a \propto -x \; \therefore \; a = -kx$ where k is a constant

The general relationship for all simple harmonic oscillators is:

$$a = -\omega^2 x = -4\pi^2 f^2 x.$$

Summary questions

1 Calculate the frequency of an oscillator with a time period of 0.25 ms.

(2 marks)

2 A simple harmonic oscillator has an amplitude of oscillation of 30 mm and a frequency of 1.2 Hz. The oscillator passes through the equilibrium position at $t = 0\,\text{s}$. Calculate:

a its displacement at $t = 0.25\,\text{s}$ *(2 marks)*

b its maximum acceleration. *(2 marks)*

3 a State the properties shared by all simple harmonic oscillators.

(2 marks)

b Two pendulums, A and B, are set in motion. Pendulum A has half the amplitude and twice the frequency of pendulum B.

Calculate the ratio $\dfrac{\text{maximum acceleration of pendulum A}}{\text{maximum acceleration of pendulum B}}$ *(2 marks)*

11.2 Modelling simple harmonic oscillation

Specification references: 5.1.1 a(v), 5.1.1.b (vii), 5.1.1c(ix)

Displacement, velocity, and acceleration of simple harmonic oscillators

Figure 1 shows how the displacement, velocity, and acceleration of a simple harmonic oscillator vary over time. It is very important to learn the phase relationships between these three quantities.

- Velocity is the rate of change of displacement. The gradient of the displacement–time graph at any instant is the velocity at that instant.

- The velocity variation is a quarter of a cycle $\left(\dfrac{\pi}{2}\text{radian}\right)$ ahead of the displacement variation. For example, the displacement variation passes through zero a quarter of a cycle after the velocity variation passes through zero.

- Acceleration is the rate of change of velocity. The gradient of the velocity–time graph at any instant gives the acceleration at that instant.

- The acceleration variation is a quarter of a cycle $\left(\dfrac{\pi}{2}\text{radian}\right)$ ahead of the velocity variation. The acceleration cycle is therefore π radian ahead of the displacement cycle.

The displacement of the oscillator in Figure 1 is described by the equation:

$$x = A\cos 2\pi ft \text{ or } x = A\cos \omega t$$

The velocity v of the oscillator at time t is given by:

$$v = \frac{dx}{dt} -2\pi fA \sin 2\pi ft = -\omega A \sin \omega t$$

The acceleration a of the oscillator at time t is given by:

$$a = \frac{dv}{dt} -4\pi^2 f^2 A \cos 2\pi ft = -\omega^2 A \cos \omega t$$

As $x = A\cos 2\pi ft$, $a = -4\pi^2 f^2 x = -\omega^2 x$

As $4\pi^2 f^2$ is a constant for a given harmonic oscillator, this equation is of the form: $a \propto -x$

(a)

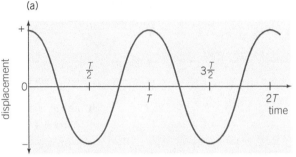

(b)

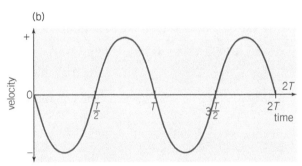

(c)

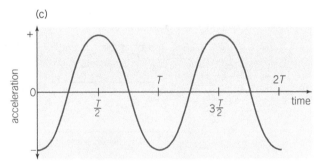

▲ **Figure 1** *Graphs of (a) displacement, (b) velocity, and (c) acceleration against time for a simple harmonic oscillator*

Common misconception: Acceleration at zero velocity

Acceleration and velocity are often confused and it is sometimes thought that the acceleration of a body is zero if the body has zero velocity. This is not the case, and in simple harmonic motion the maximum acceleration of the oscillator occurs when the velocity is zero.

Revision tip

Cosines and sines have values from −1 to 1 so the maximum magnitudes of displacement, velocity, and acceleration are found by setting the sine or cosine term to 1 or −1. This gives:

maximum displacement = amplitude, A

maximum velocity = $2\pi fA$

maximum acceleration = $4\pi^2 f^2 A$

Modelling simple harmonic oscillators

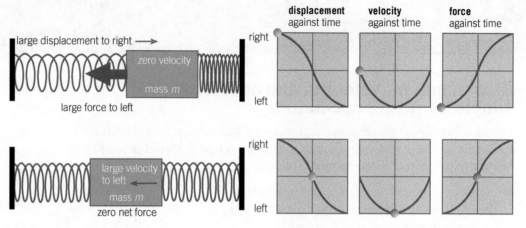

▲ **Figure 2** *Everything about harmonic motion follows from the fact that the restoring force (and so the acceleration) is proportional to the negative of the displacement*

Imagine a mass held between two springs as shown in Figure 2. The mass is displaced $+x$ to the right. When the mass is released the force F on the mass will produce an acceleration $-a$.

From Hooke's law, $F = -kx$ ∴ $a\dfrac{-kx}{m}$ where k is the force constant of the system.

The acceleration is zero as the mass passes through the equilibrium point of the oscillation.

The equation for the oscillation of the mass can be written as:

$$\frac{\Delta^2 x}{\Delta t^2} = \frac{-kx}{m}$$

This equation can be used to iteratively model the situation shown in Figure 2 using the scheme shown in Figure 3.

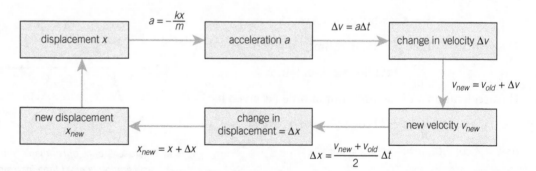

▲ **Figure 3** *Flow chart showing calculations for the simple harmonic oscillation in Figure 2*

This iterative model produces a reasonable picture of a single oscillation of the system, but when the model is run for a large number of iterations it produces an oscillation with an ever-increasing amplitude. This doesn't happen in simple harmonic oscillation and shows a limitation of the model.

Summary questions

1 The graph in Figure 4 shows how the acceleration of a simple harmonic oscillator varies with time.

▲ **Figure 4**

a Write down the equation that describes how the displacement of this oscillator varies with time where A is the amplitude of the oscillation and ω is the angular frequency of the oscillation. *(1 mark)*

b Copy the graph and add lines representing the variation of velocity with time and the variation of displacement with time. Label the lines. *(2 marks)*

2 The weight on the end of a pendulum (called the 'bob') oscillates in simple harmonic motion. The frequency of the oscillation is 0.90 Hz. The amplitude of the oscillation is 0.030 m. Calculate:

a the maximum velocity of the pendulum bob *(2 marks)*

b the maximum acceleration of the pendulum bob. *(2 marks)*

3 An iterative model of the oscillations of a mass held between two springs is made using the following data:
mass = 0.6 kg, force constant $k = 18$ N kg^{-1}, amplitude of oscillation = 0.12 m, time interval between iterative calculations = 0.05 s
The model follows the scheme shown in Figure 2. Table 1 shows the first few iterations of the model. You can see that the velocity has been held at zero for the first 0.05 s.

a Copy and complete Table 1 using either simple calculations or a spreadsheet. Don't round your answers.

▼ **Table 1**

t / s	x / m	a / m s^{-2}	Δv / m s^{-1}	v_{new} / m s^{-1}	Δx / m
0.00	0.12	−3.6	0.0	0.0	0.0
0.05	0.12	−3.6	−0.18	−0.18	−0.0045
0.10	0.1155	−3.465	−0.17325	−0.35325	−0.01333
0.15	0.102169	−3.06506	−0.15325	−0.5065	−0.02149
0.20					
0.25					
0.30					
0.35					

(4 marks)

b Use your completed table to make an estimate of the time period of the oscillation. *(2 marks)*

c The time period of the oscillation modelled is 1.15 s. Explain the difference in this value and your answer to part **b**. *(2 marks)*

The equation $a = -4\pi^2 f^2 x$ is a general equation which can be applied to specific oscillating systems. In this section it is applied it to the oscillation of mass on a spring and the oscillation of a simple pendulum.

The oscillations of a mass on a spring

In Topic 11.1, Introducing simple harmonic oscillators, you saw that the acceleration of a mass on a spring is given by

$$a = -\frac{kx}{m}$$

Substituting, $a = -4\pi^2 f^2 x$

$$4\pi^2 f^2 x = \frac{kx}{m}$$

Therefore,

$$f = \frac{1}{2\pi}\sqrt{\frac{k}{m}}$$

Therefore,

$$T = 2\pi\sqrt{\frac{m}{k}}$$

 Practical: Measuring the period of a mass on a spring

- A mass is hung from a spring as shown in Figure 1.
- The mass is lifted a small distance above the equilibrium position and released.
- The time for (say) 10 oscillations is measured to find the time period of the system.
- The process is repeated for different masses.
- If the time period of the oscillation follows the equation $T = 2\pi\sqrt{\frac{m}{k}}$ a graph of T^2 against m will produce a straight line through the origin. A graph of $\log T$ against $\log m$ will produce a straight line with a gradient of 0.5.

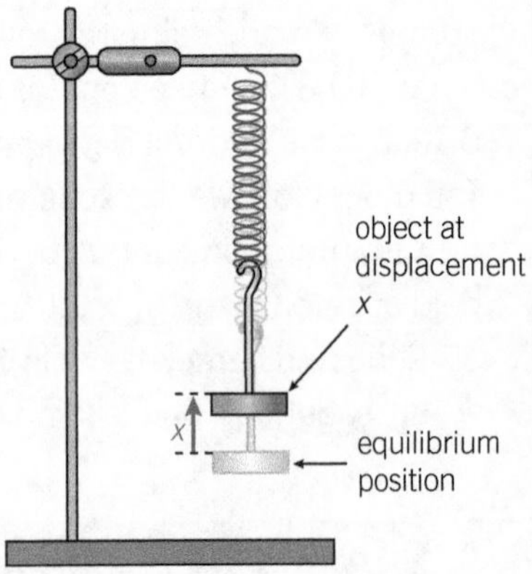

object at displacement x

equilibrium position

▲ **Figure 1** *Investigating the oscillations of a mass on a spring*

The oscillations of a simple pendulum

A restoring force acts on the mass m at the end of a pendulum of length L when it is displaced by a small displacement x from the equilibrium position. This force accelerates the mass such that

$a = -g\dfrac{x}{L}$ where g is the gravitational field strength.

Substituting, $a = -4\pi^2 f^2 x$

$$4\pi^2 f^2 x = g\frac{x}{L}$$

Therefore

$$4\pi^2 f^2 = \frac{g}{L}$$

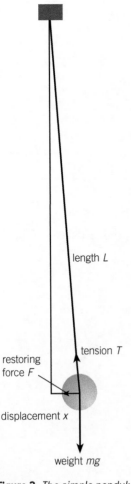

length L

tension T

restoring force F

displacement x

weight mg

▲ **Figure 2** *The simple pendulum*

Therefore
$$f = \frac{1}{2\pi}\sqrt{\frac{g}{L}}$$

$$T = \frac{1}{f} = 2\pi\sqrt{\frac{L}{g}}$$

 Worked example: The simple pendulum

A pendulum oscillating in simple harmonic motion has a time period of 2.0 s. Calculate the length of the pendulum. ($g = 9.8\,\text{N kg}^{-1}$)

Step 1: Select and rearrange the correct equation.
$$T = 2\pi\sqrt{\frac{L}{g}} \quad \therefore L = \frac{gT^2}{4\pi^2}$$

Step 2: Substitute and evaluate.
$$L = \frac{9.8\,\text{N kg}^{-1} \times 4.0\,\text{s}^2}{4\pi^2} = 0.99\,\text{m (2 s.f.)}$$

Summary questions

1 Calculate the time period of a pendulum of length 4.00 m.   (*2 marks*)

2 A 0.7 kg mass oscillates between two springs in simple harmonic motion. The frequency of the oscillation is 0.85 Hz.
   a Calculate the force constant of the system.   (*2 marks*)
   b The amplitude of oscillation is 0.020 m. Calculate the magnitude of the maximum acceleration of the system.   (*2 marks*)

3 A pendulum of length L has a time period on Earth of 2.8 s. Calculate the time period of the same pendulum oscillating on the Moon if $g_{\text{Earth}} = 6.2g_{\text{Moon}}$ (*2 marks*)

4 A 0.20 kg mass oscillates on a spring in simple harmonic motion. The amplitude of the oscillation is 0.08 m. The maximum velocity is $0.35\,\text{m s}^{-1}$. Calculate the force constant k of the system.   (*2 marks*)

11.4 Resonance

Specification references: 5.1.1a(vii), 5.1.1a(viii) 5.1.1b(iii), 5.1.1b(viii), 5.1.1.c(ix), 5.1.1d(ii)

Key term

Free oscillation: An oscillation due to the action of a restoring force without any damping or driving forces.

Key term

Forced oscillation: An oscillation driven by the action of a periodic driving force.

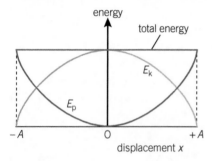

▲ **Figure 1** *Variation of kinetic energy and potential energy with displacement in an oscillator*

Free and forced oscillations

An undamped pendulum will swing at the same amplitude at its particular **natural frequency** for all time, it will continue swinging forever. This is an example of a free oscillation.

A loudspeaker is an example of a driven or forced oscillation. Variations of current in the coil of the loudspeaker force it to vibrate at the same frequency as the variations in current. If the current in the speaker coil is varying at, say, 340 Hz, the speaker will vibrate at this frequency.

Energy of a harmonic oscillator

The energy of a harmonic oscillator shifts back and forwards between kinetic energy and potential energy. In the case of a mass between springs the energy of the oscillator moves between kinetic and elastic potential energy, in the case of a simple pendulum the energy shifts between kinetic and gravitational potential energy. It is simplest to consider the oscillations of a mass between springs as shown in Topic, 11.2, Modelling simple harmonic oscillation, Figure 2.

- When the displacement is a maximum the velocity of the oscillator is zero. At this point all the energy of the system is elastic potential energy:
$E_p = \frac{1}{2}kx^2$
At this point, displacement = amplitude, $x = A$ so this can be written:
$E_p = \frac{1}{2}kA^2$

- When the oscillator passes through the equilibrium point, $x = 0$. At this point all the energy of the oscillator is kinetic energy E_k.

- Generally, total energy $E_{total} = \frac{1}{2}mv^2 + \frac{1}{2}kx^2 = E_k + E_p = \frac{1}{2}kA^2$

Figure 1 shows the variation of the energy of a simple harmonic oscillator with displacement.

Figure 2 shows the variation of energy with time. This graph is showing one complete oscillation (the time period of the oscillator is 1.0 s). Note that the potential energy and kinetic energy peak twice during each oscillation.

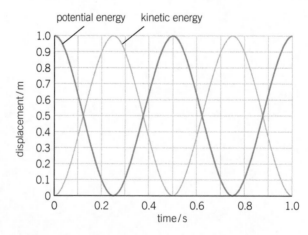

▲ **Figure 2** *Variation of kinetic energy and potential energy in an oscillator over time*

Revision tip: Amplitude and energy

Note that the energy of an oscillator is proportional to its amplitude squared. This is true of all oscillations, including electromagnetic waves and sound.

Worked example: Mass between springs

A 0.50 kg mass is held between two springs and is free to oscillate horizontally. The force constant k of the system is 20 N m^{-1}. The amplitude of the oscillation is 0.15 m.

a Calculate the energy of the system.

b Calculate the maximum velocity of the mass.

a $E = \frac{1}{2}kA^2 = 0.5 \times 20 \text{ N m}^{-1} \times 0.15^2 \text{ m}^2 = 0.23 \text{ J} \text{ (3 s.f.)}$

b The velocity is a maximum when the mass passes through the equilibrium point. That is, when E_k = total energy (as E_p = 0 at this point).

$\frac{1}{2}mv^2 = 0.225 \text{ J}$ (using unrounded value) $v = \sqrt{\dfrac{2 \times 0.225 \text{ J}}{0.50 \text{ kg}}} = 0.95 \text{ m s}^{-1}$

Damped oscillations

Real pendulums do not oscillate forever. The amplitude of the oscillation decreases until the oscillation stops. Energy gradually leaks away from them through the action of forces such as friction and drag. This gradual loss of energy from the oscillator is known as damping.

Figure 3 shows the variation of displacement with time for heavily damped, critically damped and lightly damped oscillators.

Resonance

When the driving frequency of a lightly-damped oscillator matches its natural frequency the amplitude of the oscillation will increase until the energy lost each oscillation (through damping) is equal to the energy supplied by the driver during the each oscillation.

Lightly damped systems can show dramatic resonance effects. Bridges are fitted with 'dampers' to limit high-amplitude oscillations caused by resonance. Bridges without enough damping have been known to collapse (literally shake themselves to bits) due to resonant oscillations.

Figure 4 shows how the 'resonant peak' varies with the degree of damping. The x-axis shows the ratio of natural frequency to the driving frequency and you can see that the resonance peak is when the natural frequency is the same as the driving frequency. For heavily damped systems, resonance occurs at a slightly lower frequency than the natural frequency.

Key term

Resonance: The production of large-amplitude oscillations when the driving frequency of a lightly-damped oscillator matches its natural frequency.

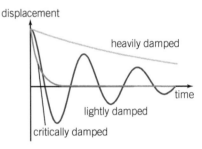

▲ **Figure 3** *Variation of displacement with time for different degrees of damping*

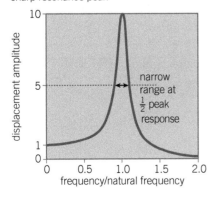

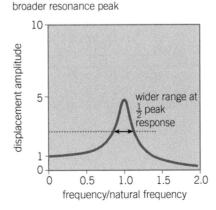

a low damping:
large maximum response
sharp resonance peak

b more damping:
smaller maximum response
broader resonance peak

▲ **Figure 4** *Damping and resonance*

Common misconceptions: Resonance graphs

Note that the amplitude of driven oscillators approaches zero when the driving frequency increases above the value of the natural frequency. The graphs are *not* symmetrical about the resonant frequency.

Practical: Observing resonance

- Resonance can be shown using the apparatus represented in Figure 5.
- The amplitude of the oscillations is measured by eye as the frequency is varied using the signal generator.
- The variation will produce a graph of amplitude against frequency similar to the left-hand graph in Figure 4.

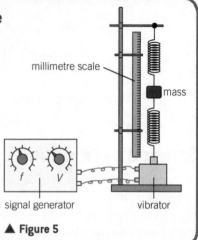

▲ **Figure 5**

Summary questions

1 Describe the energy changes over one oscillation of a freely oscillating pendulum. Assume that the gravitational potential energy of the pendulum bob is zero at the lowest point of the oscillation. The oscillation begins at the maximum displacement of the pendulum bob. You can include a labelled diagram in your answer. *(2 marks)*

2 'Resonance is found in many situations. Driven oscillators with light damping can show dramatic behaviour when resonating.' Explain the meanings of the underlined terms. *(6 marks)*

3 A mass is held between two springs and oscillates in simple harmonic motion. How do the following quantities change when the amplitude of the oscillation is halved? Note that the frequency of the oscillation does not change.
    a Total energy of the system *(1 mark)*
    b Maximum velocity of the mass *(1 mark)*
    c The maximum acceleration of the mass *(1 mark)*

4 Here are some data about a mass oscillating between two springs:
    mass = 0.4 kg, force constant of system = 60 N m^{-1}
    The total energy of the system is 0.16 J.
    Calculate the velocity of the mass at a displacement of 0.03 m.
    (3 marks)

1 A mass of 0.40 kg oscillates on a vertical spring. The time period of the oscillation is 0.80 s. The mass is replaced with a mass of 0.90 kg. What is the time period of the oscillation of the 0.90 kg mass? *(1 mark)*

A 0.35 s **B** 0.53 s **C** 1.2 s **D** 1.8 s

2 The head of an electric toothbrush oscillates at 200 Hz. The amplitude of movement of the brush head is 0.5 mm. Assuming that the motion is simple harmonic, what is the maximum acceleration of the brush head? *(1 mark)*

A 3.95 m s^{-2} **B** 250 m s^{-2} **C** 395 m s^{-2} **D** 790 m s^{-2}

3 A mass oscillates in simple harmonic motion. The total energy of the oscillation = E_1.

What is the energy of the oscillation when the amplitude of the oscillation and the frequency are *both* doubled? *(1 mark)*

A $2E_1$ **B** $4E_1$ **C** $8E_1$ **D** $16E_1$

4 The time period of a pendulum of length 1.0 m on Earth is 2.0 s. The gravitational field strength of the Moon is about one-sixth that on Earth.

  a What would the time period of the pendulum be on the Moon? *(2 marks)*

  b What length pendulum would give a time period of 2.0 s on the Moon? *(2 marks)*

5 This question is about the vibrations of a guitar string. The vibrating length of each string on a guitar is 65.0 cm, as shown in Figure 1.

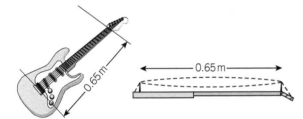

  — 0.65 m —

▲ **Figure 1**

  a The lightest string vibrates at 330 Hz. Calculate the velocity of wave along the string. *(2 marks)*

  b The amplitude of the oscillation at the mid-point of the string (the antinode of the standing wave) is 0.8 mm. Calculate:

    i the maximum velocity of the string *(2 marks)*

    ii the maximum acceleration of the string. *(2 marks)*

  c The quality factor of an oscillation is a measure of the amount of damping. The quality factor is roughly equal to the number of oscillations made before all the energy of the oscillator is transferred to the surroundings. The quality factor for guitar strings is about 1000.

  The energy remaining E after n oscillations is approximated by

$$E = E_0 e^{-0.007n}$$

  where E_0 is the initial energy in the system.

    i Show that the energy of the system will have reduced to half its original value after about 100 oscillations. *(3 marks)*

    ii Calculate the amplitude of the oscillation after 100 oscillations. (original amplitude = 0.8 mm) *(2 marks)*

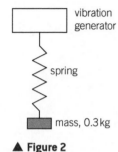

vibration generator

spring

mass, 0.3 kg

▲ **Figure 2**

d The lowest frequency string oscillates at 82 Hz. The lowest and highest strings are set in oscillation at the same instant. Assuming that the string can be heard until its energy is reduced to half its original value, explain why the lower frequency string can be heard for longer. You can use calculations in your explanation. Assume both strings have the same quality factor. *(3 marks)*

6 A mass is supported by a spring as shown in Figure 2. The force constant of the spring is 23 N m⁻¹.

a Calculate the natural frequency of oscillation of the spring and mass. *(2 marks)*

b A second spring of the same force constant is placed in parallel to the first, so that the mass is supported by two springs. What effect does this have on the frequency of the oscillation of the 0.3 kg mass? *(2 marks)*

c The vibration generator is set to 2.0 Hz and switched on. The amplitude of vibration of the generator is 1.5 mm. The amplitude of oscillations of the mass supported by two springs is measured at 6.0 mm. Explain this observation. *(2 marks)*

d Calculate the energy of the mass–spring system at an amplitude of 6.0 mm. *(2 marks)*

Centripetal acceleration

Acceleration is the rate of change of velocity.

Velocity is a vector. It has both magnitude and direction. This means that a body can change its velocity by changing its direction of travel. A change of velocity does not require a change of speed.

A body travelling in a circular path at constant speed has a centripetal (centre-seeking) acceleration towards the centre of the circle given by $a = \dfrac{v^2}{r}$ where v is the speed of the body and r the distance of the body from the centre of the circle.

Centripetal force

$$F = ma \therefore \text{ centripetal force} = \frac{mv^2}{r}$$

The centripetal force always acts towards the centre of the circle. That is, it acts at right angles to the direction of travel of the body. There is no component of force acting in the direction of travel so the speed of the body does not change.

If the centripetal force acting on a body is suddenly removed, the body will fly off at a tangent to its circular path.

The expressions for centripetal acceleration and centripetal force can be found by considering the angular velocity of the body moving in a circular path.

Angular velocity

The speed v of a particle moving in a circle of radius r is given by:

$$v = \frac{\text{circumference}}{\text{time period}} = \frac{2\pi r}{T} = 2\pi rf$$

The angular velocity ω of a body in units $\text{rad s}^{-1} = 2\pi f$. You have met this quantity in Topic 11.1, Introducing simple harmonic oscillators, where it was called angular frequency. This definition leads to another expression for the speed of a body moving in a circle of radius r:

$$v = \omega r$$

Substituting in $a = \frac{v^2}{r}$ gives: centripetal acceleration, $a = \omega^2 r$

$$F = ma \therefore \text{ centripetal force} = m\omega^2 r$$

Common misconception: Centripetal force

'Centripetal' is a description of the direction a force acts in, it is not a type of force.

A gravitational force can be centripetal, for example, the gravitational force that keeps the Earth in orbit.

A magnetic force can be centripetal, for example, the force on charged particles moving at right angles to a magnetic field.

A tension force can be centripetal, for example, when you swing a mass on the end of a string around your head the tension in the string provides the centripetal force.

Worked example: The force on the Moon

Here are some data about the orbit of the Moon:

orbital period T: 2.36×10^6 s, orbital radius r: 3.85×10^8 m, mass of moon: 7.35×10^{22} kg

Calculate:

a the angular velocity of the Moon in its orbit about the Earth
b the centripetal acceleration of the Moon
c the gravitational force exerted by the Earth on the Moon.

a Angular velocity $= 2\pi f = \dfrac{2\pi}{T} = \dfrac{2\pi}{2.36 \times 10^6 \, \text{s}} = 2.66 \times 10^{-6} \, \text{rad s}^{-1}$

b Centripetal acceleration $a = \omega^2 r = (2.66 \times 10^{-6})^2 \, \text{rad}^2 \, \text{s}^{-2} \times 3.85 \times 10^8 \, \text{m}$
$= 0.00272 \, \text{m s}^{-2}$

c The gravitational force on the Moon is the centripetal force $= m\omega^2 r = 2.00 \times 10^{20} \, \text{N}$

Summary questions

1 A particle moves in a circle of radius 2.0 m. It takes 1.2 s to make one revolution.
   a Calculate the angular velocity of the particle in rad s^{-1}.   (2 marks)
   b Calculate the speed of the particle in m s^{-1}.   (2 marks)
   c The radius of the circle is doubled. The time for one revolution remains the same. How does the change of radius affect the
      i angular velocity and **ii** the speed of the particle?   (2 marks)

2 A mass M of 1.8 kg is attached to a thread and whirled in a horizontal circle of radius 1.5 m. The force required to break the thread is 20.0 N. Calculate the speed at which the thread breaks.   (3 marks)

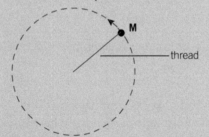

▲ Figure 1

3 A vehicle of mass 1000 kg is driven around a roundabout of radius 25 m on a flat surface at a speed of 15 miles per hour (6.7 m s^{-1}). The vehicle does not skid.
   a Calculate the value of the (centripetal) frictional force acting on the vehicle at this speed.   (2 marks)
   b Explain why a more massive vehicle travelling at the same speed around the roundabout may skid.   (3 marks)

12.2 Newton's law of gravitation

In 1687, a book was published which revolutionised the way that scientists think about the Universe. The book's title, 'The Principle of Natural Philosophy' may not be familiar to you, but the name of its author, Isaac Newton, certainly should be. The book includes Newton's theory of gravity, perhaps the first mathematically-based theory in science to have universal scope.

The law of gravitation

The starting point of Newton's thinking can be stated in a few words: *All particles in the Universe attract all other particles.*

- The gravitational force is an example of an inverse-square relationship; the force between two bodies is proportional to the reciprocal of the square of their separation.

- This is stated algebraically as $F_{grav} \propto -\dfrac{Mm}{r^2}$ where M and m are the masses of the two bodies and r is the separation of the centres of the two bodies. The negative sign shows that the force is attractive.

- With the gravitational constant G, the component of the gravitational force acting between the centres of mass of the bodies is:
$$F_{grav} = -\frac{GMm}{r^2}$$
The gravitational constant G has a value of $6.7 \times 10^{-11}\,\mathrm{N\,m^2\,kg^{-2}}$.

- The gravitational force from an extended body (such as a planet) acts as if all the mass is concentrated at the centre of the body.

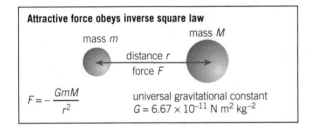

Attractive force obeys inverse square law

mass m mass M

distance r
force F

$F = -\dfrac{GmM}{r^2}$ universal gravitational constant
$G = 6.67 \times 10^{-11}\,\mathrm{N\,m^2\,kg^{-2}}$

▲ **Figure 1** *Newton's law of gravitation*

 Worked example: The International Space Station

The International Space Station orbits at a height of about 400 km above the surface of the Earth. Use the data below to calculate an estimate of the magnitude of the force between the Earth and the space station.

Data: mass of space station: $4.2 \times 10^5\,\mathrm{kg}$, mass of Earth: $6.0 \times 10^{24}\,\mathrm{kg}$, radius of Earth = 6400 km

Step 1: Distance between centres of the two masses (in m) $= 6.4 \times 10^6\,\mathrm{m} + 4 \times 10^5\,\mathrm{m}$
$= 6.8 \times 10^6\,\mathrm{m}$

Step 2: Substitute values into the correct equation and evaluate.

magnitude of force $= \dfrac{GMm}{r^2} = \dfrac{6.7 \times 10^{-11}\,\mathrm{N\,m^2\,kg^{-2}} \times 6.0 \times 10^{24}\,\mathrm{kg} \times 4.2 \times 10^5\,\mathrm{kg}}{(6.8 \times 10^6\,\mathrm{m})^2}$
$= 3.7 \times 10^6\,\mathrm{N}$

Revision tip

As you can see in the Worked example, the equation giving the gravitational force refers to the distance r between the centres of the two bodies. Data about artificial satellites sometimes gives the height of the satellite above the surface of the planet rather than the distance of the satellite from the planet's centre.

Key term

Gravitational field: A gravitational field is a region of space in which a mass is subject to a force.

Gravitational fields

The gravitational field strength g describes the gravitational effect of a body of mass M at a distance r: $g = -\dfrac{Mm}{r^2}$. This is another example of an inverse square relationship. The units of gravitational field strength are $N\,kg^{-1}$.

The direction and magnitude of a field can be represented by field lines or by vectors, as shown in Figure 2.

Field lines   **Vectors in space**

Field direction shown by direction of lines

Field strength shown by closeness of lines

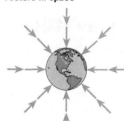

Field direction shown by vector direction

Field strength shown by length of vector

▲ **Figure 2** *Gravitational field lines*

 Worked example: Supermassive black hole

At the centre of the Milky Way galaxy there is a supermassive black hole of mass about 8.2×10^{36} kg.

A star called S2 orbits the centre of the black hole at a distance of about 1.8×10^{13} m.

Calculate and estimate the field strength of the black hole at the distance of S2.

Step 1: Choose the correct equation: $g = -\dfrac{GM}{r^2}$

Step 2: Substitute and evaluate: $g =$
$-\dfrac{6.7 \times 10^{-11}\,N\,m^2\,kg^{-2} \times 8.2 \times 10^{36}\,kg}{(1.8 \times 10^{13}\,m)^2}$
$= -1.7\,N\,kg^{-1}$

Summary questions

1 Show that the units of the gravitational force constant G can be given as $N\,m^2\,kg^{-2}$. *(2 marks)*

2 Neil Armstrong, the first person to walk on the Moon, had a mass (including spacesuit and breathing apparatus) of about 160 kg. Calculate his weight on the Moon.
mass of Moon = 7.3×10^{22} kg, radius of Moon: 1.7×10^6 m   *(2 marks)*

3 Figure 3 shows the variation of the gravitational field strength of the Earth with distance above the surface.
   a What is the force on a 10 kg mass at a height of 1.5×10^7 m above the surface? *(2 marks)*
   b The relationship between field strength and distance above the surface is not an inverse-square relationship.
      i Explain the term 'inverse-square relationship'. *(1 mark)*
      ii Explain how the graph shows that this relationship is not inverse square. *(2 marks)*

4 Geostationary satellites orbit above the equator in the same direction as the spin of the Earth with an orbital period of exactly one day (23 hours and 56 minutes). These orbits allow the satellites to stay above the same position on the Earth's surface at all times. This question calculates the radius of such orbits.
   a Remembering that the gravitational force on a satellite of mass m_s is centripetal, show that the speed² of the satellite in orbit is given by $v^2 = \dfrac{GM}{R}$ where M is the mass of the Earth and R is the radius of orbit. *(2 marks)*
   b The speed of an object travelling in a circle of radius R is given by $v = \dfrac{2\pi R}{T}$ where T is the time for one orbit (orbital period). Use this relationship and the equation given in **a** to show that: $R^3 = \dfrac{GMT^2}{4\pi^2}$ *(2 marks)*
   c Calculate the height above the Earth's surface of a geostationary satellite orbit.
      mass of Earth = 6.0×10^{24} kg, radius of Earth = 6.4×10^6 m *(3 marks)*

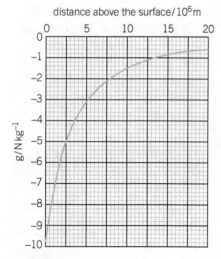

distance above the surface/10^6 m

▲ **Figure 3**

12.3 Gravitational potential in a uniform field

Specification references: 5.1.2a(i), 5.1.2 a(ii), 5.1.2b(i), 5.1.2b(iv), 5.1.2c(i), 5.1.2c(ii)

The gravitational field of a point mass is radial. This means that the field lines extend from the point mass like spokes on a bicycle wheel. The gravitational field near the Earth, by contrast, is uniform. It has the same magnitude and direction everywhere.

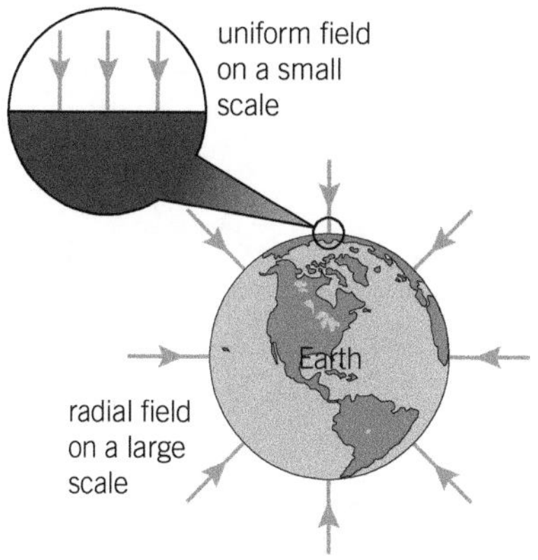

Gravitational potential

Near the surface of the Earth, the change in gravitational potential energy with height $mg\Delta h$ is always the same for equal changes in height Δh. This is because the field is uniform.

It is often useful to consider gravitational potential, the energy per kilogram of material, units $J\,kg^{-1}$. For calculations near the surface of the Earth the gravitational potential is often measured relative to a zero value set at sea level. Taking g as $9.8\,N\,kg^{-1}$, the potential increases by $9.8\,J\,kg^{-1}$ for every metre raised.

Equipotential surfaces

You can think of, say, a football pitch as being an equipotential surface. One metre above the pitch there is another equipotential surface that is $9.8\,J\,kg^{-1}$ greater than that on the ground.

Potential surfaces are three-dimensional but are often represented in two dimensions, as in Figure 2.

▲ **Figure 1** *Near the surface of the Earth the field is approximately uniform*

Key term

Equipotential surface: An equipotential surface is a surface on which all points are at the same potential.

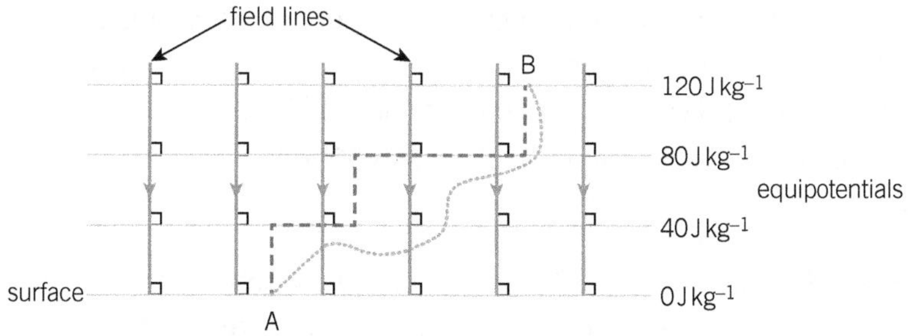

▲ **Figure 2** *Field lines and equipotentials*

- The spacing of the equipotentials is constant, showing that the field is uniform. Constant spacing of equipotentials of constant potential difference is a distinguishing characteristic of a uniform field.

- The gravitational field lines are always at right angles to the equipotentials.

- There is no work done changing displacement by Δs along an equipotential, therefore, work done $\Delta E = F\Delta s = 0$. Therefore, there is no component of gravitational force F acting along the equipotential.

- The change in potential (the potential difference) between two points in a gravitational field is independent of the route taken. As long as the change in vertical displacement is the same, so is the change in potential. The potential difference between points A and B in Figure 2 is the same for both the routes shown.

Motion in a uniform field

A projectile follows a parabolic path in a uniform gravitational field. The force on the projectile is always vertically downwards. There is no horizontal component of the gravitational force.

Figure 3 represents the motion of two projectiles which have been projected horizontally in a uniform gravitational field. The kinetic energy gained by each projectile depends only on the height fallen.

Change in kinetic energy = change in gravitational potential energy

$$\Delta mgh = \Delta \frac{1}{2}mv^2 \therefore \Delta gh = \Delta \frac{1}{2}v^2$$

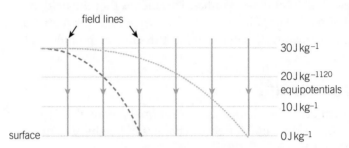

▲ **Figure 3** *Parabolic motion in a uniform gravitational field*

The vertical component of velocity of both particles will be the same when they hit the ground. Note that the velocity gained is independent of the mass of the projectile. This predicts that a feather dropped from, say, 2 m will hit the ground at the same speed as a hammer dropped from the same height. This is not observed on Earth because of the effects of the fluid the objects are falling through – the air.

Summary questions

1 The gravitational field strength on the surface of the Moon is about 1.7 N kg⁻¹.
   a Calculate the potential difference between the lunar surface and a height 1.8 m above the surface. *(2 marks)*
   b Calculate the vertical velocity of a feather released from rest at a height of 1.8 m above the lunar surface just before it hits the surface. *(2 marks)*

2 A ball is projected at an angle of 30° to the horizontal with an initial speed of 40 m s⁻¹. Calculate the maximum vertical height reached by the ball. *(3 marks)*

3 One of the balls in Figure 3 is projected horizontally with an initial velocity of 30 m s⁻¹. The mass of the ball is 0.09 kg.
   a Use information from the figure to calculate the kinetic energy of the ball just before it strikes the ground. *(2 marks)*
   b Calculate or state:
     i the horizontal velocity of the ball just before it strikes the ground *(1 mark)*
     ii its vertical velocity *(2 marks)*
     iii its speed. *(2 marks)*

12.4 Gravitational potential in a radial field

Specification references: 5.1.2a(iii), 5.1.2b(i), 5.1.2b(ii), 5.1.2b(iii), 5.1.2b(iv), 5.1.2c(v), 5.1.2c(vi)

Gravitational potential wells

You have seen that for calculations near the Earth the potential at the surface is set to the zero value at sea level. For calculations involving greater separations it is easier to set the zero as the potential an infinite distance from the gravitational mass.

Energy has to be transferred (work done) to move a 1 kg mass from the surface of the Earth to a point an infinite distance away. As the potential at this distance is zero, the potential at the surface of the Earth is negative. The surface of the Earth is at the bottom of a potential well. The larger the planet is, the deeper the potential well.

The equations for gravitational potential energy and gravitational potential are:

$$\text{gravitational potential energy, } E_{\text{grav}} = -\frac{GMm}{r}$$

$$\text{gravitational potential, } V_{\text{grav}} = -\frac{GM}{r}$$

You can see from Figure 1 that equipotentials separated by equal potential difference become further apart with distance from the planet. The spacing of equipotentials is an indication of the strength of the field.

Potential and field strength

The area between the line and the x-axis of a gravitational field strength versus radius from the centre of the mass graph gives the difference in potential for the distance chosen (see Figure 2 (a)). The change in energy can be found in a similar manner from the area enclosed by a force–distance graph (see Figure 2 (b)).

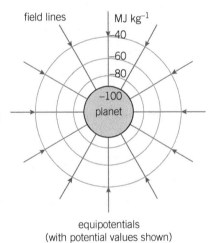

field lines   MJ kg^{-1}

equipotentials (with potential values shown)

▲ **Figure 1** *Equipotentials near a planet*

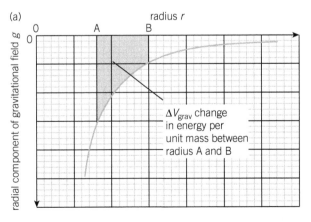

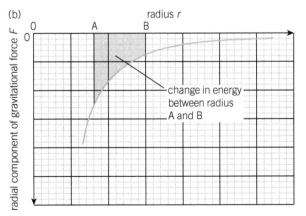

▲ **Figure 2a** *The difference in potential is the area under the graph of field against radius*
b *The difference in energy is the area under the graph of force against radius*

Worked example: The potential on Europa

Europa is a natural satellite of Jupiter.

The radius of Europa is 1.56×10^6 m. The mass of Europa is 4.80×10^{22} kg.

a Calculate the potential at a height of 7.00×10^4 m above the surface of the satellite.

b An unpowered spacecraft of mass 120 kg has a velocity of 200 m s^{-1} at a height of 7.0×10^4 m above the surface of Europa, falling directly towards the centre of Europa. Calculate the velocity at which it strikes the surface.

Data: potential at surface of Europa = -2.06×10^6 J kg^{-1}

a

Step 1: Calculate distance from centre of Europa of a height 7.0×10^4 m above the surface.

distance from centre = 1.56×10^6 m + 7.0×10^4 m = 1.63×10^6 m

Step 2: Select correct equation, substitute and evaluate.

$$V_{grav} = -\frac{GM}{r} = -\frac{6.7 \times 10^{-11}\,\text{N m}^2\,\text{kg}^{-2} \times 4.80 \times 10^{22}\,\text{kg}}{1.63 \times 10^6\,\text{m}} = -1.97\,0^6\,\text{J kg}^{-1}\ (3\ \text{s.f.})$$

b

Step 1: Δkinetic energy = Δ potential energy = $m\Delta V_{grav}$

= 120 kg × [-1.97×10^6 J kg^{-1} − ($-$) 2.06×10^6 J kg^{-1}] = 1.1×10^7 J

Step 2: Kinetic energy at a height of 7.0×10^4 m = $\frac{1}{2}$ × 120 kg × 200^2 m^2 s^{-2} = 2.40×10^6 J

Step 3: Kinetic energy at surface = 1.1×10^7 J + 2.4×10^6 J = 1.34×10^7 J

Step 4: $v = \sqrt{\dfrac{2E_k}{m}} = \sqrt{\dfrac{2 \times 1.34 \times 10^7\,\text{J}}{120\,\text{kg}}} = 470\ \text{m s}^{-1}\ (2\ \text{s.f.})$

Note that you add the kinetic energies, *not* velocities.

This calculation can be performed without using the mass of the spacecraft, but the steps are more easily shown by considering values of kinetic energy.

Field and potential gradient

- The change in potential ΔV with change in radius Δr from the centre of the mass as Δr approaches zero is often referred to as the potential gradient and is written as $\frac{dV}{dr}$.

- The radial component of the field strength at any point in space is equal to the *negative* of the potential gradient at that point.

- The field strength can be found by drawing a tangent to the potential versus radius curve, as shown in Figure 3.

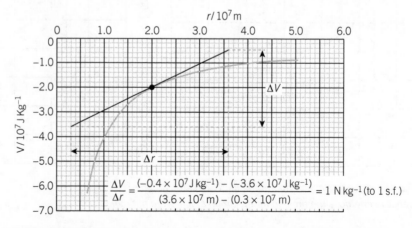

▲ **Figure 3** *The field strength for the Earth is the negative of the gradient of a graph of potential against radius*

- In a similar manner, the force on a mass can be found from the negative of the gradient of a graph of potential energy against radius, as shown in Figure 4.

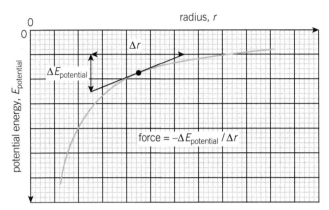

▲ **Figure 4** *The force is the negative of the gradient of a graph of potential energy against radius*

Revision tip
When you have finished working through this topic you will find it useful to go back through the chapter, write down the equations covered and ensure that you understand the differences between, for example, the field strength equation and the potential equation.

Summary questions

1 **a** Explain the difference between gravitational potential and gravitational potential energy. *(2 marks)*

 b Explain why gravitational potential is always a negative value when the potential at an infinite distance is set at zero. *(2 marks)*

2 Here are some data about the Moon: radius = 1.74×10^6 m; mass = 7.35×10^{22} kg

 a Calculate the potential energy of a 2.0 kg mass on the lunar surface. *(2 marks)*

 b State the initial kinetic energy needed to project the mass from the surface of the Moon and not to fall back. Explain your answer. *(2 marks)*

 c Calculate the velocity of the mass with the kinetic energy calculated in **b**. This is the escape velocity for the Moon. *(2 marks)*

 d Using the equations for kinetic energy and gravitational potential energy in a radial field, show that escape velocity, $v_{esc} = \sqrt{\dfrac{GM}{r}}$

 where M and r are the mass and radius of the body that is being escaped from. *(2 marks)*

3 **a** Use Figure 3 in the summary questions for Topic 12.2 to estimate the change in potential between 5×10^6 m above the surface of the Earth and 15×10^6 m above the surface of the Earth. *(4 marks)*

 b Use the equation $V_{grav} = -\dfrac{GM}{r}$ to support your value from **a**.

 Data for the Earth: radius = 6.4×10^6 m, mass = 6.0×10^{24} kg *(3 marks)*

13

OUR PLACE IN THE UNIVERSE
13.1 Measuring the Solar System
Specification references: 5.1.3 a(i), 5.1.3 a(iii), 5.1.3b(i), 5.1.3c(ii)

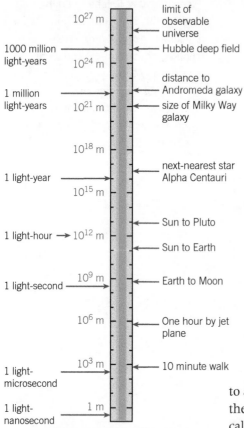

▲ Figure 1 *Distances can be expressed in units of light travel time*

Synoptic link

You have met logarithmic scales a number of times already, including in Topic 4.4, Choosing materials.

Light travel time

The Solar System is a collection of planets and other objects orbiting the Sun. Although it takes many years for spacecraft to reach the outer planets, the scale of the Solar System is tiny compared to that of the galaxy which is itself dwarfed by the immensity of the Universe.

Astronomers and other scientists use the light-year, the distance light travels through space in one year, as a measure of these vast distances. One light-year is about 9.5×10^{15} m.

Shorter distances can be given in light-seconds where one light-second is 3.0×10^8 m. Light-years and light-seconds are examples of distances expressed in 'light travel time'.

Figure 1 shows a range of distances expressed in light travel time. You can see that the scale is logarithmic, which allows a wide range of distances to be represented on a single diagram.

Measuring distances and velocities in the Solar System

Radar (**ra**dio **d**etection **a**nd **r**anging) can be used to measure distances within the Solar System. A pulse of radio waves is sent out from Earth to a given object (the planet Venus, for example). The time interval between the emission of the pulse and the return of the reflected pulse is used to calculate the distance, remembering that the pulse has travelled to the object and back during that time interval.

This method can be extended to measure velocities by taking two distance measurements over a known time interval. The component of the velocity of the object along the line between the Earth and the object is found by dividing the difference in distance by the time interval. This method is shown in Figure 2.

It makes the assumptions that the speed of the signal is the same in both directions and that the moment of reflection occurs exactly halfway through the time interval between the emitted pulse and the received signal.

 Worked example: The distance to the Moon

A pulse sent from Earth is reflected on the lunar surface and the reflected signal is detected. The time interval between emission and subsequent detection of the reflected signal is 2.5 s. Calculate the distance from the point on the surface of the Earth from which the pulse was emitted to the point on the lunar surface that reflected the pulse. Assume that the pulse travels at 3×10^8 m s^{-1} throughout the journey.

Step 1: Distance travelled by pulse = speed × time = 3×10^8 m s^{-1} × 2.5 s = 7.5×10^8 m

Step 2: Earth–Moon distance = $\dfrac{\text{distance travelled by pulse}}{2} = \dfrac{7.5 \times 10^8 \text{ m}}{2}$

$= 3.8 \times 10^8$ m (2 s.f.)

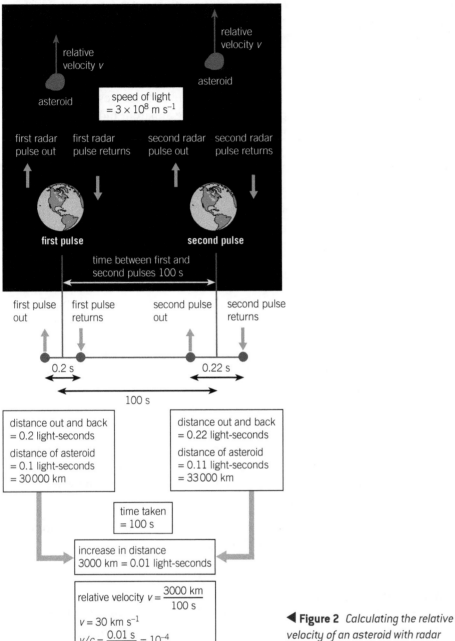

◀ **Figure 2** *Calculating the relative velocity of an asteroid with radar pulses*

Summary questions

1 **a** Calculate the distance of the Sun in light-seconds. (distance to Sun = 1.5×10^{11} m) (2 marks)

   b The star Sirius A is 8.6 light-years from Earth. Calculate its distance in metres. (1 year = 3.2×10^7 s) (2 marks)

2 Use the information in Figure 1 to calculate how long it would take to reach the Sun from Earth at walking speed. Express your answer in years. (3 marks)

3 At one point in its orbit, the dwarf planet Pluto is about 6×10^{12} m from Earth. Explain, with calculations, why radar measurement of such a distance is not practical.

   You should consider the time delay in sending and receiving a pulse of electromagnetic radiation. You should also consider the proportion of the original energy of the pulse that will strike an area of 1 m^2 on the surface of Pluto. (surface area of sphere = $4\pi r^2$) (7 marks)

13.2 Measuring the Universe

Specification references: 5.1.3 a(iv), 5.1.3 c (i)

You have seen in Topic 13.1, Measuring the Solar System, that radar can be used to measure distances within the Solar System. Distances to the nearest stars can be measured using parallax. This is the apparent movement of the near star against a background of distant stars as the Earth orbits the Sun. As some stars are more luminous than others, you cannot assume that the brighter the star is, the nearer it is to the Earth.

In 1912, it was found that a certain type of star, a Cepheid variable, varies in brightness in a manner that depends upon its absolute luminosity. This discovery led to the measurement of the distance to a fuzzy patch of light that turned out to be in a galaxy some 900 000 light-years from Earth.

Measuring speed using Doppler shift

You have seen in Topic 7.1, Quantum behaviour, that photons of specific frequencies are emitted when an electron in an atom falls from a high energy level to a lower energy level. The frequency f of the photon emitted is given by $f = \frac{E}{h}$ where E is the difference in energy levels and h is the Planck constant. Similarly, light of specific frequencies is absorbed when it passes through a gas. This is because the energy of the photons absorbed promotes electrons to higher energy levels. This process produces the absorption spectral lines that are observed in stars.

When a star is moving away (receding) the wavelength of its spectral lines increases. This is called red-shift because the lines are shifted towards the red end of the spectrum. An approaching star shows blue-shift as the wavelength of the absorption lines is reduced.

The fractional increase in the wavelength of light $\frac{\Delta\lambda}{\lambda}$ from a receding source (for example, a galaxy) is given by the equation:

$$z = \frac{\Delta\lambda}{\lambda} = \frac{v}{c}$$

where v is the speed the galaxy is moving away and c is the speed of light. This gives accurate results when v is much less than the speed of light but Einstein's special theory of relativity modifies the equation for higher speeds.

The expanding Universe

Using red-shift data, Edwin Hubble and others found that:

- nearly all the galaxies are moving away from Earth

- the further away a galaxy is, the faster it is receding from Earth.

Although there was uncertainty in the data, a general law was established. When the recession velocity of galaxies is calculated from red-shift data, Hubble's law can be stated as:

recession speed v = constant H_0 × distance r

H_0 is called the Hubble constant. It can be found from the gradient of a graph of recession speed against distance. $\frac{1}{H_0}$ gives a measure of the time since the

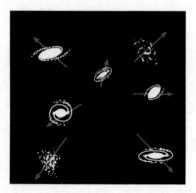
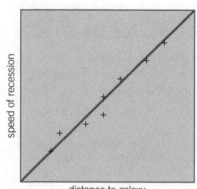

speed of recession is directly proportional to distance, $v = H_0 r$

H_0 is the Hubble constant

units of $H_0 = \dfrac{\text{speed}}{\text{distance}} = \dfrac{1}{\text{time}}$

$\dfrac{1}{H_0} = $ Hubble time

units of $\dfrac{1}{H_0} = $ time

If speed v were constant, then $\dfrac{1}{H_0} = \dfrac{r}{v} = $ time since galaxies were close together.

▲ **Figure 1** *Speed of recession is directly proportional to distance*

galaxies were close together, which is a measure of the age of the Universe. The observation that the Universe is expanding suggests that the Universe originated in a very hot, dense state from which it expanded and cooled. This is the Big Bang theory.

Cosmological red-shift

Cosmological red-shifts are very large red-shifts observed in the spectra of distant galaxies caused by the expansion of space. If light from a distant galaxy shows cosmological red-shift z $(= \frac{\Delta\lambda}{\lambda})$, space has stretched by a factor of $1 + z$ during the time the light has been travelling.

Figure 2 explains this interpretation of the observed red-shift of light from distance galaxies.

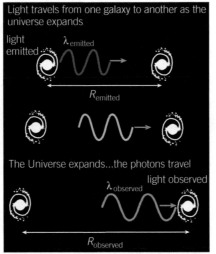

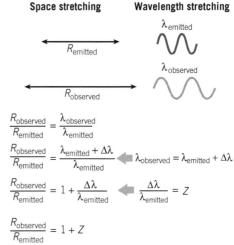

$$\frac{R_{observed}}{R_{emitted}} = \frac{\lambda_{observed}}{\lambda_{emitted}}$$

$$\frac{R_{observed}}{R_{emitted}} = \frac{\lambda_{emitted} + \Delta\lambda}{\lambda_{emitted}} \quad \Leftarrow \quad \lambda_{observed} = \lambda_{emitted} + \Delta\lambda$$

$$\frac{R_{observed}}{R_{emitted}} = 1 + \frac{\Delta\lambda}{\lambda_{emitted}} \quad \Leftarrow \quad \frac{\Delta\lambda}{\lambda_{emitted}} = z$$

$$\frac{R_{observed}}{R_{emitted}} = 1 + z$$

▲ **Figure 2** *The cosmological red-shift measures the stretching of space*

🖩 Worked example: Cosmological red-shift

A galaxy as a red-shift $z = 0.197$. Calculate how much the Universe has expanded during the time the light from the galaxy has been travelling.

Step 1: Choose the equation and substitute the values.

$$\frac{R_{observed}}{R_{emitted}} = 1 + z = 1 + 0.197 = 1.197$$

$$\therefore R_{observed} = 0.197 = R_{emitted}$$

Step 2: Write the conclusion.

The Universe has expanded by about 20% since the light was emitted from the galaxy.

Cosmic microwave background radiation

- The cosmic microwave background radiation originates from when the Universe became cool enough for photons to travel freely through space.
- This occurred when the temperature of the Universe had dropped to about 3000 K.
- The typical wavelength of the photons at that time (about 300 000 years after the Big Bang) was about 1 μm.
- These photons are now stretched to wavelengths of the order of 1 mm. This is in the microwave region of the electromagnetic spectrum and corresponds to a temperature of about 3 K.
- The cosmic microwave background provides convincing evidence that the Universe began in a hot, dense state.

Measurements of the microwave background show that its temperature is nearly, but not quite, uniform. This shows that the early Universe was smooth, with little temperature variation. This supports the model of the Universe developing from a hot, dense state. The tiny variation in the temperature of the microwave background shows that a slight variation in temperature was present in the early Universe, suggesting non-uniformities that allowed galaxies and stars to form.

Common misconception: Doppler shift and cosmological red-shift

Doppler shift occurs when the source of the waves is moving relative to the observer. The change in pitch of an ambulance siren as the ambulance approaches and recedes is an example of Doppler shift. Cosmological red-shift is due to the lengthening of the wavelength of light as the light travels through expanding space. The Doppler shift of a receding source and the cosmological red-shift both have the same outcome (an increase in wavelength of the waves from the source) but have very different explanations.

In the beginning...

there was the Big Bang...

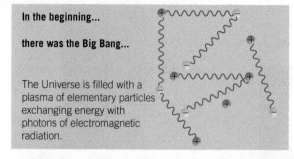

The Universe is filled with a plasma of elementary particles exchanging energy with photons of electromagnetic radiation.

300 000 years after the Big Bang

**temperature 3000 K
typical wavelength of radiation, 1 μm**

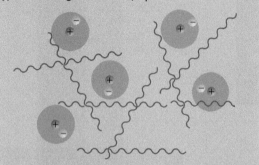

As the temperature falls, atoms form as electrons are held in orbit around nuclei of protons and neutrons.

The Universe becomes transparent to photons, which no longer interact so easily with atoms and so travel unaffected through the Universe.

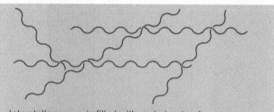

Interstellar space is filled with a photon 'gas' (and some atoms). The temperature of this gas is proportional to the energy of the photons.

The energy of a photon is proportional to its frequency. Therefore the temperature of the photon gas is proportional to the frequency of the radiation.

...14 billion years after the Big Bang

**temperature 2.7 K
typical wavelength of radiation, 1 mm**

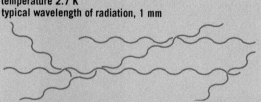

The Universe expands, stretching the wavelength of the photons. The greater the wavelength, the lower the frequency. The temperature of the photon gas falls.

▲ **Figure 3** *Cosmic microwave background radiation*

Summary questions

1 A galaxy is observed to have a redshift of $z = 0.22$. Calculate how much the Universe has expanded during the time the light from the galaxy has been travelling.
(2 marks)

2 The cosmic microwave background has been described as 'the biggest red-shift in the Universe'. Explain this statement.
(2 marks)

3 Two recent values for the Hubble constant H_0 are $69.32 \text{ km s}^{-1} \text{ Mpc}^{-1}$ and $67.80 \text{ km s}^{-1} \text{ Mpc}^{-1}$. The uncertainty in both values is about $\pm 0.8 \text{ km s}^{-1} \text{ Mpc}^{-1}$. Calculate an estimate for the maximum and minimum age of the Universe (in years) based on these values.
$1 \text{ Mpc} = 3.09 \times 10^{22} \text{m}$, $1 \text{ year} = 3.2 \times 10^7 \text{ s}$
(4 marks)

13.3 Special relativity

Specification references: 5.1.3 a(i), 5.1.3 a (ii)

Relative motion

How fast do you walk? The usual answer to this is around 3 miles per hour. But what about when you are walking along the carriage of a train? Imagine the train is travelling in a straight line at 90 miles per hour and you walk along the carriage in the same direction as the moving train. Is your velocity +3 miles an hour or +93 miles per hour?

Relative to the train, you are walking at 3 miles per hour. Relative the countryside you are passing through, you are moving at 93 miles per hour. All velocities are relative.

Wristwatch time

A stationary clock is simply a clock that is not moving with respect to its surroundings. Being 'at rest' (i.e., not moving) is the same as saying 'moving with me'. A clock at rest is one that you carry with you. The time that such a clock records is called 'wristwatch time' and is denoted by the Greek letter tau τ.

Einstein's postulates

Einstein's theory of Special Relativity states that travelling at uniform velocity relative to another object changes nothing about the physics of the situation. He put forward two 'postulates' to clarify this idea.

- Physical laws take the same form for all observers, no matter what their state of uniform motion in a straight line.

- The speed of light c is a universal constant. It has the same value, regardless of the motion of the observer.

The first postulate echoes ideas Galileo formulated some 350 years before Einstein's work. The second postulate goes beyond Galileo's thinking.

Imagine that you are shining a torch, pointing it straight ahead. If you could measure the speed of light from the torch you would find it always to be exactly $299\,792\,458\,\mathrm{m\,s^{-1}}$, no matter how fast you were travelling. A stationary observer would also measure the speed of the light from your torch as the same value.

Space–time diagrams

Space–time diagrams represent objects moving through space and time. Note the following:

- Time is shown on the y-axis.

- Distance is shown on the x-axis in units of $\frac{x}{c}$ (light-seconds).

- The diagrams are drawn from the point of view of a given observer (or 'platform'). This platform moves up the time-axis.

- Lines representing the paths of objects through space and time are called worldlines.

- A light pulse travels at 1 light-second per second, so its worldline travels at 45° across the diagram.

> **Synoptic link**
>
> You have met relative motion in Topic 8.2, Vectors.

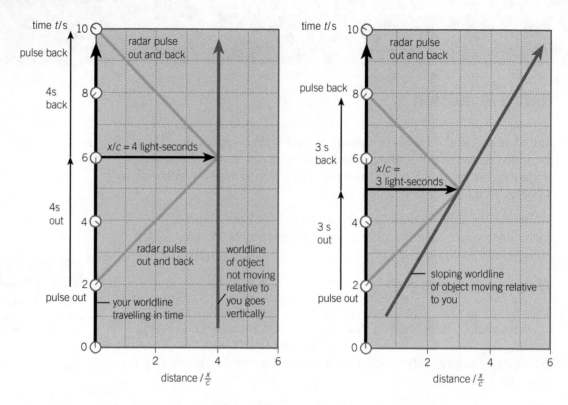

Distance is measured by reflecting a radar pulse, then measuring the time sent and the time received back. The clock used travels with you and the radar equipment (at rest).

Assumptions:
speed *c* is constant so reflection occurs halfway through the out-and-back time
speed *c* is not affected by the motion of the distant object

▲ **Figure 1** *Space–time diagrams*

Time dilation and the relativistic factor γ

A moving clock moves more slowly from the viewpoint of a stationary observer. The observer records a time *t* whereas the time recorded by the moving clock (the 'wristwatch time') is τ. These times are related by the equation:

$$t = \frac{\tau}{\sqrt{1 - \frac{v^2}{c^2}}}$$

The 'relativistic factor' γ is given as:

$$\gamma = \frac{1}{\sqrt{1 - \frac{v^2}{c^2}}}$$

Hence: $\qquad\qquad\qquad t = \gamma\tau$

This phenomenon is called 'time dilation' because the time experienced by the moving clock is stretched into a longer time for the stationary observer. Time dilation is a consequence of the speed of light being constant for all observers.

Imagine that you travelled at 90% of the speed of light (0.9*c*) for one year (measured by a clock moving with you). Stationary observers would measure your journey time to be 2.3 years.

Worked example: Mean lifetimes of pions

The mean lifetime of particles is related to their half-life by the equation: $\dfrac{\text{half-life}}{\ln 2}$

Pions have a mean lifetime of 26 ns when at rest. What is the mean lifetime of pions travelling at $2.6 \times 10^8\,\text{m s}^{-1}$ as measured by a stationary observer?

Step 1: Choose the correct equation and substitute values.

$$t = \frac{\tau}{\sqrt{1 - \dfrac{v^2}{c^2}}} = \frac{26ns}{\sqrt{1 - \dfrac{(2.6 \times 10^8\,\text{m s}^{-1})^2}{(3.0 \times 10^8\,\text{m s}^{-1})^2}}}$$

Note that the mean lifetime of the moving pions remains at 26 ns measured by the clock moving with them.

Step 2: Evaluate. It is good practice to write down the intermediate stages to help avoid errors.

$$t = \frac{26ns}{\sqrt{1 - 0.751\ldots}} = \frac{26ns}{\sqrt{0.248\ldots}} = 52ns$$

A stationary observer would record that the mean lifetime of the particles had doubled.

Summary questions

1 Look at Figure 1.
   a What feature of the right-hand diagram shows that the moving object is indeed moving? *(1 mark)*
   b How can you tell that the moving object is travelling slower than the speed of light? *(1 mark)*

2 Calculate the relativistic factor for an object moving at half the speed of light. *(2 marks)*
3 Calculate the relativistic factor for an object moving at $2.9 \times 10^8\,\text{m s}^{-1}$. *(2 marks)*
4 A particle has a half-life of 0.7 ns when it is at rest. Calculate its half-life when travelling at $0.99c$ when measured by a stationary observer. *(2 marks)*

5 Calculate the velocity of a particle with a relativistic factor of 2.5. *(3 marks)*

1 The Earth orbits the Sun at a distance of 1.5×10^{11} m. It takes 3.2×10^7 s to make one orbit. What is the centripetal acceleration of the Earth? *(1 mark)*

   A 9.2×10^{-4} m s^{-2} **B** 1.4×10^{-3} m s^{-2}

   C 2.8×10^{-3} m s^{-2} **D** 5.8×10^{-3} m s^{-2}

2 Two balls, each of mass *m* are separated by distance *r* between their centres. The gravitational force between the balls is *F*. The mass of each ball is doubled and the distance separating them is doubled. What is the force between them after these changes have been made? *(1 mark)*

   A $\dfrac{F}{2}$ **B** F **C** $2F$ **D** $4F$

3 You are standing on some bathroom scales in a lift. When the lift is stationary the scales record your weight as *W*. The lift accelerates upwards at $2\,\text{m s}^{-2}$. What is the reading on the scales? (take $g = 10\,\text{m s}^{-2}$) *(1 mark)*

   A $0.8\,W$ **B** $1.0\,W$ **C** $1.2\,W$ **D** $1.4\,W$

4 Here are three statements about the Universe.

   1 The microwave background radiation is nearly completely uniform across the sky

   2 The speed of recession of distant galaxies is proportional to the distance to the galaxy

   3 Much of the mass of the Universe consists of dark matter or dark energy.

   Which statement(s) give(s) evidence that the Universe is expanding from a hot, dense state? *(1 mark)*

   A Statements 1, 2, and 3

   B Statements 1 and 2 only

   C Statements 2 and 3 only

   D Statement 1 only

5 A radar pulse from Earth to an asteroid makes a return journey in 50.2 s.

   Calculate the distance to the asteroid at the time of measurement, stating any assumptions you make. *(3 marks)*

6 **a** Explain the statement:

   The gravitational force on a body in a circular orbit is a centripetal force. *(2 marks)*

   b A planet of mass *m* orbits a star of mass *M* at a distance *r*. Show that the mass of the star can be given by $E = \dfrac{4\pi^2 r^3}{GT^2}$ where *G* is the universal gravitational constant and *T* is the time for one orbit. *(2 marks)*

   c Mars orbits the Sun at a distance of 2.3×10^{11} m. It takes 6.0×10^7 s to make one orbit. Calculate the mass of the Sun. *(2 marks)*

7 Figure 1 shows equipotentials around a planet. There is a constant potential difference between each equipotential line.

   a Explain why no work is done when moving along an equipotential surface. *(2 marks)*

   b State how the diagram shows that the gravitational field decreases with distance from the surface of the planet. *(1 mark)*

   c On a copy of the diagram, draw a field line through point *X*. *(2 marks)*

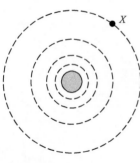

▲ Figure 1

d The potential at the surface of the planet is $-6.3 \times 10^7 \, \text{J kg}^{-1}$.

State the energy required to move a 1 kg mass from the surface of the planet to a great distance away (effectively, infinite distance). Use your answer to calculate the velocity required for a projectile, launched from the surface of the planet, to escape from the gravitational potential well of the planet. *(3 marks)*

e The radius of the planet is $6.4 \times 10^6 \, \text{m}$. The potential at X is $-9.6 \times 10^6 \, \text{J kg}^{-1}$. Calculate the height of point X above the surface of the planet. *(3 marks)*

8 A student is very confused about the difference between gravitational field strength, gravitational force and gravitational potential. This is what he writes:

'Gravitational field strength is just another name for gravity, which is the same as gravitational force. Gravitational potential at a place is the energy required to get from there to a long way off. Gravitational potential varies with $\frac{1}{\text{distance}^2}$ from the centre of mass. You can find the change in gravitational potential from the gradient of a graph of field strength against distance from the centre of mass.'

List the mistakes the student has made and give the correct version.

(5 marks)

9 The half-life of a type of sub-atomic particle at rest is $17 \, \mu\text{s}$. Calculate the half-life measured by laboratory observers when a beam of particles is accelerated to $0.85c$. *(2 marks)*

10 This question is about determining the age of the Universe.

Hubble's law states that $v = H_0 r$ where v is the velocity at which a distant galaxy is moving away from Earth, r is the distance from Earth, and H_0 is the Hubble constant.

a Describe how the velocity at which a galaxy is moving away from Earth is measured. *(2 marks)*

b Explain why Hubble's law supports the idea that the Universe started with a Big Bang. *(2 marks)*

c A recent value for the Hubble constant is $67.1 \, \text{km s}^{-1} \, \text{Mpc}^{-1}$, where $1 \, \text{MPc} = 3.09 \times 10^{22} \, \text{m}$.

   i Show that the units $\text{km s}^{-1} \, \text{Mpc}^{-1}$ are equivalent to s^{-1}. *(1 mark)*

   ii Convert $67.1 \, \text{km s}^{-1} \, \text{Mpc}^{-1}$ into s^{-1}. *(1 mark)*

d The age of the Universe is given by $\frac{1}{H_0}$. Calculate the age in years suggested by the value for the Hubble constant. *(2 marks)*

11 A motorcyclist travels in a circular arc of radius 15 m at a speed of $20 \, \text{m s}^{-1}$.

a Calculate the centripetal acceleration of the motorbike and rider. *(2 marks)*

b The combined mass of the cycle and rider is 300 kg. Calculate the centripetal force on the cycle and rider. *(1 mark)*

c Explain why corners in roads should be ridden through more slowly in wet conditions. *(3 marks)*

Investigating the behaviour of gases

The 17th and 18th centuries saw great developments in the knowledge of the behaviour of gases. A theoretical picture of gases as simple particles exerting a pressure through bouncing off the walls of their container also developed throughout the 18th and 19th centuries.

Boyle's law

Boyle's law states that, when the mass and temperature of a sample of gas is kept constant, the pressure p is inversely proportional to the volume V, giving:

$$pV = \text{constant}$$

This relationship is shown in the graph in Figure 1.

What happens if the volume of gas is kept the same but more gas is pumped into the container? If the mass of gas is doubled the pressure will also double because this is the same as putting the original mass of gas into half the volume.

So, at constant temperature: $\quad p \propto \dfrac{\text{mass}}{V}$ or $p \propto$ density ρ

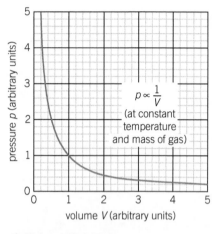

▲ **Figure 1** *Boyle's law*

Practical: Pressure–volume relationship for a gas

- Figure 2 shows an apparatus commonly used to investigate the relationship between the pressure and volume of a fixed mass of gas at constant temperature.
- Increasing the pressure of the air in the reservoir forces oil into the tube, decreasing the volume of the gas in the tube.
- The pressure of the air reservoir is assumed to be the same as the pressure of the trapped air so the variation of volume of trapped air and its pressure can be investigated.

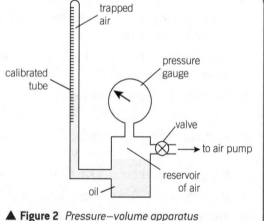

▲ **Figure 2** *Pressure–volume apparatus*

Revision tip

One litre (1 L) is a volume of $1.0 \times 10^{-3}\,\text{m}^3$.

Worked example: Air in a bicycle tyre

A bicycle tyre has a volume of $4.0 \times 10^{-3}\,\text{m}^3$. The pressure of air in the tyre is $3.2 \times 10^5\,\text{Pa}$ above the atmospheric pressure of $1.0 \times 10^5\,\text{Pa}$. Calculate the volume the air in the tyre would occupy at atmospheric pressure, assuming its temperature remains constant.

Step 1: The absolute air pressure in the tyre = $3.2 \times 10^5\,\text{Pa} + 1.0 \times 10^5\,\text{Pa} = 4.2 \times 10^5\,\text{Pa}$

Step 2: From Boyle's law, $pV = \text{constant}$. Therefore, $p_1V_1 = p_2V_2$. In this case, the pressure changes from $4.2 \times 10^5\,\text{Pa}$ to $1.0 \times 10^5\,\text{Pa}$.

Step 3: $4.2 \times 10^5\,\text{Pa} \times 4.0 \times 10^{-3}\,\text{m}^3 = 1.0 \times 10^5\,\text{Pa} \times V_2$

$$\therefore V_2 = \frac{4.2 \times 10^5\,\text{Pa} \times 4.0 \times 10^{-3}\,\text{m}^3}{1.0 \times 10^5\,\text{Pa}} = 1.7 \times 10^{-2}\,\text{m}^3 \ (2\text{ s.f.})$$

Moles, molar mass, and the Avogadro constant

The kinetic theory of gases explains gas pressure by picturing a gas as many, many tiny particles which exert a force on their container from the many collisions they make with the walls. This idea explains Boyle's law: halve the volume of the gas and the number of collisions between the gas particles and the walls will double, doubling the pressure on the walls.

The important quantity here is the number of particles in a volume of gas rather than the mass of gas. This quantity is measured by the mole (symbol mol) where $1 \, mol = 6.02 \times 10^{23}$ particles. This number is known as the Avogadro constant, N_A. The mass of 1 mol of a substance is called its molar mass. For example, the molar mass of carbon-12 atoms is $12.0 \, g \, mol^{-1}$. The molar mass of O_2 molecules is $32 \, g \, mol^{-1}$.

A sample of n moles of a substance will have N particles where $N = n \times N_A$.

Relationships between pressure, volume, and temperature

Charles' law considers the relationship between the volume of a fixed mass of gas at constant pressure and the temperature of the gas. He discovered that the volume increases linearly with temperature as shown in Figure 3.

If the volume of a fixed mass of gas remains constant as the gas is heated, the pressure of the gas also increases linearly with temperature. This is called the **pressure law**.

Absolute zero and the kelvin temperature scale

Look at Figure 3. If the line is extrapolated backwards it will eventually meet the temperature axis. At this point its volume will be zero. This implies that the particles of the gas are not moving. They have no kinetic energy. The temperature at which this occurs is absolute zero, $-273 \, °C$.

The kelvin scale of temperature starts at absolute zero, $0 \, K$. Each degree in the scale represents the same temperature difference as 1 degree Celsius. For example, $0 \, °C = 273 \, K$ and $100 \, °C = 373 \, K$.

Using the Kelvin scale, Charles' law becomes $V \propto T$ (at constant pressure) and the pressure law is $P \propto T$ (at constant volume).

Synoptic link

The kinetic theory is considered in more detail in Topic 14.2, The kinetic model of gases.

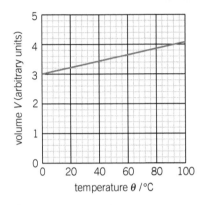

▲ **Figure 3** *Charles' law*

 Practical: Determining absolute zero

- Figure 4 shows a capillary tube containing a trapped sample of air. As the capillary tube is of constant cross-section the length of the air sample is proportional to its volume.
- The tube is placed in a tall glass beaker of water and the length of the air column measured for a range temperatures.
- Extrapolating the linear graph of length of air column versus temperature to zero length gives an estimate of absolute zero, though there are likely to be large uncertainties in the data.

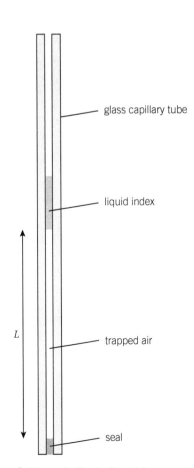

▲ **Figure 4** *Charles' law tube apparatus*

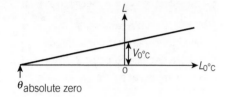

▲ **Figure 5** *Obtaining an estimate of absolute zero through extrapolation of the graph line*

Revision tip

Always remember to change degrees Celsius into kelvin before any calculations involving the ideal gas law.

The ideal gas law

For an ideal gas, the relationships can be combined into a single relationship:

$$pV \propto NT \text{ for a constant mass of gas}$$

This relationship can be expressed as an equation:

$$pV = NkT$$

where k is the Boltzmann constant, $1.38 \times 10^{-23} \, \text{J K}^{-1}$.

The relationship can be considered in terms of the number of moles of gas present n, rather than the number of particles, N. In this case: $pV = nRT$ where R is the gas constant, $8.31 \, \text{J mol}^{-1} \text{K}^{-1}$.

It is worth remembering that the Boltzmann constant is simply the gas constant divided by the Avogadro number, that is:

$$k = \frac{R}{N_A}$$

 Worked example: Using $pV = nRT$

A cylinder contains 200 g of helium (molar mass = 4.0 g mol⁻¹) at temperature of 19 °C and a pressure of 2.0 × 10⁶ Pa. Calculate the volume of the cylinder.

Step 1: Convert the temperature into kelvin: 19 + 273 = 292 K

Step 2: $V = \dfrac{nRT}{p}$ where $n = \dfrac{200 \, \text{g}}{4.0 \, \text{g mol}^{-1}} = 50 \, \text{mol}$

$$V = \frac{50 \, \text{mol} \times 8.31 \, \text{J mol}^{-1} \text{K}^{-1} \times 292 \, \text{K}}{2.0 \times 10^6 \, \text{Pa}} = 0.061 \, \text{m}^3 \, (2 \, \text{s.f.})$$

Summary questions

1. A gas cylinder of volume 2.5 litres contains 9.6 g of oxygen (O_2) at a temperature of 25 °C. The molar mass of oxygen is 32 g mol⁻¹.
   a What is the temperature of the gas in kelvin? *(1 mark)*
   b How many moles of gas are in the cylinder? *(1 mark)*
   c How many oxygen molecules are in the container? *(1 mark)*
   d What is the pressure in the container? *(2 marks)*

2. A cylinder contains 56 g of nitrogen (N_2) gas at a pressure of 4.1 × 10⁵ Pa. More nitrogen is pumped into the cylinder without changing the temperature of the gas. The pressure rises to 4.7 × 10⁵ Pa. How many moles of nitrogen have been added to the cylinder? (molar mass of nitrogen = 28 g mol⁻¹) *(3 marks)*

3. A container of volume 20 litres contains 20 g of argon (molar mass = 40 g mol⁻¹) and 10 g of helium (molar mass = 4.0 g mol⁻¹). The gases are at a temperature of 300 K. Calculate the pressure exerted on the walls of the container. *(3 marks)*

14.2 The kinetic model of gases

Specification references: 5.2.1 a(ii), 5.2.1 a(iv), 5.2.1 a(v), 5.2.1a(vi), 5.2.1 b(i), 5.2.1 c (iii)

Ideal gases

An ideal gas has the following characteristics:

- It comprises molecules that do not interact with one another at all.
- The volume occupied by the molecules within the gas is negligible.
- All the collisions of the particles with each other and with the walls of the container are perfectly elastic. No energy is lost in collisions.

The model of an ideal gas is a simplification, but it is a very useful one.

Modelling a gas

Consider a single molecule of mass m in the box shown in Figure 1.

The molecule is moving at speed c in the x-direction. If it makes elastic collisions with the walls of the box it will bounce back and forwards in the x-direction, changing from speed $+c$ to $-c$ when it bounces off the right-hand end. Each collision with the right-hand wall produces an impulse of $+2mc$ on that wall. Similarly, the molecule exerts an impulse of $-2mc$ each time it bounces off the left-hand wall. The time Δt between collisions at the right-hand wall is given by $\frac{2x}{c}$.

$$\text{As force} = \frac{\text{impulse}}{\Delta t}, \text{ force on the right-hand wall} = \frac{2mc}{2x/c} = \frac{mc^2}{x}$$

Now consider N molecules in the same box, moving randomly in all possible directions. You can assume, as indicated in Figure 2, that one-third will be moving in the x-direction, one-third in the y-direction and one-third in the z-direction.

Synoptic link

This topic uses ideas about momentum and impulse covered in Topic 9.2, Newton's laws of motion and momentum.

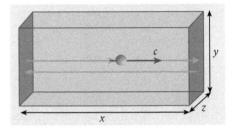

▲ **Figure 1** *A molecule in a box*

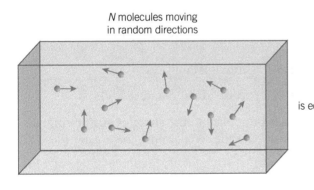

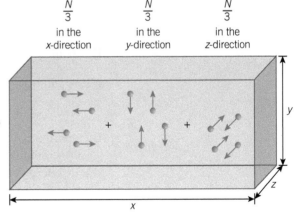

▲ **Figure 2** *Many molecules in a box*

The average force on the right-hand end will be:

$$F = \frac{1}{3} \times \frac{Nmc^2}{x}$$

The pressure on the right-hand end of the box is:

$$p = \frac{F}{A} = \frac{F}{yz} = \frac{1}{3} \times \frac{Nmc^2}{xyz}$$

As volume of the box, $V = x \times y \times z$:

$$\text{pressure } p = \frac{1}{3} \times \frac{Nmc^2}{v} \text{ or } pV = \frac{1}{3}Nmc^2$$

It is assumed that all the molecules are moving at the same speed, *c*. The final form of the equation uses the mean of the *square* of the speeds. This has the symbol $\overline{c^2}$.

The final form of the equation is:

$$pV = \frac{1}{3}Nm\overline{c^2}$$

When considering molecular speeds use the square root of the mean square speed, $\sqrt{\overline{c^2}}$. This is often written as c_{rms}.

 Worked example: Root mean square speed

Four molecules have speeds 200 m s⁻¹, 200 m s⁻¹, 240 m s⁻¹, and 250 m s⁻¹. Calculate the root mean square speed of the molecules.

Step 1: Find the mean square speed:

$$\frac{(200\,\text{m s}^{-1})^2 + (200\,\text{m s}^{-1})^2 + (240\,\text{m s}^{-1})^2 + (250\,\text{m s}^{-1})^2}{4}$$

Step 2: Calculate the root mean square speed.

$$= \sqrt{\frac{(200\,\text{m s}^{-1})^2 + (200\,\text{m s}^{-1})^2 + (240\,\text{m s}^{-1})^2 + (250\,\text{m s}^{-1})^2}{4}}$$

$$= \sqrt{\frac{200\,100\,\text{m}^2\,\text{s}^{-2}}{4}} = \sqrt{50\,025\,\text{m}^2\,\text{s}^{-2}} = 224\,\text{m s}^{-1}$$

Temperature and the energy of molecules

The average kinetic energy of a molecule in a gas: $E_k = \frac{1}{2}m\overline{c^2}$

As $pV = \frac{1}{3}Nm\overline{c^2}$ you can write: $pV = \frac{2}{3}N\left(\frac{1}{2}m\overline{c^2}\right)$

As $pV = NkT$ it follows that: $kT = \frac{2}{3}\left(\frac{1}{2}m\overline{c^2}\right)$

Therefore: $\frac{1}{2}m\overline{c^2} = \frac{3}{2}kT$

This relationship leads to the useful approximation:

average energy *E* of a particle at temperature $\approx kT$

The approximation $E \approx kT$ can also be applied to the energies of vibrating particles in liquids and solids, the higher the temperature the greater the kinetic energy of the vibrations.

Model answer: Root mean square speed and temperature

Air is a mixture of gases including nitrogen and oxygen. Calculate the ratio $\dfrac{c_{rms}\,(\text{nitrogen})}{c_{rms}\,(\text{oxygen})}$ in a sample of air. Molar mass of nitrogen (N_2) = 28 g mol⁻¹, molar mass of oxygen = 32 g mol⁻¹.

It may appear that you have not been given enough information to calculate the ratio. You have, but it takes a little thought. The temperature of the gas is the same throughout the sample so you can write

Step 1: $\frac{1}{2}m_n\overline{c_n^2} = \frac{1}{2}m_o\overline{c_o^2}$ where 'n' and 'o' represent nitrogen and oxygen.

Step 2: Rearranging and simplifying: $\dfrac{\overline{c_n^2}}{\overline{c_o^2}} = \dfrac{m_o}{m_n}$

> You are not given the mass of individual molecules, m_n and m_0 but the ratio of the molar masses will be the same as the ratio of molecular masses, so

Step 3: $\dfrac{\sqrt{\overline{c_n^2}}}{\sqrt{\overline{c_o^2}}} = \dfrac{\sqrt{32}}{\sqrt{28}} = \sqrt{\dfrac{8}{7}} = 1.07$

The random walk of molecules in a gas

Although gas molecules are of negligible size compared to the volume of the gas, they still collide with one another. Each collision changes the direction of the molecules in an entirely random manner. For a given length between collisions L, the displacement from the starting point after N steps is $L\sqrt{N}$. On average, an air molecule will travel about 100 nm between collisions, a distance called its mean free path.

 Worked example: Displacement of a nitrogen molecule.

At room temperature, the r.m.s. speed of a nitrogen molecule is about $500\,\text{m s}^{-1}$. The mean free path length of nitrogen molecules is about 100 nm. Calculate the displacement from its starting point of a nitrogen molecule after a period of random movement of 90 s.

Step 1: Total distance covered in 90 s = $500\,\text{m s}^{-1} \times 90\,\text{s} = 45\,000\,\text{m}$

Step 2: Number of collisions $= \dfrac{45\,000\,\text{m}}{1 \times 10^{-7}\,\text{m}} = 4.5 \times 10^{11}$ collisions

Step 3: Displacement = mean free path $\times \sqrt{N} = 1 \times 10^{-7}\,\text{m} \times \sqrt{4.5 \times 10^{11}} = 0.067\,\text{m}$

There is a great difference between the total distance travelled (45 km) and the total displacement (6.7 cm). This explains why diffusion of gases is slow.

Summary questions

1 Calculate:
   a the kinetic energy of a molecule of oxygen gas at 298 K   (*1 mark*)
   b the r.m.s. speed of oxygen molecules at this temperature.
   [molar mass of $O_2 = 32\,\text{g mol}^{-1}$]   (*2 marks*)

2 A cylinder contains air at the very low pressure of 350 Pa. The volume of the cylinder is $6.5 \times 10^{-4}\,\text{m}^3$. The air is at a temperature of 295 K. The molar mass of air is $29\,\text{g mol}^{-1}$. Calculate:
   a the r.m.s. speed of the air molecules in the cylinder   (*2 marks*)
   b the number of molecules in the cylinder.   (*2 marks*)

3 It takes about 100 s for a molecule in a gas to make a displacement of 0.05 m from its starting point.
   Calculate the displacement made in the same time if the temperature of the gas is doubled. Assume that the density of the gas remains the same.   (*2 marks*)

14.3 Energy in matter

Specification references: 5.2.1 a(i), 5.2.1 b(i), 5.2.1 c (ii), 5.2.1 d(i)

The first law of thermodynamics

The first law of thermodynamics equates the change in internal energy ΔU of a system with the work done on a system W and the energy thermally transferred to a system Q:

$$\Delta U = W + Q$$

Note that either or both of W and Q can be negative.

If the volume of a substance does not change so no work is done on or by the substance the change in internal energy can be linked to the change in temperature $\Delta \theta$ by the equation:

$$\Delta U = mc\Delta \theta$$

where m is the mass of the substance and c is a constant for the material, the specific thermal capacity, with units $J\,kg^{-1}\,K^{-1}$.

Model answer: Specific thermal capacity

A cup contains 200 g of water at 90 °C Calculate the energy transferred to the surroundings as the water cools from 90 °C to 65 °C. The specific thermal capacity of water is 4200 J kg^{-1} K^{-1}.

This simple calculation can be performed in one step, but remember to convert the mass into kg. The temperature change is 35 °C which is also a temperature *change* of 35 K.

Energy transferred to surroundings $= mc\Delta\theta = 0.2\,kg \times 4200\,J\,kg^{-1}\,K^{-1} \times 35\,K = 29.4\,kJ$.

Practical: Determining specific thermal capacities

- Figure 1 shows a simple experiment to determine an estimate for the specific thermal capacity of a liquid.
- The same method can be used to find the specific thermal capacity of a solid if the sample has holes drilled to accept the immersion heater and the thermometer.
- The electrical work W (found from $E = IVt$) can be equated to the change in internal energy ΔU if care is taken to reduce Q, the energy transferred from or to the substance by other means.

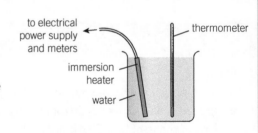

▲ **Figure 1** *Measuring the specific thermal capacity of water*

Summary questions

1 A 1.2 kW heater is immersed in 1.5 kg of water at 20 °C. The water is heated for 4.0 minutes. Calculate the maximum final temperature of the water and explain why this is a maximum value. (specific thermal capacity of water 4.2×10^3 J kg^{-1} K^{-1}) *(3 marks)*

2 A metal block of mass 0.8 kg is heated by a 48 W electrical h eater inside the block. The rate of rise of temperature of the block is 3.8 °C per minute. Calculate the specific thermal capacity of the block, assuming no energy losses to the heater or the surroundings. *(2 marks)*

3 0.2 kg of water at 80 °C is added to 1.4 kg of water at 40 °C. Calculate the maximum final temperature of the water, assuming no energy losses to the surroundings. *(2 marks)*

Temperature and the energy of particles

You have seen that the mean energy per particle in an ideal gas is given by $\frac{3}{2}kT$.

You often only need an order of magnitude value for the energy of a particle and can use the approximation $E = kT$ for the mean particle energy at temperature T.

Processes and activation energies

Many processes need a certain amount of energy to take place. Figure 1 shows a typical example in which the energy of the products is less than the energy of the reactants. However, the process needs an input of energy to be possible. This is the **activation energy** E.

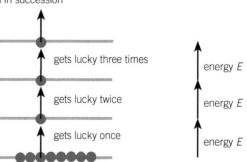

▲ **Figure 1** *Activation energy and change in energy between reactants and products*

Things happen between 15kT and 30kT

A useful rule of thumb to remember is that an activation process will happen at an appreciable rate (in a human timescale) if the activation energy is in the range $15kT$ to $30kT$. For example, the energy required for a water molecule to leave the water surface is about $16kT$ at room temperature. That's why sweat evaporates and wet clothes dry on an airing rack in a warm house.

 Worked example: Electron emission from platinum wire

It takes about 2×10^{-19} J to remove an electron from the surface of a platinum wire. Calculate the ratio $\dfrac{E}{kT}$ for this activation process at 298 K.

Substitute the values into the equation and perform the calculation.

$$\text{ratio} = \frac{2 \times 10^{-19}\,\text{J}}{1.38 \times 10^{-23}\,\text{J K}^{-1} \times 298\,\text{K}} = 49$$

This ratio is outside the 15–30 range so there will not be an appreciable emission of electrons from the metal surface at this temperature.

Energy exchange, probability, and the Boltzmann factor f

Flip a coin; the chance of it showing 'heads' is 0.5. Flip it again; the chance of two heads in a row is 0.25 or 0.5^2. The chance of a coin showing n heads in a row is 0.5^n.

Now consider a simple model of energy change amongst particles as they interact with one another. Assume that all particles gain or lose energy in equally-sized quanta E, allowing them to climb up or down the ladder of energy levels illustrated in Figure 2.

If a given particle has a probability f of gaining energy E from an interaction, the probability of it gaining energy E twice in succession is f^2. The chance of it making n energy-gaining interactions in a row, or 'getting lucky' n times in a

One particle may acquire energy E several times in succession

gets lucky three times

gets lucky twice

gets lucky once

energy E

energy E

energy E

▲ **Figure 2** *Particles can 'get lucky' and acquire energy to climb the ladder of energy levels*

With many particles, a fraction f acquire energy E at each step of the ladder.

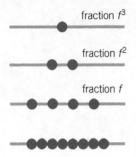

fraction f^3

fraction f^2

fraction f

▲ **Figure 3** *Numbers of particles at different energies*

row is f^n. This probability is the same value as the fraction f of particles on the higher energy level to the energy level below. This is illustrated in Figure 3.

The fraction f is known as the Boltzmann factor. It is the ratio given by:

$$f = \frac{\text{number of particles } N_X \text{ on the } X^{\text{th}} \text{ level}}{\text{number of particles } N_{X-1} \text{ on the } (X-1)^{\text{th}} \text{ level}}$$

In the example in Figure 3, this ratio is 0.5.

The Boltzmann factor is usually given in the form $f = e^{-E/kT}$ where E is the energy difference between levels and T is the absolute (kelvin) temperature.

Worked example: Boltzmann factor for electron emission from platinum wire

It takes about 2×10^{-19} J to remove an electron from the surface a platinum wire. Calculate the Boltzmann factor for this process at 298 K and 1000 K.

Step 1: Substitute values into the equation: $f = e^{-E/kT}$

$$f = e^{-\frac{2\times10^{-19}\,\text{J}}{1.38\times10^{-23}\,\text{JK}^{-1}\times298\,\text{K}}}$$

Step 2: Evaluate: $f = 7.6 \times 10^{-22}$

Performing the same calculation for 900 K $\left(\text{where } \frac{E}{kT} \text{ is about 16, within the range}\right.$ of 15–30 discussed in Topic 15.1, The ratio $\left.\frac{E}{kT}\right)$ gives a value $f = 1.0 \times 10^{-7}$. This demonstrates that the Boltzmann factor is usually a very small fraction, even for processes that we observe to happen over human timescales.

The Boltzmann factor, energy, and temperature

Figure 4 shows how the Boltzmann factor varies with absolute temperature for three different values of energy E. This diagram is worth spending some time over. You can see that the weak van der Waals bonds have a higher Boltzmann factor than the stronger hydrogen and covalent bonds. The *higher* Boltzmann factor shows that such bonds are more likely to break at any given temperature.

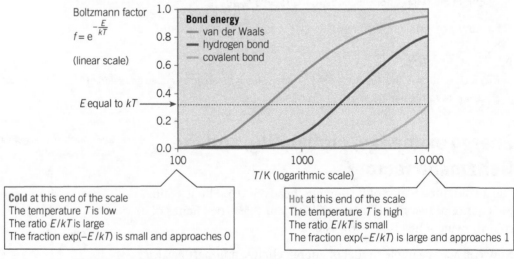

▲ **Figure 4** *How the Boltzmann factor f varies with temperature T*

Examples of activation processes

Liquids flow when molecules in the middle of the liquid gain sufficient energy (the activation energy) through interactions ('getting lucky') to break out of the 'cage' formed by the surrounding molecules.

Liquids evaporate when molecules at the surface gain enough energy to break away from their neighbours. Like all activation processes, these occur more readily at higher temperatures. That's why honey is runnier in a warm room than in the fridge, and puddles disappear more quickly on a warm day.

The rate of an activation process is proportional to the Boltzmann factor for the process. For example, the rate of evaporation of a liquid will increase if the chance of a molecule gaining sufficient energy to evaporate increases: double the chance, double the rate. So:

$$\text{rate} \propto e^{-E/kT}$$

Thus:

$$\text{rate} = C\,e^{-E/kT} \quad \text{where } C \text{ is a constant}$$

Therefore:

$$\ln \text{rate} = \ln C - \frac{E}{kT}$$

A graph of $\ln \text{rate}$ against $\frac{1}{T}$ will produce a straight line of gradient $-E$.

Viscosity of liquids

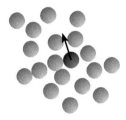

Evaporation of liquids

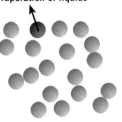

▲ **Figure 5** *Random thermal agitation of the surroundings provides the energy for liquids to flow and to evaporate*

Summary questions

1   What value of $\frac{E}{kT}$ corresponds to a Boltzmann factor of 10^{-8}? *(2 marks)*

2   Copy and complete Table 1. *(6 marks)*

▼ **Table 1**

E/J	T/K	$\dfrac{E}{kT}$	$f = e^{-\frac{E}{kT}}$
3×10^{-19}		25	
3×10^{-19}	600		
	550		1.9×10^{-11}

3   It takes about 3.5×10^{-20} J to break the bonds of a particular gas molecule. This is called 'dissociation'.
    Calculate the proportion of the molecules dissociated at 298 K.
    (2 marks)

4   The rate of escape *I* of electrons from a hot filament is given by the relationship:
    $$I = C\,e^{-E/kT}$$
    where *C* is a constant and *E* is the energy required for an electron to escape. Use this data to find *E*:
    current *I* at 900 K = 0.04 µA, current *I* at 1000 K = 0.16 µA   *(3 marks)*

Revision tip
There are many processes in which the rate *r* varies as $Ce^{-\frac{E}{kT}}$

The rates, r_1 and r_2 of such processes at temperatures T_1 and T_2 can be compared using the equation:

$$\ln\left(\frac{r_2}{r_1}\right) = \frac{E}{k}\left(\frac{1}{T_1} - \frac{1}{T_2}\right), \text{ eliminating}$$

the constant *C*.
This technique can be used in Question 4.

1 A cylinder contains mass M of hydrogen gas (molar mass $0.002\,kg\,mol^{-1}$) at pressure P.

An identical cylinder contain the same mass of helium gas (molar mass $0.004\,kg\,mol^{-1}$) at the same temperature. What is the pressure of the helium in the cylinder? *(1 mark)*

A $\dfrac{P}{2}$　　**B** P　　**C** $\sqrt{2}\,P$　　**D** $2P$

2 Five molecules of gas have the speeds given below:

$120\,m\,s^{-1}$　　$200\,m\,s^{-1}$　　$250\,m\,s^{-1}$　　$500\,m\,s^{-1}$　　$500\,m\,s^{-1}$

What is the root mean square speed of the five molecules? *(1 mark)*

A $160\,m\,s^{-1}$　　**B** $310\,m\,s^{-1}$　　**C** $300\,m\,s^{-1}$　　**D** $350\,m\,s^{-1}$

3 $1.80\,m^3$ of an ideal gas is at a temperature of $25.0\,°C$ and a pressure of $1.20\times10^5\,Pa$.

It is heated to a temperature of $55.0\,°C$ and its pressure increases to $1.30\times10^5\,Pa$.

What is the final volume of the gas? *(1 mark)*

A $1.82\,m^3$　　**B** $1.83\,m^3$　　**C** $3.65\,m^3$　　**D** $3.66\,m^3$

4 $1.2\,kg$ of water is heated from room temperature using a $1400\,W$ immersion heater.

　a Calculate the initial rate of rise of temperature of the water.
　　(specific thermal capacity of water $= 4200\,J\,kg^{-1}K$) *(2 marks)*

　b Explain why you would expect the rate of rise of temperature to change during the heating. *(2 marks)*

5 A sealed container of volume $4.4\times10^{-3}\,m^3$ contains $0.7\,mol$ of O_2 molecules. The temperature of the gas is $25\,°C$. Calculate the pressure of the gas. *(2 marks)*

6 Combine the equations $pV = nRT$ and $pV = \dfrac{1}{3}Nm\overline{c^2}$ to calculate the root mean square speed of a helium atom (molar mass $0.004\,kg\,mol^{-1}$) at $293\,K$. *(3 marks)*

7 A process has an activation energy of $50\,kJ\,mol^{-1}$.

　a Calculate the activation energy per particle. (Avogadro constant $= 6.0\times10^{23}\,mol^{-1}$) *(1 mark)*

　b Calculate the Boltzmann factor for this process at $T = 298\,K$. *(2 marks)*

8 Bromine, Br_2 is a brown gas of molar mass $0.16\,kg\,mol^{-1}$.

　a Show that the r.m.s. speed of bromine molecules at $293\,K$ is about $210\,m\,s^{-1}$.

　　(Avogadro constant $= 6.0\times10^{23}\,mol^{-1}$) *(2 marks)*

　b The bromine is released into a transparent container of air. The brown colour is observed to slowly diffuse through the container.

　　On average, a bromine molecule travels $100\,nm$ between each collision with another particle, each 'step' is $100\,nm$. The *displacement d* a gas molecule makes from its starting point in such circumstances is given by $d = x\sqrt{N}$ where x is the distance between collisions (mean free path) and N is the number of steps the molecule has made. Show that it will take about half an hour for a particle to move a displacement d of $0.2\,m$ from its starting point. *(3 marks)*

　c The molar mass of oxygen, O_2 is one-fifth the molar mass of bromine. Calculate the average displacement an oxygen molecule in the container will make in the same time. Show and explain all your working. *(3 marks)*

9 0.25 kg of an unknown liquid at 80 °C is in a beaker. A volume of the same liquid at 5 °C is added to the beaker until the temperature of the liquid in the beaker falls to 60 °C. Calculate the mass of liquid added to the beaker. Assume that all the energy transferred from the hot liquid goes to raising the temperature of the cold liquid added. *(2 marks)*

10 About 2.3×10^6 J is required to evaporate 1 kg of water.

The molar mass of water is 0.018 kg.

  a Calculate an estimate for the energy required for a single water molecule to escape into the vapour. *(2 marks)*

  b The average energy E of a particle at temperature T is given by $E \approx kT$.

  Use your answer to **a** to calculate the Boltzmann factor for the evaporation of water at a temperature of 20 °C. *(2 marks)*

  c Explain why the rate of evaporation roughly doubles when the temperature rises to 32 °C, include calculations in your answer. *(3 marks)*

11 A student uses apparatus similar to that shown in Figure 1 to investigate the relationship between pressure and temperature of a fixed volume of gas.

Use ideas from kinetic theory to describe and explain the variation of pressure with temperature you would expect to observe if the dry air behaved as an ideal gas and explain how the apparatus could be used to determine absolute zero of temperature. *(6 marks)*

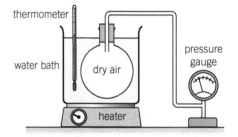

▲ **Figure 1**

12 Figure 2 shows the relationship between pressure and volume of a fixed mass of gas at constant temperature.

  a A student states that the graph shows that pressure $\propto \dfrac{1}{volume}$. Suggest a graph that could be drawn using the same data that would show whether the student was correct. Explain your reasoning. *(3 marks)*

  b Copy the graph and add a second line representing the relationship between pressure and volume for the same mass of gas at a higher constant temperature. Explain your reasoning. *(2 marks)*

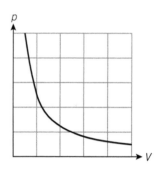

▲ **Figure 2**

13 This question is about the atmosphere of the Sun.

The surface of the Sun is at a temperature of about 6000 K. The energy E required to remove the electron from a hydrogen atom, the ionisation energy, is 13.6 eV.

  a Show that the ratio $\dfrac{E}{kT}$ is in the range 15–30, the range where processes will happen at an appreciable rate. *(1 mark)*

  b Hydrogen atoms in the Sun are ionised by collisions. The Boltzmann factor gives an estimate of the proportion of collisions which have enough energy to ionise an atom. Show that the Boltzmann factor for ionising hydrogen atoms on the surface of the Sun is about 5×10^{-12}. *(1 mark)*

  c Suggest and explain why ionised hydrogen is easily detectable in the Sun's surface, even though the proportion of collisions having sufficient energy to ionise an atom appears small. You may use an arithmetical example in your argument. *(4 marks)*

Field and flux

The study of magnetism and electromagnetism depends on a few simple concepts. Two of these are the idea of a magnetic field and the idea of magnetic flux. Both of these help visualise the invisible.

Figure 1 shows the magnetic field around a bar magnet. The field is represented by lines of flux. Note that the flux lines never cross and that they have a direction, from the N-pole to the S-pole. Look at the identical shaded areas X and Y. The flux lines are packed more tightly at X which shows that the field is stronger at X. The name for the measure of the strength of the magnetic field, the magnetic flux density, reflects this relationship; the more field lines passing through a given area, the stronger the field. The symbol for magnetic flux density is B, and the flux density is often referred to as the B-field.

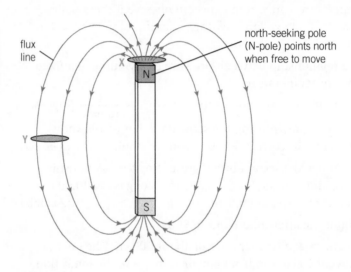

flux line

north-seeking pole (N-pole) points north when free to move

▲ **Figure 1** *Magnetic field and magnetic flux*

Long, current-carrying coils (solenoids) produce fields of similar shapes to those of bar magnets. The parallel, equally-spaced flux lines within the coil show that the field is uniform in this region.

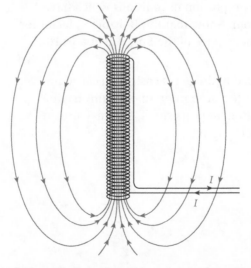

▲ **Figure 2** *Magnetic field in and near a solenoid*

Getting it straight

Lines of flux tend to shorten and straighten. In Figure 3 the magnets rotate towards one another, straightening and shortening the lines of flux.

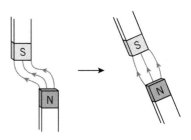

▲ **Figure 3** *Lines of flux tend to shorten and straighten*

Flux Φ and flux density B

These are related by the equation $\Phi = BA$ with Φ measured in weber (Wb) and B measured in $Wb\,m^{-2}$, provided that the area A is perpendicular to the lines of flux. Diagrams of magnetic fields are often drawn with the direction of the field perpendicular to the diagram. A cross represents a field going into the plane of the paper and a dot represents a field coming out of the paper.

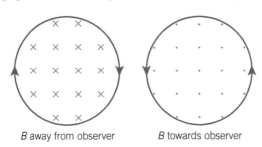

B away from observer   B towards observer

▲ **Figure 4** *Magnetic field in a section through a solenoid*

 Worked example: Flux density

A circular coil of cross-sectional area 25 cm² has a flux of 3.4×10^{-5} Wb passing perpendicularly through it. Calculate the flux density in the coil.

Step 1: You must remember to convert the area into m². 1 m² = 100 cm × 100 cm =

$10\,000\ cm^2$ area in $m^2 = \dfrac{25}{10\,000} = 0.0025\,m^2$

Step 2: $\Phi = BA \therefore B = \dfrac{\Phi}{A} = \dfrac{3.4 \times 10^{-5}\,Wb}{0.0025\,m^2} = 0.014\,Wb$

Electromagnetic induction

A change of flux in a circuit induces an e.m.f. across that circuit. The magnitude of the induced e.m.f. ε is proportional to the rate of change of flux Φ:

$$\varepsilon \propto \frac{\Delta\Phi}{\Delta t}$$

A change of flux in a coil of two turns will induce twice the e.m.f. as the same change of flux in a coil of one turn. This leads to the concept of flux linkage, illustrated in Figure 5, where:

flux linkage = number of turns × flux through one coil

Induced e.m.f. = rate of change of flux linkage, that is, $\varepsilon = \dfrac{\Delta N\Phi}{\Delta t}$ where N is the number of turns.

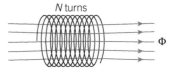

▲ **Figure 5** *Flux linkage = N Φ*

Lenz's law and Faraday's law

Lenz's law states that the direction of the induced e.m.f. is always such to act *against* the change that causes the induced e.m.f. This is a consequence of the conservation of energy.

For example:

- a changing flux in a solenoid will induce an e.m.f. in the solenoid
- the e.m.f. across the solenoid will produce a current through the solenoid

Revision tip

Lenz's law is a very useful memory aide but in examination questions you will be expected to give more explanation than simply stating the law.

Revision tip

When you are asked to explain an example of induction, have Faraday's law in your mind as it forms the basis of explanations of the induction effects met in the course.

- the induced current will produce its own flux
- the induced flux will act *against* the changing flux producing it, that is, in the opposite direction to the changing flux.

As a consequence of Lenz's law, the equation for induced e.m.f. is written:

$$\varepsilon = -\frac{\mathrm{d}(N\Phi)}{\mathrm{d}t}$$

This is often called Faraday's law. The minus sign is a reminder of Lenz's law. This simple equation encapsulates many of the ideas about electromagnetism covered in the course.

Summary questions

1 A coil of cross-sectional area $2.2 \times 10^{-5}\,\mathrm{m}^2$ has 600 turns. The flux linkage in the coil is $3.0 \times 10^{-4}\,\mathrm{Wb}$. Calculate:
   a   the flux linking one turn of the coil   (*1 mark*)
   b   the flux density in the coil.   (*2 marks*)

2 The flux linkage in a coil changes by 20 Wb over a period of 5 s at a steady rate. Calculate the induced e.m.f. across the coil.   (*1 mark*)

3 The flux through a coil decreases from $1.6 \times 10^{-6}\,\mathrm{Wb}$ to $0.8 \times 10^{-6}\,\mathrm{Wb}$ in 0.42 s. The coil has 200 turns. Calculate the induced e.m.f. across the coil.   (*2 marks*)

4 A circular coil of 500 turns has a diameter of 8.0 cm. The flux density in the coil is $3.2 \times 10^{-4}\,\mathrm{Wb\,m^{-2}}$. The direction of the flux in the coil reverses at a steady rate over a period of 0.4 s. Calculate the induced e.m.f. across the coil.   (*3 marks*)

16.2 Transformers

Specification references: 6.1.1a(i), 6.1.1a(iv), 6.1.1b(i), 6.1.1c(iii), 6.1.1c(iv), 6.1.1d(iii)

Electric and magnetic circuits

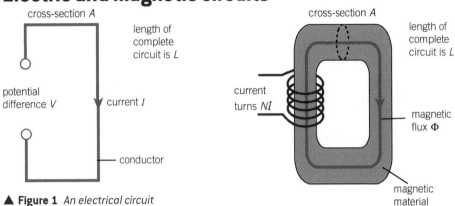

▲ **Figure 1** *An electrical circuit*

▲ **Figure 2** *A magnetic circuit*

The equivalent of p.d. in the magnetic circuit is the 'current-turns'. This is the current through the coil multiplied by the number of turns. This

▼ **Table 1** *Comparison of magnetic and electric circuits*

Magnetic circuit	Electrical circuit analogy
current turns NI	potential difference V
flux Φ	current I
permeability	conductivity

can be thought of as driving the flux through the magnetic material in an analogous manner to p.d. driving a current through a conductor.

Just as a p.d. will drive a large current through a circuit loop of high conductance, so the magnetic circuit will give a large flux if the material has a high permeance.

In an electrical circuit, conductance $G = \sigma \frac{A}{L}$, where σ is the conductivity of the material. You can see that the conductance of a circuit loop of conductivity σ wil be increased by increasing the cross-sectional area of the material and decreasing its length. It is the same with the magnetic circuit. For a high permeance of the circuit you would choose a material of high permeability (analogous to conductivity), and the circuit loop should be as short as possible with as large a value of A as possible. For magnetic circuits, short, fat circuit loops are desirable.

> **Revision tip**
> Permeance is a property of a particular magnetic circuit.
> Permeability is a property of the material the flux passes through.

Mind the gap

The magnetic permeability of iron is about 200 000 times greater than that of air. If there is an air gap in a magnetic circuit the permeance of the circuit is reduced and the flux through circuit is reduced. This is similar to an electrical circuit with a small resistance (analogous to iron in a magnetic circuit) in series with a large resistance (analogous to the air gap).

Transformers

A transformer is an electromagnetic machine often constructed with two coils wrapped around an iron core. The primary coil is connected to an alternating current (a.c.) supply. The a.c. in the primary coil induces an alternating e.m.f. in the secondary coil.

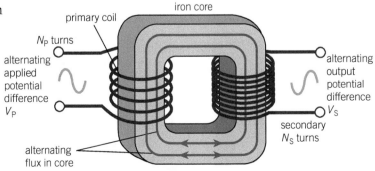

▲ **Figure 3** *Induction in the secondary coil of a transformer*

The rate of change of flux in the core is given by:

$$\frac{d\Phi}{dt} = \frac{V_p}{N_p}$$

As very little flux leaks into the air, the flux will be the same in both coils. Remembering Lenz's law, the e.m.f. induced in the secondary coil is the rate of change of flux linkage in the coil:

$$V_s = - N_s \times \frac{d\Phi}{dt}$$

As both coils have the same flux through them at all times:

$$\frac{V_p}{N_p} = \frac{d\Phi}{dt} = -\frac{V_s}{N_s}$$

so: $\dfrac{V_p}{N_p} = -\dfrac{V_s}{N_s}$

This is the transformer equation. The minus sign shows that the alternating p.d. across the secondary coil is 180° out of phase with the alternating p.d. across the primary coil (Figure 4). The equation can be rearranged as:

$$\frac{V_p}{V_s} = -\frac{N_p}{N_s}$$

where $\dfrac{N_p}{N_s}$ is called the turns ratio of the transformer.

In an ideal transformer, where energy losses can be ignored, the output power of the secondary coil will be the same as the power supplied into the primary coil.

Therefore, in an ideal transformer:

$$I_p V_p = I_s V_s \text{ or } \frac{I_s}{I_p} = \frac{N_p}{N_s}$$

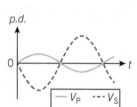

p.d.

— V_P ···· V_S

▲ **Figure 4** V_p and V_s are in antiphase

Revision tip

Step-up transformers have more turns on the secondary coil than on the primary coil: $N_s > N_p$

Step-down transformers have fewer turns on the secondary coil than on the primary coil: $N_s < N_p$

Revision tip

Permeance is a property of a particular magnetic circuit. Permeability is a property of the material(s) that flux passes through.

Eddy currents

Iron is often used for transformer cores because it has a high magnetic permeability, producing a magnetic circuit of high permeance.

But iron is also a good electrical conductor. The changing flux in the circuit induces e.m.f.s in the core itself which produce eddy currents in the core (Figure 5).

By Lenz's law, the flux produced by the eddy currents will oppose the flux created by the primary coil and reduce the efficiency of the transformer, dissipating wasted energy as thermal energy within the core.

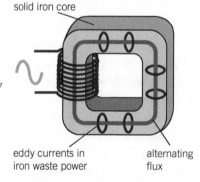

solid iron core

eddy currents in iron waste power

alternating flux

▲ **Figure 5** Eddy currents in a solid iron core

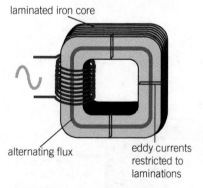

laminated iron core

alternating flux   eddy currents restricted to laminations

▲ **Figure 6** Eddy currents are reduced in a laminated iron core

---

🖩 **Worked example: Transformers**

An ideal transformer has 800 turns on its primary coil and 1240 turns on its secondary coil. The primary voltage is 20 V and the current in the primary coil is 3.2 A. Calculate a the voltage across the secondary coil b the current in the secondary coil.

a Step 1: Rearrange the transformer equation: $\dfrac{V_p}{N_p} = \dfrac{V_s}{N_s} \therefore V_s = \dfrac{V_p}{N_p} \times N_s$

Step 2: Substitute values and evaluate: $V_s = \dfrac{20\,V \times 1240}{800} = 31.0\,V$

b Step 1: Rearrange equation: $\dfrac{I_s}{I_p} = \dfrac{N_p}{N_s} \therefore I_s = \dfrac{N_p}{N_s} \times I_P$

Step 2: Substitute values and evaluate: $I_s = \dfrac{800}{1240} \times 3.2\,A = 2.06\,A$ [3 s.f.]

Practical: Investigating transformers

- The simple apparatus shown in Figure 7 can be used to investigate transformer action by measuring p.d. and current in the primary and secondary circuits using a.c. meters or oscilloscopes.

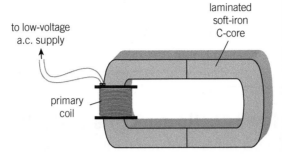

▲ **Figure 7** *Simple transformer (secondary coil not yet added)*

- You can confirm the transformer equations given above and also investigate:
  - the effect of changing the relative positions of the coils
  - the effect of decreasing the permeance of circuit by introducing sheets of paper between the two C-cores
  - the effect of changing the load resistance of the secondary circuit.

Summary questions

1 Complete Table 2 for an ideal transformer with turns ratio $\frac{N_p}{N_s} = 0.08$. *(2 marks)*

▼ **Table 2**

V_P	I_P	V_S	I_S
12.0 V			0.20 mA

2 A transformer has a turns ratio $\frac{N_p}{N_s} = 0.1$.

   a The voltage across the primary coil of a simple transformer is 12.0 V. State the voltage across the secondary coil, assuming ideal behaviour. *(1 mark)*

   b The core develops a crack, introducing a small air gap. Explain the effect this has on the permeance of the magnetic circuit and the induced voltage. *(4 marks)*

3 Explain how eddy currents are produced in transformers with solid cores and the effect these currents have on the efficiency of the transformer. Explain how eddy currents can be reduced. *(6 marks)*

a

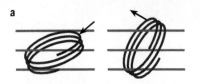

turn the coil so that more flux goes through it

b

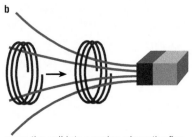

move the coil into a region where the flux density is larger

c

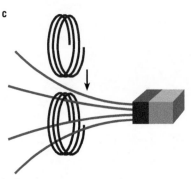

slide the coil so that more flux goes through it

▲ **Figure 1** *Creating a changing flux with a constant magnetic field*

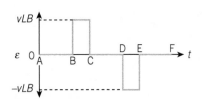

▲ **Figure 3** *e.m.f. induced by the movement in Figure 2*

Generators and dynamos

A generator uses motion to produce the flux changes needed to induce an e.m.f. 'Dynamo' is an older term for generator so the newer term is used throughout, and you are advised to do the same.

Moving coils in magnetic fields

Figure 1 shows three ways the flux through a coil can be changed. In each case, a change in flux linkage $N\Phi$ in time interval Δt will result in an induced e.m.f.

Figure 2 shows a one-turn coil entering and leaving a region of uniform field (the shaded region). The coil moves with constant velocity.

● From position A to B there is no e.m.f. induced as there is no change of flux through the coil.

● From B to C the flux changes from zero to a maximum value of $B \times$ area of coil = LWB (where L is length of coil and W is width of coil). The flux through the coil changes at a uniform rate so the e.m.f. is constant over this period.

● The value of the e.m.f. can be linked to the velocity of the coil relative to the field v as follows:

$$\varepsilon = \frac{\Delta\Phi}{\Delta t} \text{ (ignoring the sign of the e.m.f.)} = \frac{LWB}{\Delta t}$$

$$v = \frac{W}{\Delta t} = \therefore \Delta t = \frac{W}{v} \therefore \varepsilon = \frac{LWB}{W/v}. = vLB.$$

If the coil has N turns, $\varepsilon = NvLB$.

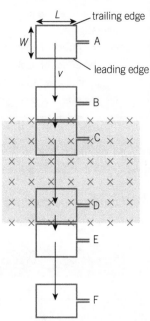

▲ **Figure 2** *A coil moving through a uniform field*

● From C to D there is no flux change in the coil (even though the coil is moving through a field) so there is no induced e.m.f.

● From D to E the flux changes from maximum value to zero. A constant e.m.f. of magnitude vLB is induced in the opposite direction to that induced between B and C (see Figure 3).

The equation $\varepsilon = vLB$ can also be used to find the e.m.f. induced across a straight conductor of length L moving at right angles to a magnetic field of strength B.

Synoptic link

You will recognise the form of this equation from Topic 11.1, Introducing simple harmonic oscillators.

Practical: Induced e.m.f. in a coil with a moving magnet

● Clamp a coil with its axis vertically and drop a small bar magnet through it (Figure 4).

● The induced e.m.f. changes as the magnet enters, accelerates through, and leaves the coil.

● The voltage–time graph produced with results from a data logger or oscilloscope can be analysed and interpreted in terms of the motion of the bar magnet relative to the coil and the shape of its B-field.

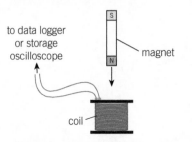

▲ **Figure 4** *Magnet falling through coil*

Coil rotating in a uniform magnetic field

Figure 5 represents a coil of area A rotating in a magnetic field of flux density B. The flux through the coil is given by $BA\cos\theta$. If the coil is rotating with angular speed, $\omega = 2\pi f$ the flux at any instant is given by:

$$\Phi = BA\cos 2\pi ft$$

A coil of N turns will have a flux linkage given by:

$$N\Phi = NBA\cos 2\pi ft.$$

$$\text{induced e.m.f.} = -(\text{rate of change of flux linkage})$$

This relationship is illustrated in Figure 6.

Real generators

Real generators are engineered to have as large a flux as possible. This can be done in two ways: increasing the permeance of the magnetic circuit and using an electromagnet. Figure 7 illustrates a possible design. The rotating electromagnet (the **rotor**) provides the changing flux in the iron core (the stator).

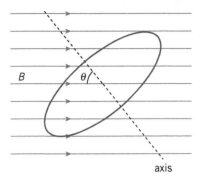

▲ **Figure 5** *Rotating coil in a uniform B-field*

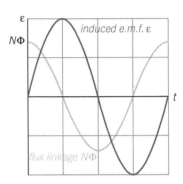

▲ **Figure 6** *Flux linkage and induced e.m.f. in the rotating coil*

Summary questions

1 Look at Figure 6. Explain the following features:
   a the induced e.m.f. when $N\Phi$–t graph is the steepest *(2 marks)*
   b the induced e.m.f. is zero when the $N\Phi$–t graph is a maximum or minimum *(2 marks)*
   c increasing $N\Phi$ produces a negative e.m.f and decreasing $N\Phi$ produces a positive e.m.f. *(1 mark)*

2 An e.m.f. of 2.4 V is induced across a straight conductor of length 0.40 m as it moves at 3.2 m s^{-1} at right angles to a uniform magnetic field. Calculate the strength of the field. *(2 marks)*

3 A 400-turn coil of area 6.4×10^{-3} m^2 is placed in a uniform magnetic field of strength 28.0 mWb m^{-2}. (see Figure 8). At time $t = 0$ s the flux linkage is zero.
   a Calculate the flux linkage after the coil has turned through 90° from its position at $t = 0$ s. *(2 marks)*
   b The coil rotates at 30 Hz. Use your answer to **a** to calculate the average e.m.f. induced during the first quarter rotation of the coil from $t = 0$ s. Explain why your answer gives the *average* e.m.f. over this time. *(3 marks)*

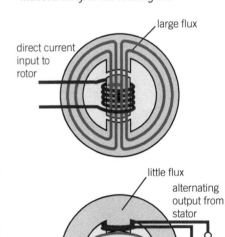

▲ **Figure 7** *A practical generator design*

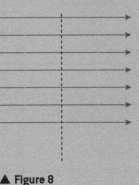

▲ **Figure 8**

16.4 Flux changes and force

Specification references: 6.1.1a[iii], 6.1.1c[i], 6.1.1c[ii], 6.1.1d[ii].

The catapult force

A wire carrying a current generates its own field. Figure 1 shows a uniform magnetic field (the three horizontal lines) and the field around a straight conductor carrying a current into the paper (the direction represented by the cross in the circle). When the current-carrying conductor is placed in the uniform field the field distorts as shown. Because flux lines tend to shorten, a downward force results. This is known as the catapult force.

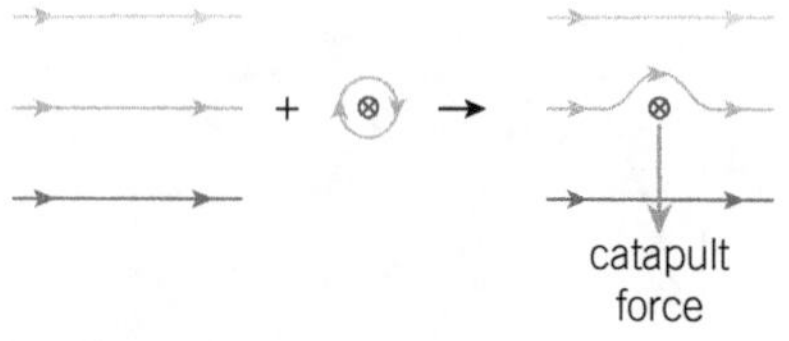

A current-carrying coil in a uniform magnetic field

The catapult force can produce rotation in a current-carrying coil. Such a coil forms the armature. This is the rotating part of an electric motor. Figure 2 shows a coil ABCD which is carrying a current I as shown. Side AB of the coil is in the same situation as in Figure 1 and so has a downward catapult force (because the flux lines tend to contract). Side CD experiences an upwards catapult force. Sides BC and DA are parallel to the lines of flux, so no force acts on them. The two forces produce a turning force (torque) that rotates the coil anticlockwise. A switching mechanism (a commutator) reverses the connections to the coil every half turn to allow the coil to continue to rotate. Without a commutator the coil would come to rest in a vertical position.

Real motors are more complex. They may use multi-turn coils, iron cores and some designs use alternating magnetic fields and don't require commutators.

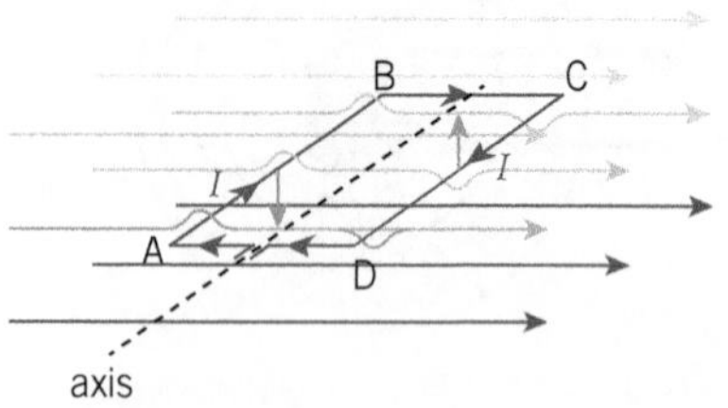

▲ **Figure 1** *The catapult force*

> ### Revision tip
> All motors rely on stretching and shortening lines of flux. A coil will experience a force in the direction that allows the flux lines to shorten and straighten.

Force on a straight wire in a uniform field

You have seen in Topic 16.3, Generators, that the e.m.f. induced across a wire of length L moving with velocity v perpendicular to a field of strength B is given by $\varepsilon = vLB$.

Look at Figure 3. There is an induced current I flowing in the wire, so:

the electrical power generated = $I\varepsilon = IvLB$

This power is produced by the force F required to move the rod at velocity v so is equal to Fv.

▲ **Figure 2** *Rotation of an armature coil*

mechanical power delivered = electrical power generated

$Fv = IvLB$ so $F = ILB$

The strength of the magnetic field can be measured in $Wb\,m^{-2}$ or an equivalent unit, the tesla, T, where $1\,T = 1\,Wb\,m^{-2}$.

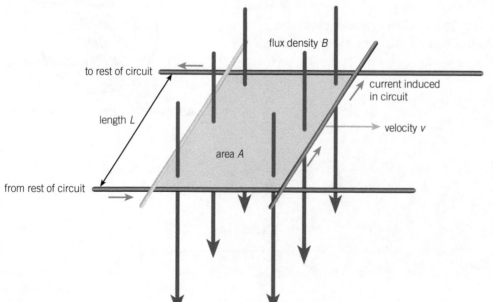

▲ **Figure 3** *Combining F = ILB and ε = vLB*

Practical: Using a balance to measure *B*-fields

- Figure 4 shows a stiff wire of length *L* passing through a uniform magnetic field created by the two slab magnets. The wire is held rigid and the balance is zeroed or tared.
- When a current passes through the wire, the catapult force on the wire will produce an equal and opposite force on the magnets and change the reading on the balance.
- Changing the current in the wire will change the force on the balance.
- A graph of force against current can be plotted and the strength of the *B*-field determined.

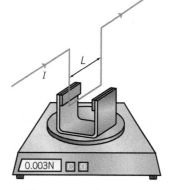

▲ **Figure 4** *Apparatus for measuring B-field*

Motors as generators

Every generator is also a motor and every motor is also a generator. If you rotate a generator by hand you will notice a resistance to motion as soon as the generator drives a current to the load. The generator, acting as a motor, pushes against you. Similarly, once a motor starts spinning it generates an e.m.f., often

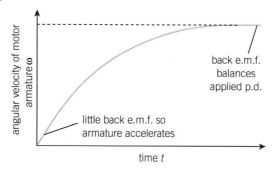

▲ **Figure 5** *Back e.m.f. opposes motor rotation*

called a back e.m.f. which opposes the p.d. driving the motor. The growth of the back e.m.f. limits the speed of a motor. As the angular velocity of the armature increases so does the back e.m.f. The angular velocity of the motor will reach a maximum when the back e.m.f. balances the applied p.d.

Summary questions

1 A wire of length 28 cm is perpendicular to a magnetic field of 4.8×10^{-3} T. Calculate the force on the wire when it carries a current of 2.3 A. (*2 marks*)

2 Calculate the force per centimetre on a straight wire carrying a current of 1.6 A in a uniform magnetic field of strength 140 mT. The field is perpendicular to the current. (*2 marks*)

3 Look at Figure 4.
   a State why the horizontal length of wire *L* experiences a force when it carries a current but the vertical sections of the wire in the field do not experience a force. (*1 mark*)
   b Estimate the smallest difference in current in the wire that can be detected by the system. Use this data about the experimental set-up: length $L = 0.040$ m, uniform field strength between magnets = 180 mT, resolution of balance = 0.0001 kg (*4 marks*)

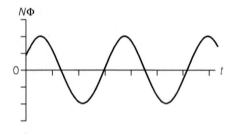

▲ Figure 1

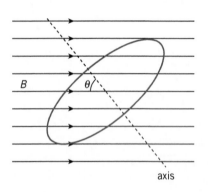

▲ Figure 2

1   A wire of length 72.0 cm carries a current of 62 mA in a field of uniform flux density acting at right angles to the direction of the current. The force on the wire is 1.2×10^{-3} N.

What is the flux density of the field?   (1 mark)

A 5.4×10^{-5} Wb m^{-2} B 2.7×10^{-2} Wb m^{-2}

C 5.4×10^{-2} Wb m^{-2} D 2.7×10^{-1} Wb m^{-2}

2   An ideal transformer has 400 turns on its primary coil and 620 turns on its secondary coil. The primary current is 0.64 A. The primary voltage is 12.0 V a.c. What are the values for voltage across the secondary coil and current through the coil?   (1 mark)

A 18.6 V, 0.41 A   B 18.6 V, 0.99 A   C 7.74 V, 0.99 A   D 7.74 V, 0.41 A

3   Figure 1 shows how the flux linkage through a coil varies over time. The time for one cycle is 0.2 s. The maximum flux through coil is 0.0036 Wb. The coil has 180 turns.

a   Calculate the maximum flux linkage in the coil.   (1 mark)

b   Use the graph to estimate the magnitude of the maximum induced e.m.f. and state the value of the flux linkage through the coil at times of maximum induced e.m.f.   (2 marks)

c   Explain the effect on the maximum induced e.m.f. of doubling the frequency of the flux linkage variation and doubling the number of terms at the same time.   (3 marks)

4   Figure 2 shows a coil rotating in a field of flux density 0.045 Wb m^{-2}. The radius of the coil is 0.05 m. The coil has 260 turns.

a   Show that the flux linking the coil is about 0.08 Wb when $\theta = 35°$.   (2 marks)

b   The coil rotates so that θ changes from 90° to 0° in 0.18 s. Calculate the magnitude of the average e.m.f. induced across the coil during this time. Explain why your answer gives an average value.   (3 marks)

c   The maximum value of the e.m.f. can be found from the equation:

maximum e.m.f. = $2\pi f \times$ maximum flux linkage

where f is the frequency of the rotation of the coil.

Calculate the maximum e.m.f. induced across the coil.   (3 marks)

5   A coil of wire is in a uniform magnetic field. Explain why an e.m.f. is induced across the coil when it is crushed, reducing its area.   (2 marks)

6   A wire of length 0.12 m carries a current of 8.0 A at right angles to a uniform field of flux density 0.090 Wb m^{-2}.

a   Calculate the force on the wire.   (1 mark)

b   Calculate the work done moving wire 0.24 m at right angles to its length and at right angles to the field.   (2 marks)

c   Calculate the flux cut when the wire is moved through 0.24 m.   (2 marks)

d   Calculate e.m.f. induced in the wire if the movement described in b takes 0.26 s.   (1 marks)

7   A simple motor has a current-carrying coil of wire spinning in a magnetic field. Explain why the current drawn by the motor decreases as the motor speeds up.   (3 marks)

8   a   An aircraft of wingspan 55 m flies at 250 m s^{-1}. The vertical component of the Earth's magnetic field in the area of the aircraft is 1.6×10^{-4} T. Calculate the e.m.f. induced across the wings.   (2 marks)

b   Suggest and explain why the induced e.m.f. increases as the plane flies nearer to the North Pole.   (3 marks)

Uniform fields

You have come across mathematical similarities or analogies between different areas of physics in a number of chapters. For example, you considered exponential relationships in capacitor discharging and in nuclear decay. Similarly, the uniform electric field can be compared with the uniform gravitational field.

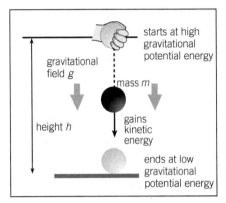
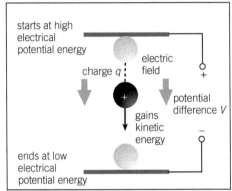

▲ **Figure 1** *Gravitational and electrical energy changes*

▼ **Table 1** *Comparing gravitational and electric fields*

	Uniform gravitational field	Uniform electric field
field strength	$g = \dfrac{F_{grav}}{m}$ [unit N kg^{-1}]	$E = \dfrac{F_{electric}}{q}$ [unit N C^{-1}]
force on test object	$F_{grav} = mg$ [unit N]	$F_{electric} = qE$ [unit N]
work done by the field on test object	$W = mgh$ [unit J] (mass m moved through vertical distance h)	$W = WEd$ [unit J] (charge q moved through potential difference V)

Electric potential difference is given by $V = \dfrac{W}{q}$ so:

$$W = Vq = qEd$$

Therefore, for a uniform field: $\quad E = \dfrac{V}{d}$

⌨ Worked example: Charge in uniform electric field

Two parallel plates have a potential difference of 120 V between them. The plates are separated by 0.025 m. Calculate a the strength of the uniform field between the plates b the force on an electron in the field c the energy transferred when an electron is accelerated from rest from the negative plate to the positive plate.

a Field strength $= \dfrac{V}{d} = 120\,V/0.025\,m = 4800\,V\,m^{-1}$

b Force $= Eq = 4800\,V\,m^{-1} \times 1.6 \times 10^{-19}\,C = 7.7 \times 10^{-16}\,N$

c Energy transferred = force × distance $= 7.7 \times 10^{-16}\,N \times 0.025\,m = 1.9 \times 10^{-17}\,J$

Note that part **c** can also be calculated by remembering that $V = \dfrac{W}{q}$, so if a charge of $1.6 \times 10^{-19}\,C$ passes through a p.d. of 120 V:

energy transfer $= 1.6 \times 10^{-19}\,C \times 120\,V = 1.9 \times 10^{-17}\,J$

Equipotentials in electric fields

Equipotential surfaces linking points of equal potential form equally spaced planes in a uniform electric field. Figure 2 shows the equal spacing in the region of uniform field and also shows how the field becomes non-uniform near the

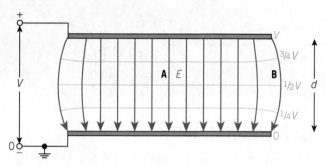

▲ **Figure 2** *Uniform electric field*

edges of the plates. The equipotential lines are perpendicular to the field lines.

The equation $E = \dfrac{V}{d}$ only applies to a uniform field, where the field lines are straight. Where field lines curve (such as at the edges of the field in Figure 2) the more general equation $E = \dfrac{dV}{dr}$ applies, where r is the distance along the field line.

Figure 3 shows the variation of potential in the central region (**A**) and at the edge (**B**). Tangents have been drawn on each graph where the field line crosses the equipotentials to find $E\left(=\dfrac{dV}{dr}\right)$. You can see that the gradient remains the same in the region of uniform field but changes in the non-uniform area where, for example, the gradient at $\frac{3}{4}V$ line is $0.96\,\dfrac{V}{d}$ but the gradient at the $\frac{1}{2}V$ line is $0.58\,\dfrac{V}{d}$

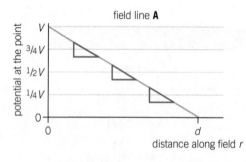

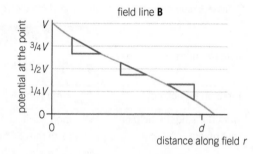

▲ **Figure 3** *Field strength obtained from a V–r graph*

Figure 4 shows the field lines between a positively charged sphere and a negatively charged plate. The equipotential line through point **X** is shown. Note that the equipotential line meets the field lines at right angles. The region enclosed in the dotted square is a region of uniform field.

Millikan's oil-drop experiment

This experiment, carried out in 1913, determined the charge of an electron. A simplified version of the apparatus is shown in Figure 5.

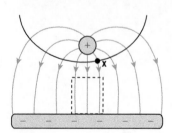

▲ **Figure 4**

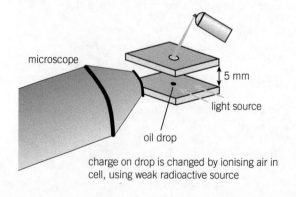

charge on drop is changed by ionising air in cell, using weak radioactive source

◀ **Figure 5** *Millikan's experimental set-up*

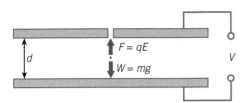

▲ **Figure 6** *Forces on a stationary oil drop*

- Tiny, charged droplets of oil are sprayed into the gap between two metal plates.
- The p.d. across the plates produces a uniform field in the gap.
- The direction and strength of the field is adjusted so that a particular drop is held stationary under the equal and opposing effects of the uniform gravitational and electric fields.
- For a stationary drop: $qE = Mg$

As $E = \dfrac{V}{d}$:
$$q\frac{V}{d} = Mg \therefore q = \frac{mgV}{d}$$

Millikan obtained thousands of values of charge on the drops and found that all of them were multiples of 1.6×10^{-19} C. He concluded that this was the value of the charge on the electron.

Summary questions

1 Two metal plates separated by 4.2 cm have a potential difference between them which produces a uniform electric field of $6000\,\text{V}\,\text{m}^{-1}$. Calculate:
   a the potential difference between the plates *(1 mark)*
   b the magnitude of the force on a proton in the uniform field between the plates. *(1 mark)*

2 Draw a copy of Figure 4 and include two more equipotential lines between point **X** and the plate. *(2 marks)*

3 2.6×10^{-18} J of work is done moving a charge of 3.2×10^{-19} C in an area of uniform electric field. Calculate the potential difference the charge has moved through. *(1 mark)*

4 In a Millikan experiment, a drop of oil of mass 9.8×10^{-15} kg is held stationary between two charged plates 5.2 mm apart in a set up similar to Figure 6. The potential difference between the plates is 520 V.
   a Calculate the field strength between the plates. *(1 mark)*
   b Calculate the charge on the drop. *(2 marks)*
   c A radioactive source is held near the apparatus, ionising the air in the gap between the plates. Explain why the drop begins to fall towards the lower plate. *(5 marks)*

17.2 Deflecting charged beams

Specification references: 6.1.2a(v), 6.1.2 b(i), 6.1.2c(ii), 6.1.2c(iv), 6.2.1c(i)

Deflecting electron beams in uniform electric fields

Figure 1 shows a set-up in which electrons are accelerated in the horizontal direction in an 'electron gun'. The electrons are then deflected in the vertical direction by a second, uniform field between deflection plates. Note that the deflection in this region is parabolic, like the path of a horizontally projected mass in a uniform gravitational field (turn the page upside down and you will see the similarity).

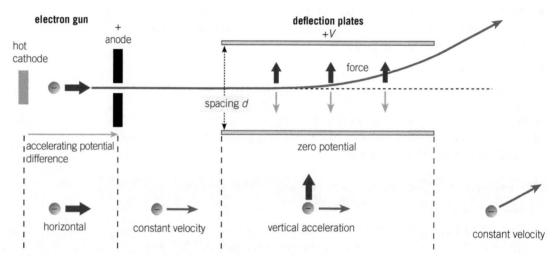

▲ **Figure 1** *Deflecting an electron beam with an electric field*

The energy gained when an electron, charge magnitude e passes through a p.d. of $V = eV$. This leads to the convenient unit of energy, the electronvolt (eV).

An electron accelerated through 900 V in an electron gun will leave the gun at a speed of about $1.8 \times 10^7\,m\,s^{-1}$. Moving this quickly, the electron will cross a 12 cm deflection region in about 7 ns. In this time, the gravitational force acting on the electron accelerates it downwards and the electron falls a distance of about $2 \times 10^{-16}\,m$. This tiny distance (smaller than an atomic nucleus) can be ignored when considering the effect of the electric field on the electron in the deflection region.

If the deflection plates in Figure 1 are separated by $d = 9.0\,cm$ and a p.d. of 300 V is applied between the plates the force on an electron from the electric field between the plates is about $5.3 \times 10^{-16}\,N$. This will produce a vertical deflection of about 6 cm as the electron travels through the field.

Moving charged particles in uniform magnetic fields

The force F on a charge q moving with speed v at right angles to a magnetic field of strength B is given by $F = qvB$.

Figure 2 shows a particle of charge q moving at right angles to the direction of a uniform magnetic field. It will experience a force qvB at right angles to its velocity. This is a centripetal force, hence, in this situation:

$$qvB\frac{mv^2}{r} = \therefore r = \frac{mv}{qB}$$

Charged particles travel in circular paths in uniform magnetic fields such as shown in Figure 2. The radius of the path depends on the momentum of the particle, its charge and the strength of the field.

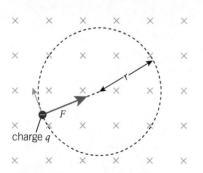

▲ **Figure 2** *Centripetal motion due to qvB*

Summary questions

1 An electron is accelerated from rest through a p.d. of 700 V. Calculate speed of the accelerated electron.
(mass of electron = 1.9×10^{-31} kg) *(3 marks)*

2 An electron is travelling at a speed of 2.0×10^6 m s^{-1} in a uniform magnetic field of strength 0.12 mT in a direction perpendicular to the field (see Figure 2).
  a Calculate the radius of the circular path followed by the electron. (mass of electron = 9.1×10^{-31} kg) *(2 marks)*
  b Calculate an estimate of the radius of the path made by a proton of similar speed as the electron in a in the same field. The mass of a proton is about 1800 times the mass of an electron. *(1 mark)*
  c The path of a charged particle travelling perpendicular to a uniform magnetic field is observed to spiral inwards. Explain what this tells you about the speed of the particle. *(2 marks)*

3 This question asks you to confirm the values given in the text for an electron accelerated through 900 V in the set-up illustrated in Figure 1.
  a Show that an electron accelerated through a p.d. of 900 V will leave the accelerating region with a speed of about 1.8×10^7 m s^{-1}.
  (2 marks)
  b The electron passes between deflection plates separated by 9.0 cm. There is a p.d. of 300 V between the plates. Show that the force on the electron in the deflection region is about 5.3×10^{-16} N. *(2 marks)*
  c Show that the vertical deflection of the electron as it travels through the plates is about 6 cm. *(4 marks)*

Synoptic link

You have considered centripetal forces on masses moving in gravitational fields in Topic 12.1, Circular motion. A force is described as centripetal if it acts at right angles to the velocity of the body, no matter what produces the force.

17.3 Charged spheres

Specification references: 6.1.2a(ii), 6.1.2a(iii), 6.1.2b(i), 6.1.2b(ii), 6.2.1b(iii), 6.1.2c(i), 6.1.2c(ii)

Coulomb's law

This gives the force F between two charges, q and Q separated by a distance r between their centres as: $F_{\text{electric}} \propto \frac{Qq}{r^2}$.

With constant of proportionality k this becomes:

$$F_{\text{electric}} = k\frac{Qq}{r^2}$$

Electric field strength $E = \frac{F_{\text{electric}}}{q} \therefore E = k\frac{Qq}{qr^2} = k\frac{Q}{r^2}$

where Q is the source of the field.

You can see the mathematical similarity between the force between two charges and the force between masses, $F_{\text{gravity}} = -G\frac{Mm}{r^2}$. However, whilst the force between masses is always attractive (hence the negative sign), the force between charges is attractive when the charges are of opposite sign but repulsive when the charges are of the same sign.

r
F1
F2
−q
+Q

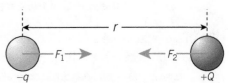

r is the position of q measured from Q

F_1 is the force on q due to Q

F_2 is the force on Q due to q

$F_1 = \frac{kqQ}{r^2} = F_2$

▲ **Figure 1** *Opposite charges attract*

Gravitational and electrical fields from point masses or charges are not the only examples of inverse-square law relationships; for example, as Figure 2 illustrates, luminous intensity also obeys an inverse-square law.

Revision tip

The electric force constant $k = 8.98 \times 10^9\ \text{N m}^2\ \text{C}^{-2}$ is often written as $k = \frac{1}{4\pi\varepsilon_0}$ where ε_0 is the permittivity of free space and has the value $\varepsilon_0 = 8.85 \times 10^{-12}\ \text{F m}^{-1}$.

r
diameter d,
area A
2r
diameter 2d,
area 4A

▲ **Figure 2** *Luminous intensity obeys an inverse square law*

Electrical potential near a charged sphere

The equations you have met so far in this section have been for point charges – you probably imagine them as small, charged spheres. A charged sphere is exactly equivalent to a point source of the same charge at its centre.

At a radial distance r from the centre of charge Q, the electrical field is $E = k\frac{Qq}{r^2}$ and the electrical potential is $V = k\frac{Q}{r^2}$.

Synoptic link

In Topic 12.2, Newton's laws of gravitation, you used the equations for gravitational point masses and saw that the gravitational field around a spherical mass is equivalent to a point mass at its centre.

Revision tip

The resultant electric field strength of two (or more) charges is the vector sum of the individual electric field strengths.

Potentials add as scalars.

Model answer: Field and potential near point charges.

A +15 μC point charge is separated from a +20 μC point charge by a distance of 50 mm (Figure 3). Calculate:

a **the field strength at X at the midpoint between the charges (a distance of 25 mm from both)**

b **the potential at the midpoint.**

50mm
+15μC
+20μC

▲ **Figure 3**

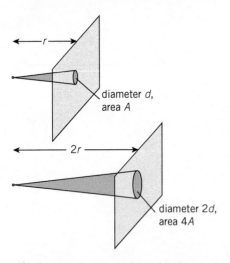

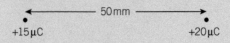

a Field strength due to +15 μC charge $= k\dfrac{Q}{r^2} = 9.0 \times 10^9 \, N\,m^2\,C^{-2} \times \dfrac{+15 \times 10^{-6}\,C}{(0.025\,m)^2} =$

$(+)2.16 \times 10^8 \, N\,C^{-2}$

Field strength due to the +20 μC charge, by the same method $= (-)2.88 \times 10^8 \, N\,m^{-2}$

So, field strength at midpoint $= -2.88 \times 10^8 \, N\,m{-2} + 2.16 \times 10^8 \, N\,C^{-2} = -0.72 \, N\,C^{-2}$

(to the left in the diagram)

> The candidate has referred to the diagram to show understanding of the addition of field strengths.

b Potential due to +15 μC charge $= k\dfrac{Q}{r} = 9.0 \times 10^9 \, N\,m^2\,C^{-2} \times + \dfrac{+15 \times 10^{-6}\,C}{0.025\,m^2} = 5.4 \times 10^6 \, V$

Potential due to the other charge $= 7.2 \times 10^6 \, V$

So, potential at midpoint $= 1.3 \times 10^7 \, V$ (2 s.f.)

> It is always better to show all working, which the candidate hasn't done in this case.

Electric fields and potential

Figure 4 shows how the electric field around a charge $-Q$ varies with radial distance. The electric field strength at a point is the force on a positive point charge of 1 C at that point. A negative charge Q will produce an attractive force on a positive charge so the graph resembles the graph of the gravitational field around a mass M.

The shaded area between the line and the x-axis gives the change in potential over distance Δr.

Synoptic link

In Topic 12.4, Gravitational potential in a radial field, you met similar graphs to the ones below. It is worthwhile looking back and comparing them.

Electric field and radius

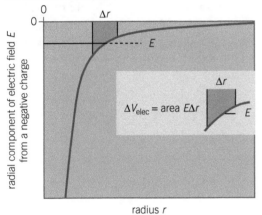

▲ **Figure 4** *The field graph gives potential*

Revision tip

It is really worth learning the equations electrical field strength, force, potential, and potential energy so that you don't use the wrong one in the pressure of an examination. It is very easy to lose marks by forgetting to square the radial distance r when calculating a field strength, for example.

Figure 5 shows the variation of potential with radial distance. Field strength E at a distance r from the charge is given by $-\dfrac{dV}{dr}$, the *negative* of the gradient of the tangent at distant r.

Electrical potential and radius

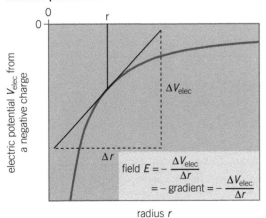

▲ **Figure 5** *The potential graph gives field*

Electric force and potential energy

The electric force on a charge q at a distance r from charge Q is given by:

$$F_{electric} = k\frac{Qq}{r^2}$$

$$\text{electrical potential energy} = qV = \frac{Qq}{r^2}.$$

Summary questions

1 a Calculate the force exerted by a proton (charge $= +1.6 \times 10^{-19}$ C) on an electron (charge $= -1.6 \times 10^{-19}$ C) at a distance of 1.0×10^{-10} m. *(2 marks)*

   b Calculate the electrical potential energy of the electron at this position. Give your answer in J and eV. *(3 marks)*

2 A hollow metal sphere of diameter 0.20 m has a potential of 800 V at its surface. What is the potential:
   a 0.10 m from the surface *(1 mark)*
   b 0.30 m from the surface? *(1 mark)*

3 A metal sphere has a charge of $+1.2 \times 10^{-9}$ C. The radius of the sphere is 0.054 m. Calculate:
   a the potential at the surface of the sphere *(2 marks)*
   b the work done taking a charge of -1.6×10^{-19} C (an electron) from the surface to a very great distance away from the sphere. *(2 marks)*

1 **a** Choose the correct unit for electric field strength from the list below.

(1 mark)

b Choose the correct unit for e.m.f. from the list below. *(1 mark)*

c Choose the unit that is equivalent to the tesla, T. *(1 mark)*

A $N C^{-1}$ **B** $Wb\,m^{-2}$ **C** $Wb\,s^{-1}$ **D** $\Omega\,A^{-1}$

2 The force between two point charges at separation r is F. What separation would increase the force to $3F$? *(1 mark)*

A $0.33r$ **B** $0.58r$ **C** $1.7r$ **D** $3.0r$

3 Which one of the graphs described in Table 1 can be used to find the electrical field strength from its gradient. *(1 mark)*

4 The electric force between two charges, Q and q is given by $F_{electric} = k\dfrac{Qq}{r^2}$ where k is a constant.

Show that the units of k are $N\,m^2\,C^{-2}$. *(1 mark)*

5 A spark plug ionises air between two metal strips separated by 0.5 mm. The air will ionise and a spark will jump across the gap when the p.d. between the strips exceeds 3.4 kV. Calculate the magnitude of the uniform field between the plates and give the unit. *(2 marks)*

6 An electron is accelerated from rest through a potential difference of 180 V.

a Calculate the velocity of the accelerated electron. *(2 marks)*

b The electron enters a region of uniform magnetic field as shown in Figure 1. The field strength in the region is 0.26 T.

Calculate the p.d. required across the horizontal plates to produce an electric force acting upwards on the electron that balances the magnetic force acting downwards.

Plate separation $d = 0.28$ m *(3 marks)*

7 Figure 2 shows the path of electrons travelling in a vacuum in an area of uniform magnetic field B. Before entering the field, the electrons have been accelerated from rest through a potential difference V.

a Show that the velocity v of an electron of charge e and mass m accelerated from rest through p.d. V is given by $\sqrt{\dfrac{2eV}{m}}$. *(2 marks)*

b Each electron experiences a force F due to the magnetic field given by $F = evB$. This force acts centripetally, causing the electrons to move in a circle of radius r.

Use the equation for centripetal force and the equation from **a** to show that $r = \dfrac{1}{B}\sqrt{\dfrac{2mV}{e}}$ *(3 marks)*

c i Use the data below to calculate the radius of the electron path in the field. *(1 mark)*

Accelerating potential difference = 680 V

Field strength = 1.8 mT

Mass of an electron = 9.1×10^{-31} kg

Charge on an electron = 1.6×10^{-19} C

ii The ratio, mass of proton : mass of electron = 1800 : 1. Explain why a proton of the same energy as the electron will have a path of radius more than 40 times that of the electron. *(2 marks)*

▼ **Table 1**

Graph	x-axis	y-axis
A	radial distance from point charge r/m	potential energy/J
B	radial distance from point charge r/m	force due to electrical field/N
C	radial distance from point charge r/m	potential/V
D	radial distance^2 from point charge r/m^2	potential energy/J

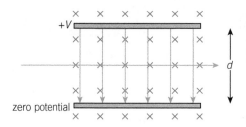

zero potential

▲ **Figure 1**

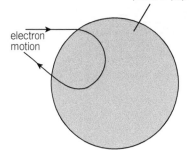

region of uniform magnetic field into plane of paper

electron motion

▲ **Figure 2**

18 LOOKING INSIDE THE ATOM
18.1 Probing the atom with alpha particles

Specification references: 6.2.1 a(ii), 6.2.1 b(i), 6.2.1 b(ii), 6.2.1 c(ii)

The discovery of the nucleus

The discovery of the electron in 1897 prompted physicists to consider the structure of the atom, and in 1909 Ernest Rutherford published results from alpha-particle scattering experiments which showed that the atom was not a single particle but a positively charged nucleus surrounded by distant electrons.

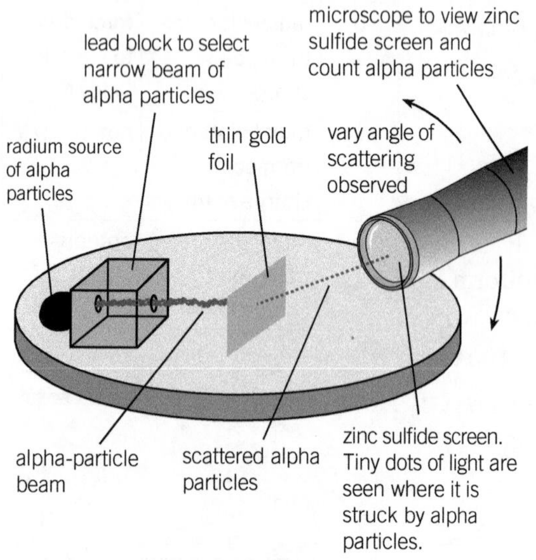

▲ **Figure 1** *Rutherford's scattering experiment*

Alpha-particle scattering

Geiger and Marsden, working under the direction of Rutherford, fired alpha particles (of energy 5 MeV) at a sheet of gold foil as shown in Figure 1.

It was expected that the alpha particles would pass through the gold foil with very little deflection. However, a very small fraction of the alpha particles 'bounced back'. That is, they were deflected more than 90° by the gold foil.

Rutherford knew that alpha particles are helium atoms which have lost their electrons and therefore carry a positive charge. From this understanding and the results of the scattering experiment he reasoned that:

- the core of the atom must be massive (on an atomic scale) to deflect alpha particles through large angles
- the core of the gold atoms and the alpha particles must both be very small (much smaller than an atom) or more alpha particles would 'hit' and bounce back – in fact, only around one alpha particle in 10 000 bounces back
- the alpha particles are deflected because of the electrical repulsion between the positively charged alpha particle and a positively charged core of the gold atoms.

Rutherford concluded that all atoms consist of a very small, massive, positively charged nucleus, surrounded at much larger distances by electrons.

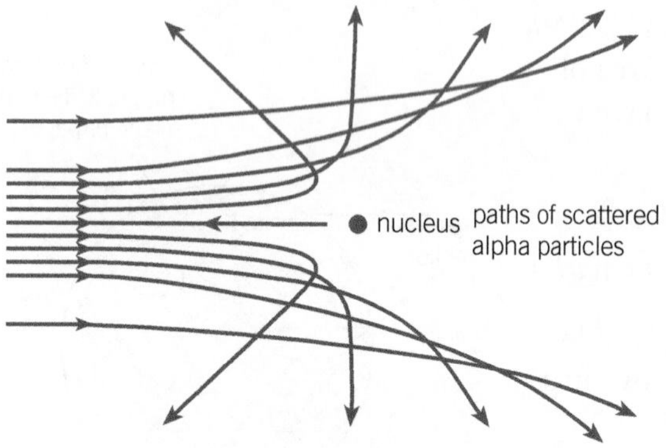

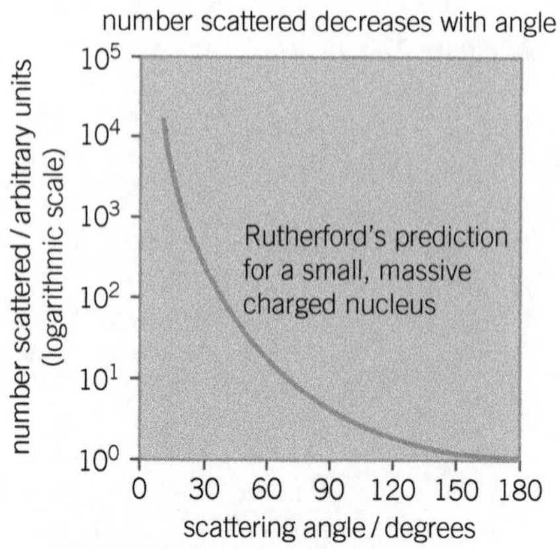

▲ **Figure 2** *Rutherford's picture of alpha-particle scattering*

This model fits experimental findings:

- Slower alpha particles are deflected through greater angles.
- Nuclei of smaller electric charge scatter alpha particles less strongly.
- The pattern of numbers of alpha particles scattered at different angles fits the pattern expected from an inverse square law for electrical repulsion.

Estimating the size of the nucleus

When an alpha particle makes a 'head-on' approach to a gold nucleus, it will slow down as it approaches, stop at the nearest point of approach, and then accelerate away from the nucleus in the opposite direction to the way it came.

The electrical potential energy of the alpha particle at the point of closest approach is equal to its initial kinetic energy at a large distance from the nucleus.

The electrical potential energy of a charge q at a distance r from charge Q is given by:

$$\text{energy} = \frac{kQq}{r} \quad \text{where } k = \frac{1}{4\pi\varepsilon_0} = 8.9 \times 10^9 \, \text{N m}^2 \, \text{C}^{-2}$$

In this case q and Q are the charges of the alpha particle and the nucleus respectively.

Synoptic link

This analysis uses ideas about the electrical potential of a point charge that you met in Topic 17.3, Charged spheres.

 ## Worked example: Estimating the radius of a silver nucleus

A 5.4 MeV alpha particle makes a 'head-on' collision with a silver nucleus. Calculate the distance of closest approach of the alpha particle to the nucleus.

Data: charge on alpha particle = $+2e$, charge on silver nucleus = $+47e$, $e = 1.6 \times 10^{-19}$ C

Step 1: Convert initial kinetic energy from MeV to J.

$5.4 \, \text{MeV} = 5.4 \times 10^6 \times 1.6 \times 10^{-19} \, \text{J} = 8.64 \times 10^{-13} \, \text{J}$

Step 2: Equate the initial kinetic energy with electrical potential energy at nearest approach.

$$\therefore 8.64 \times 10^{-13} \, \text{J} = \frac{kQq}{r} = \frac{8.9 \times 10^9 \, \text{N m}^2 \, \text{C}^{-2} \times 2 \times 1.6 \times 10^{-19} \, \text{C} \times 47 \times 1.6 \times 10^{-19} \, \text{C}}{r \, (\text{m})}$$

Note that the units on the right-hand side of the equation cancel down to N m, which is equivalent to J. Checking units is a useful method of ensuring that you are on the right track in calculations.

Step 3: Rearrange and evaluate.

$$\therefore r = \frac{8.9 \times 10^9 \, \text{N m}^2 \, \text{C}^{-2} \times 3.2 \times 10^{-19} \, \text{C} \times 7.52 \times 10^{-18} \, \text{C}}{8.64 \times 10^{-13} \, \text{J}} = 2.5 \times 10^{-14} \, \text{m}$$

This gives an estimate for the maximum radius of the nucleus. A more energetic alpha particle would give a smaller estimate for the radius as the value of the denominator in the equation in Step 3 would be larger.

Summary questions

1 An iron nucleus has 26 protons. Calculate the charge on an iron nucleus. *(2 marks)*

2 Figure 4 shows the path of an alpha particle near a nucleus. Copy the diagram.

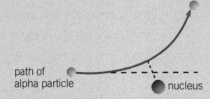

path of alpha particle

nucleus

▲ **Figure 4**

a Add a path representing an alpha particle with more energy. The path starts from the same point and in the same direction as the original path. *(2 marks)*

b Describe any change to the path if the nucleus had more protons. Explain your answer. *(2 marks)*

c Describe any change to the path if the nucleus had more neutrons. Explain your answer. *(2 marks)*

3 Calculate the distance of closest approach of a proton of energy 2.4 MeV to a nucleus of gold. (proton number of gold = 79) *(3 marks)*

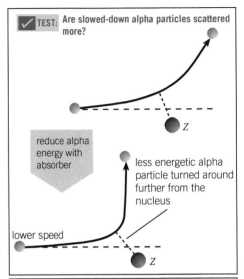

TEST: Are slowed-down alpha particles scattered more?

reduce alpha energy with absorber

less energetic alpha particle turned around further from the nucleus

lower speed

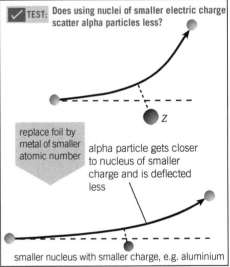

TEST: Does using nuclei of smaller electric charge scatter alpha particles less?

replace foil by metal of smaller atomic number

alpha particle gets closer to nucleus of smaller charge and is deflected less

smaller nucleus with smaller charge, e.g. aluminium

▲ **Figure 3** *Careful investigation of alpha-particle scattering supported the nuclear model*

Revision tip

When you draw the path of an alpha particle near a nucleus, remember these two points:

1 The path will curve the most at the point of nearest approach.

2 The path approaching the nucleus should curve in the same way as the path leaving the nucleus. The deflection will be the same whether the alpha particle is approaching from the right of the nucleus or the left.

Accelerating charges

A charge q of mass m accelerated through a potential difference V gains kinetic energy qV.

$$\frac{1}{2}mv^2 = qV$$

$$\therefore v = \sqrt{\frac{2qV}{m}}$$

 Worked example: Accelerating electrons

An electron is accelerated through a p.d. of 12 kV. Calculate the velocity of the accelerated electron.

Data: mass of an electron = 9.1×10^{-31} kg, $e = 1.6 \times 10^{-19}$ C

Step 1: Substitute and evaluate: $v = \sqrt{\dfrac{2 \times 1.6 \times 10^{-19}\,C \times 12\,000\,V}{9.1 \times 10^{-31}\,kg}} = 6.5 \times 10^6\,m\,s^{-1}$

The equation given above suggests that there is no limit to the velocity a particle can reach. However, this is *not* the case. No particle with mass can travel at the speed of light. For high potential differences, relativistic effects must be taken into account.

Einstein's equation, $E_{rest} = mc^2$

The equations used for momentum ($p = mv$) and kinetic energy work well at low speeds but for higher speeds Einstein's equations must be used.

Momentum is given by $p = \gamma mv$ where γ is the relativistic factor, given by:

$$\gamma = \frac{1}{\sqrt{1 - \dfrac{v^2}{c^2}}}$$

The energy of a free particle has two parts:

total energy = kinetic energy + rest energy

$= \gamma mc^2$ for a particle of mass m

For a particle at rest, $\gamma = 1$ so total energy = rest energy, $E_{rest} = mc^2$, perhaps the most famous equation in science.

The masses of particles can be expressed in energy units. The mass of an electron (9.1×10^{-31} kg) expressed in electronvolts is about 0.5 MeV. You can simply think of mass as being the rest energy.

> **Revision tip**
>
> When the velocity of a body is much less than c, $\dfrac{v^2}{c^2}$ is close to zero so $\gamma \approx 1$. Therefore at slow speeds, $p = \gamma mv$ becomes $p = mv$. This shows that at slow speeds Newton's momentum relationship works well.

 Worked example: Rest energy of a neutron

The mass of a neutron is 1.7×10^{-27} kg. Calculate its rest energy in MeV.

Step 1: Calculate rest energy in joules.

$E_{rest} = mc^2 = 1.7 \times 10^{-27}\,kg\,(3.0 \times 10^8\,m\,s^{-2})^2 = 1.53 \times 10^{-10}$ J

Step 2: Convert joules into MeV.

1 eV = 1.6×10^{-19} J

$\dfrac{1.53 \times 10^{-10}\,J}{1.6 \times 10^{-19}\,J\,eV^{-1}} = 9.56 \times 10^7\,eV = 960\,MeV$

Another expression for γ

From the equations above you can see that:

$$\frac{\text{total energy}}{\text{rest energy}} = \frac{\gamma mc^2}{mc^2} = \gamma$$

As total energy = kinetic energy + rest energy:

$$\gamma = 1 + \frac{\text{kinetic energy}}{\text{rest energy}}$$

When $v \approx c$, $\gamma \gg 1$, and momentum $p = \gamma mv \approx \gamma mc$

As $E_{\text{total}} = \gamma mc^2$, when $v \approx c$, $p \approx \dfrac{E_{\text{total}}}{c}$

The final equation also gives the momentum of a photon of energy E.

The linear accelerator

Figure 1 shows the principle of the linear accelerator. Bunches of charged particles are accelerated between pairs of cylindrical electrodes. The particles move at constant speed as they travel through the electrodes. An alternating p.d. ensures that the p.d. is in the correct direction to accelerate the particles as they leave the cylindrical electrodes, increasing the energy of the particles in steps as they pass between the electrodes.

Electron scattering

Electrons scatter off the nucleus in a similar manner to alpha particles.

The kink in the graph in Figure 2 shows the effect of diffraction. Electrons can be thought of as having a wavelength given by the de Broglie equation $\lambda = \dfrac{h}{p}$

The kink shown in Figure 2 is a diffraction minimum superimposed on the Rutherford scattering curve.

This is found at an angle θ where $\theta \approx \dfrac{1.22\lambda}{\text{nuclear diameter}}$

The wavelength of the electron depends on its energy. An electron with a wavelength of the order of magnitude of the atomic nucleus requires the electron to have an energy of several hundred MeV. This is far greater than the rest energy of 0.51 MeV.

For such high energies, $p \approx \dfrac{E}{c}$ so $\lambda \approx \dfrac{hc}{E}$

Revision tip

At 10% of the speed of light ($0.1c$), the relativistic factor is about 1.005, a correction of about 0.5%. Above $0.1c$ relativistic effects become increasingly clear. At $0.2c$ the correction is about 2%.

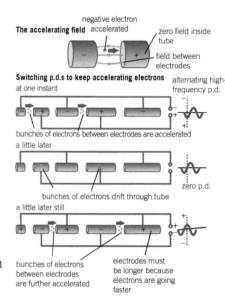

▲ **Figure 1** *Principle of the linear accelerator*

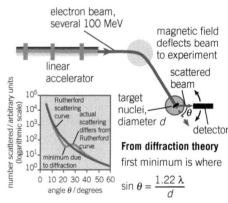

▲ **Figure 2** *Diffraction of electron beams by nuclei*

Summary questions

1 Calculate the rest energy of an alpha particle, mass 6.64×10^{-27} kg. Give your answer in GeV.   *(2 marks)*

2 An electron, rest energy 0.51 MeV, is accelerated in a linear accelerator through a potential difference of 0.9 MV. Calculate:
   a the kinetic energy of the accelerated electron in joules   *(2 marks)*
   b the relativistic factor for the accelerated electron   *(2 marks)*
   c the velocity of the electron.   *(3 marks)*

3 Copy and complete Table 1, comparing the relativistic factor γ for different ratios of speed of a particle (v) and speed of light c.   *(2 marks)*

▼ **Table 1**

$\dfrac{v}{c}$	γ
0.1	1.005
0.4	
	1.5

4 Electrons of energy 280 MeV are scattered by target nuclei giving a diffraction minimum at 22°. Calculate an estimate for the diameter of a target nucleus.   *(4 marks)*

18.3 Inside the nucleus

Specification references: 6.2.1 a(v), 6.2.1 a(vi), 6.2.2 b(i)

The structure of the nucleus

Experiments throughout the first decades of the 20th century gradually led physicists to an understanding of the structure of the nucleus. The picture was completed with the discovery of the neutron in 1932.

Atomic nuclei are composed of protons and neutrons. Both particles have approximately the same mass. Protons have a charge equal and opposite to that of an electron. Neutrons, as the name suggests, are neutral.

In a neutral atom, the number of protons is equal to the number of electrons which determine its chemical properties.

Figure 1 shows how the nucleus is represented.

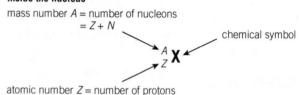

Inside the nucleus

mass number A = number of nucleons
$= Z + N$

atomic number Z = number of protons

chemical symbol

$$_{Z}^{A}X$$

$_{2}^{4}$**He**

$_{3}^{7}$**Li**

atomic number Z	mass number A	neutron number N
2	4	2
3	7	4

⊕ proton ◯ neutron

▲ **Figure 1** *Protons add mass and charge to the nucleus, neutrons simply add mass*

Neutrons add mass to the nucleus without adding charge. Atoms of the same chemical element often have exactly the same chemical properties but slightly different masses. These isotopes have the same proton number but different number of neutrons, and so have a different nucleon number. A difference in the number of neutrons in a nucleus can make an isotope radioactive.

Inside the nucleon

In the second half of the 20th century, more powerful accelerators increased the energies of the accelerated particles, and many new kinds of particles were produced in particle collisions. These results led to an understanding of the internal structure of nucleons and other particles.

Nucleons are not fundamental, indivisible particles but are combinations of more fundamental particles called quarks.

Protons and neutrons are composed of two types of quark: the up quark, u (charge $= +\frac{2}{3e}$) and the down quark, d (charge $= -\frac{1}{3e}$).

Protons (overall charge $= +1e$) are composed of two up quarks and one down quark (uud).

The quark composition of a neutron is ddu.

Quark list

	electric charge		electric charge
● up	$+\frac{2}{3}e$	◯ anti-up	$-\frac{2}{3}e$
● down	$-\frac{1}{3}e$	◯ anti-down	$+\frac{1}{3}e$

Proton p = uud

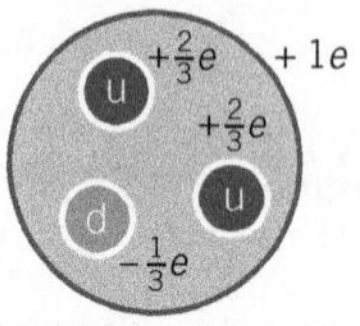

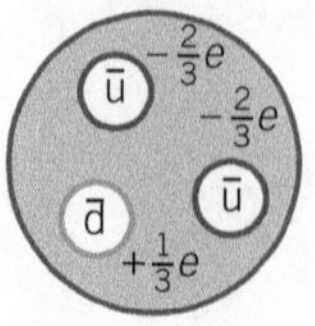

total charge = 1e
u + u + d = p
$+\frac{2}{3}e$ $+\frac{2}{3}e$ $-\frac{1}{3}e = 1e$

Neutron n = udd

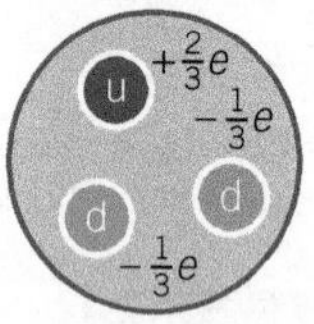

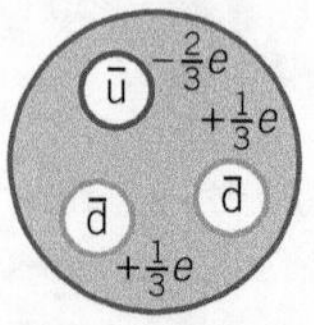

total charge = 0
u + d + d = n
$+\frac{2}{3}e$ $-\frac{1}{3}e$ $-\frac{1}{3}e = 0$

Antiproton p̄ = ūūd̄

total charge = −1e
ū + ū + d̄ = p̄
$-\frac{2}{3}e$ $-\frac{2}{3}e$ $+\frac{1}{3}e = -1e$

Antineutron n̄ = ūd̄d̄

total charge = 0
ū + d̄ + d̄ = n̄
$-\frac{2}{3}e$ $+\frac{1}{3}e$ $+\frac{1}{3}e = 0$

▲ **Figure 2** *The nucleon family is built from two kinds of quark*

Antiparticles are represented with a line above the usual symbol. For example, an antiproton (charge = −1e) can be represented as $\overline{u}\overline{u}\overline{d}$, 'anti-up, anti-up, anti-down'.

Other quark combinations are possible. Four of these are shown in Figure 3.

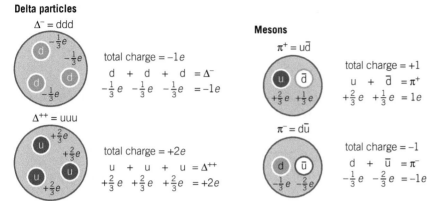

... and their antiparticles $\overline{d}\overline{d}\overline{d}$ and $\overline{u}\overline{u}\overline{u}$

▲ **Figure 3** *Quarks explain other particles*

Quarks and gluons

Electrons accelerated to energies of 20 GeV can map the charge distribution inside individual nucleons. An electron is deflected when it collides with a quark inside a nucleon and some of its energy is transferred, leading to the creation of a jet of new particles. Many of these new particles are mesons. The scattering detected is consistent with the existence of the three particles within a nucleon.

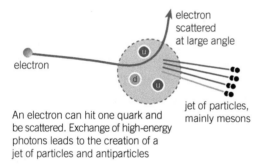

An electron can hit one quark and be scattered. Exchange of high-energy photons leads to the creation of a jet of particles and antiparticles

▲ **Figure 4** *At high energies individual quarks scatter electrons*

Quarks are bound together by the exchange of particles called **gluons.** These also lead to forces which attract nucleons to one another. This force is known as the strong interaction.

Summary questions

1 a Copy and complete the equation representing the decay of radium to radon. *(2 marks)*

$$^{224}_{88}\text{Ra} \rightarrow \,^{4}_{2}\text{He} + \,^{\square}_{\square}\text{Rn}$$

b State the number of neutrons in a radon nucleus. *(1 mark)*

2 How many quarks are there in a radium $\left[^{224}_{88}\text{Ra}\right]$ nucleus? *(1 mark)*

3 Show how a combination of three quarks can be used to construct each of the following: proton, neutron, antiproton, and antineutron. *(4 marks)*

Particles and antiparticles

Antiparticles have equal and opposite electric charge to their particle counterparts and have the same rest energy. They also have equal and opposite 'spin'.

Particles and antiparticles are classified into two groups:

- Leptons: fundamental particles which interact through the weak interaction. The weak interaction is responsible for beta decay. Electrons are leptons.
- Hadrons: these are composite particles made up of quarks that interact through the strong interaction. Protons and neutrons are hadrons.

Ordinary matter is made from one type of lepton (the electron) and two types of hadron (the proton and neutron). These particles, together with the neutrino, account for almost all the visible matter in the Universe.

▼ **Table 1** *The world around you*

Lepton	Electric charge	Rest energy/MeV		Quark	Electric charge	Rest energy/MeV
electron	−1e	0.511		d down	−1/3e	8
positron	+1e	0.511		u up	+2/3e	4
v_e electron-neutrino	0	very near 0		$\bar{d}$ anti-down	+1/3e	8
$\bar{v}_e$ anti-electron-neutrino	0	very near 0		$\bar{v}$ anti-up	−2/3e	4

Annihilation

Positrons are the antiparticles of electrons. They are emitted from nuclei in a process called β⁺ decay. When a positron interacts with an electron the two particles annihilate one another. Matter has been destroyed but the energy of the matter is still present, carried away by a pair of gamma-ray photons.

You can see from Figure 1 that *total* energy is conserved, that is, rest energy + kinetic energy. The diagram also shows how momentum and charge are conserved as well.

The number of leptons (the lepton number) is also conserved. The number before and after the event is zero: an electron has a lepton number of +1, a positron has a lepton number of −1.

Pair creation

A positron and an electron are created in pair production by a gamma-ray photon of sufficient energy near a massive nucleus. Such a gamma-ray photon must have energy equal to at least $2mc^2$, the rest energy of an electron and a positron. This comes to 1.022 MeV.

A 1.022 MeV gamma photon cannot create an electron–positron pair in free space. Momentum must be conserved and the gamma photon has momentum *p* given by:

$$p = \frac{E}{c}$$

Pair creation occurs near a nucleus which carries away some momentum so that both energy and momentum are conserved.

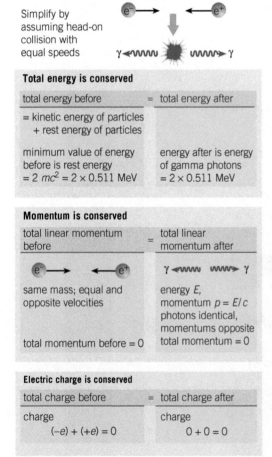

Simplify by assuming head-on collision with equal speeds

Total energy is conserved

total energy before	= total energy after
= kinetic energy of particles + rest energy of particles	
minimum value of energy before is rest energy = 2 mc^2 = 2 × 0.511 MeV	energy after is energy of gamma photons = 2 × 0.511 MeV

Momentum is conserved

total linear momentum before	= total linear momentum after
same mass; equal and opposite velocities	energy E, momentum p = E/c photons identical, momentums opposite
total momentum before = 0	total momentum = 0

Electric charge is conserved

total charge before	= total charge after
charge (−e) + (+e) = 0	charge 0 + 0 = 0

▲ **Figure 1** *Total energy, momentum, and electric charge are always conserved in electron–positron conservation*

Worked example: Muon–antimuon pair production

Muons are leptons. The rest energy of a muon is 105 MeV.

a What is the minimum energy of a gamma photon required to create a muon–antimuon pair? Give your answer in MeV and joules.

b Calculate the frequency of the gamma photon.

a The minimum energy required will equal the rest energy of the two particles created.

rest energy of particles = 2 × 105 MeV = 210 MeV

value in joules = 210 × 10^6 eV × 1.6 × 10^{-19} J eV^{-1} = 3.4 × 10^{-11} J

b Substitute and evaluate: $f = \dfrac{E}{h} = \dfrac{3.4 \times 10^{-11}\,\text{J}}{6.6 \times 10^{-34}\,\text{J s}} = 5.1 \times 10^{22}$ Hz

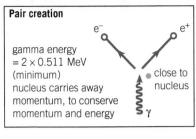

Pair creation

gamma energy
= 2 × 0.511 MeV
(minimum)
nucleus carries away
momentum, to conserve
momentum and energy

e⁻   e⁺
close to
nucleus
γ

▲ **Figure 2** *Pair creation*

Beta decay

Beta-minus decay is the decay of a neutron into a proton, electron, and an antineutrino. Beta-plus decay is the decay of a proton into a neutron, positron, and a neutrino.

An example of a beta-minus decay is strontium-90 decaying into yttrium-90.

$$^{90}_{38}\text{Sr} \rightarrow {}^{90}_{39}\text{Y} + {}^{0}_{-1}\text{e} + {}^{0}_{0}\bar{\nu}$$

Neutrinos are leptons. The lepton number on the left-hand side of the equation is zero. The lepton number on the right-hand side is 1 (electron, a lepton) + −1 (antineutrino, an anti-lepton) = 0. Lepton number is conserved.

The difference in rest energy of the strontium and yttrium nuclei is 0.546 MeV, so every beta particle released should have the same energy, 0.546 MeV. However, this is not the case. Beta particles are emitted with range of energies, as shown in the energy spectrum graph in Figure 3.

The neutrino, a particle with no charge and tiny mass takes away the 'missing' energy from the decay, as represented in Figure 4.

Beta decay of strontium-90, including antineutrino emission

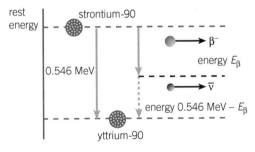

rest
energy
strontium-90
β⁻
energy E_β
0.546 MeV
$\bar{\nu}$
energy 0.546 MeV − E_β
yttrium-90

▲ **Figure 4** *Antineutrinos carry away the 'missing' energy in the beta decay of strontium-90*

Energy spectrum of beta decay of strontium-90

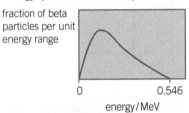

fraction of beta
particles per unit
energy range

0   0.546
energy/MeV

▲ **Figure 3** *Energy spectrum of the beta decay of strontium-90*

Summary questions

1 Show that the electric charge, nucleon number, and lepton number are conserved in the strontium decay given in the text. *(3 marks)*

2 The tau particle is a lepton of rest energy about 3500 times that of an electron. Explain how an electron-positron annihilation can produce a tau–antitau pair even though the rest energy of a tau lepton is about 3500 times that of an electron. *(2 marks)*

3 Calculate the minimum energy of a gamma photon required to create a tau–antitau pair. [mass of a tau particle = 3.2 × 10^{-27} kg] *(2 marks)*

18.5 Electrons in atoms

Specification references: 6.2.1 (a) iii, (a) (iv), b(iii)

Atomic energy levels

When an electron falls from one energy level to another, as represented in Figure 1, a photon is emitted that has energy corresponding to the energy difference between the two levels.

When light from sodium streetlamps or neon signs is passed through a diffraction grating a spectrum showing sharp, discrete spectral lines is produced. Each spectral line is produced by electrons dropping between particular energy levels. Red spectral lines represent a smaller energy drop (lower energy photons) than violet lines.

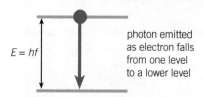

$E = hf$ — photon emitted as electron falls from one level to a lower level

▲ **Figure 1** *Photon emission*

> ### 🖩 Worked example: Energy levels
>
> The spectrum from a helium vapour lamp has a prominent blue line of wavelength about 450 nm. This is produced by electrons making a transition between two energy levels. Calculate the energy difference between the levels required to produce such a line.
>
> **Step 1:** Choose the correct equation.
>
> energy difference between levels = energy of photon emitted
>
> $$E = \frac{hc}{\lambda}$$
>
> **Step 2:** Substitute and evaluate.
>
> $$= \frac{6.6 \times 10^{-34}\,\text{J s} \times 3 \times 10^{8}\,\text{m s}^{-1}}{450 \times 10^{-9}\,\text{m}} = 4.4 \times 10^{-19}\,\text{J}$$

Electron standing waves

Evidence from spectra shows that electrons occupy specific, fixed energy levels. This observation is explained by modelling the atom as a positive nucleus which produces a potential energy well in which the negative electrons are trapped.

The trapped electrons form standing waves, in some respects like the standing waves on a plucked guitar string. The possible de Broglie waves are limited by the width of the potential well.

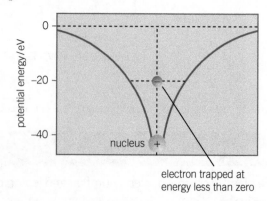

▲ **Figure 2** *An electron trapped in a potential well*

The de Broglie relationship states: $p = \dfrac{h}{\lambda}$

As the energy of the electron is quite small, the non-relativistic expression can be used:

$$E_k = \frac{1}{2}mv^2 = \frac{p^2}{2m}$$

$$\therefore E_k = \frac{h^2}{2m\lambda^2}$$

The smaller the width of the potential well that constrains the electron wave, the smaller the wavelength is and so the greater the momentum and kinetic energy of the electron.

A simplified model of the hydrogen atom

To simplify the model, imagine the potential well to be a box of width d. You can see from Figure 3 that only certain wavelengths of standing wave are possible. This produces a number of allowed energy levels, labelled by a quantum number n starting at the ground state, $n = 1$, the lowest energy state.

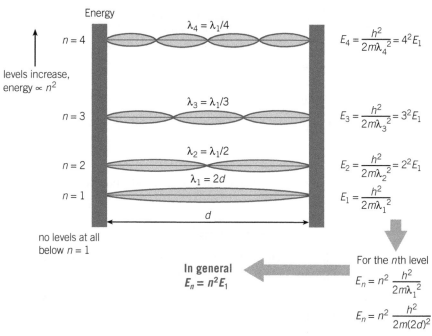

▲ **Figure 3** *Standing waves lead to discrete energy levels*

Although this simple model gets the basic idea right you can see from Figure 3 that it suggests that the gaps between levels increases as n increases. This is not the case. Electron energy levels of hydrogen increase as $\frac{1}{n^2}$. This relationship is diagrammatically represented in Figure 4.

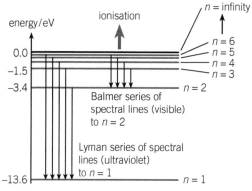

▲ **Figure 4** *As n increases, E_n gets closer to zero*

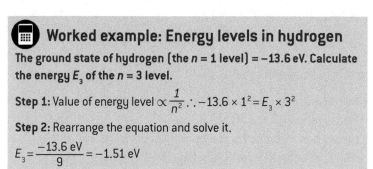

> ### ⊞ Worked example: Energy levels in hydrogen
>
> The ground state of hydrogen (the $n = 1$ level) = −13.6 eV. Calculate the energy E_3 of the $n = 3$ level.
>
> **Step 1:** Value of energy level $\propto \frac{1}{n^2} \therefore -13.6 \times 1^2 = E_3 \times 3^2$
>
> **Step 2:** Rearrange the equation and solve it.
>
> $E_3 = \frac{-13.6 \text{ eV}}{9} = -1.51 \text{ eV}$
>
> This result matches the value suggested in Figure 4.

The ionisation energy is just the energy needed to get an electron from the lowest level at −13.6 eV up to zero energy, when it is free. The ionisation energy of hydrogen is 13.6 eV.

Using the simplified model of the hydrogen to estimate the minimum radius of the hydrogen atom

The electron in a hydrogen atom is bound to the nucleus so its total energy must be negative. The attraction of the nucleus gives it negative potential energy. But if the electron is boxed into a closed space, the standing waves require it to have momentum, and therefore kinetic energy. The kinetic energy gets bigger the smaller the box. As the width of the box gets smaller the total energy increases towards zero.

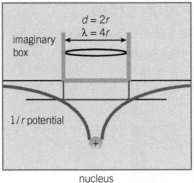

Replace $1/r$ potential by a box of width $d = 2r$
Calculate kinetic energy for waves $\lambda = 2d = 4r$
Calculate potential energy at r

standing wave $\lambda/2 = d$
momentum $p = h/\lambda$
kinetic energy $= p^2/2m$

▲ **Figure 5** *How small can a hydrogen atom be?*

For an atomic 'box' of width $d = 2r$ the electric potential energy is given by:

$$E_p = \frac{e^2}{4\pi\varepsilon_0 r}$$

The kinetic energy of a de Broglie wave trapped in an atom of radius $r = \frac{\lambda}{4}$ is given by:

$$E_k = \frac{h^2}{2m\lambda^2} = \frac{h^2}{32mr^2}$$

As the 'box' gets smaller, reducing r, the potential energy will become more negative. For example, when r is halved the magnitude of the potential energy will double. However, the kinetic energy of the particle ($\propto \frac{1}{r^2}$) will increase by a factor of four.

At the minimum radius $E_k + E_p = 0$. If the kinetic energy is of greater magnitude than the potential energy the electron will escape.

Summary questions

1 Calculate the wavelength of the light emitted when an electron makes the transition from the -2.6×10^{-19} J energy level to the -6.0×10^{-19} J energy level in a mercury atom. *(3 marks)*

2 The energy levels in a hydrogen atom are given by: $E_n = \dfrac{-13.6\text{ eV}}{n^2}$

   a Show that this is equivalent to $E_n = \dfrac{-2.18 \times 10^{-18}\text{ J}}{n^2}$ *(1 mark)*

   b Explain why the equation in **a** shows that the ionisation energy of hydrogen is -2.18×10^{-18} J. *(2 marks)*

   c Calculate the values in joules for the energy levels $n = 1$ to $n = 4$ and represent the levels on a diagram similar to Figure 4. *(4 marks)*

3 a Calculate the kinetic energy of an electron of wavelength 3.2×10^{-10} m. $(m_e = 9.1 \times 10^{-31}$ kg$)$ *(2 marks)*

   b Use your answer from **a** to show that an electron can be bound in a hydrogen atom of radius 8.0×10^{-11} m. Make your reasoning clear. *(4 marks)*

Using ionising radiation

Ionising radiation produces ions in the materials it passes through. Ionising radiation can be used in the treatment of cancer but it can also lead to the development of cancer. Ionising radiations have many uses in medicine and industry, but must be treated with caution to minimise exposure where it is not required.

The properties of α, β, and γ radiation determine their uses. Table 1 gives an overview of some of the properties of these radiations.

▼ **Table 1**

	Nature	Range in air	Ionising ability
Alpha radiation	helium nucleus	a few centimetres	strongly ionising
Beta radiation	fast moving electron	around a metre	weakly ionising
Gamma radiation	high-energy photon	follows the inverse-square law	far less ionising than the charged nuclear radiations

Absorption of nuclear radiations

The range of ionising radiations in denser materials than air (e.g., aluminium) is less than the range in air because there are more atoms to interact per metre of path.

Practical: Studying the absorption of α, β, and γ radiation

Figure 1 shows how you can investigate the absorption of nuclear radiations.

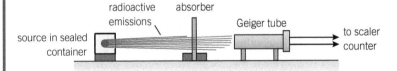

▲ **Figure 1** *Apparatus for investigating absorption of radiation by different materials*

- Take a background reading without the source present. This is subtracted from all readings present to find the counts from the source. This is known as the corrected count.
- Measure the counts in a given time interval as different thicknesses and/or materials of absorber are placed between the source and the detector.
- Minimise the time spent performing this experiment and only handle the sources with tongs.

This experiment shows the following:

- Alpha particles are stopped by a few millimetres of paper or thin metal foil.
- Beta particles are stopped by a few millimetres of aluminium.
- Gamma rays are not completely stopped by a few millimetres of lead.

Synoptic link

You considered some the physics of radioactive decay in Topic 10.1, Radioactive decay and half-life. You may find it useful to refer to that topic before working through Topics 19.1, Ionising radiation, and 19.2, Effects of radiation on tissue.

Revision tip

The range in air is a consequence of the ionising ability of the radiations. Alpha particles ionise strongly, transferring all the energy from the particles in a few centimetres of air. Eventually the alpha particle captures two electrons and forms a helium atom.

It takes about 14 eV to ionise nitrogen. Photons of visible light have energies of around 2 eV so cannot ionise the air they travel through. Ultraviolet photons have sufficient energy to cause ionisation.

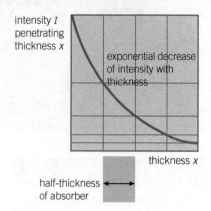

intensity I penetrating thickness x

exponential decrease of intensity with thickness

thickness x

half-thickness of absorber

Absorption by successive thicknesses

intensity reduced to one half by each block

▲ **Figure 2** *Exponential decrease of gamma ray intensity with thickness of absorber*

Revision tip

The absorption of gamma rays in lead follows the same mathematical form as radioactive decay and decay of charge on a capacitor as described in Topics 10.1, Radioactive decay and half-life, 10.2, Another way of looking at radioactive decay, and 10.4, Modelling capacitors.

Absorption of gamma rays by lead

To a good approximation, the intensity of gamma radiation decreases exponentially with thickness of lead: a given thickness of material reduces the number of gamma-ray photons by a constant fraction.

Representing the original intensity of the radiation (with no absorber present) as I_0, the intensity I when an absorber of thickness x is present is given by $I = I_0 e^{-\mu x}$ where is a constant for the material called the absorption coefficient, which has the unit m^{-1}. This equation leads to an expression for 'half-thickness' $x_{1/2}$ of an absorber:

$$x_{1/2} = \frac{\ln 2}{\mu}$$

The half-thickness of an absorber is the thickness of material required to halve the intensity of the radiation. The value for the absorption coefficient and hence the half-thickness depends on a number of factors including the density of the material and the energy of the gamma-ray photons.

Effect of ionising radiation on living tissue

Ionising radiation damages cells and their DNA. The more energy that is transferred to the cells, the more damage is caused. However, the relationship between energy and damage is not straightforward as other factors are important. These are described in Topic 19.2, Effects of radiation on tissue. For example, testes and ovaries are roughly 10 times more sensitive to radiation than skin and bone surfaces.

Summary questions

1   It takes about 14 eV to ionise a nitrogen atom. Estimate by calculation the number of atoms ionised by an alpha particle of energy 5 MeV.
      (2 marks)

2   Describe how you would measure the background count using the apparatus shown in Figure 1.   *(3 marks)*
3   Explain why an alpha particle source a few centimetres from the body is far less dangerous than one inside the body.   *(4 marks)*

4   Show that the equation $I = I_0 e^{-\mu x}$ leads to an expression for half-thickness $x_{1/2} = \frac{\ln 2}{\mu}$. You may find it helpful to refer to Topic 10.2, Another way of looking at radioactive decay.   *(3 marks)*
5   The corrected count rate for a gamma ray source with no absorber present is found to be 600 Bq. This falls to 520 Bq when 2 mm of lead is placed between the source and the detector. Calculate:
      a   the absorption coefficient of the lead   *(2 marks)*
      b   the half-thickness of the lead.   *(2 marks)*

19.2 Effects of radiation on tissue

Specification references: 6.2.2 (b) (i), (c) (i), (c) (ii), (c) (iii)

Radiation dose

Radiation dose is a measure of the energy absorbed by tissues exposed to radiation.

Effective dose

The amount of damage depends on the type of radiation and on the type of tissue exposed. The gray is not a good enough measure for predicting possible consequences of exposure to radiation. Instead, the sievert (Sv), a measure of effective dose, is used.

The quality factors for radiations are given in Figure 1. The dose equivalent takes into account the quality factor of the radiation but does not consider the type of tissue irradiated.

Radiation quality factors		
radiation	factor	dose equivalent of 1 gray/Sv
alpha	20	20
beta	1	1
gamma	1	1
X-rays	1	1
neutrons	10	10

▲ **Figure 1** *Radiation quality factors for estimation of effective dose and dose equivalent – the round numbers show that they are not precisely understood*

Synoptic link

You considered some of the physics of radioactive decay in Topic 10.1, Radioactive decay and half-life, and Topic 10.2, Another way of looking at radioactive decay.

Key term

Absorbed dose: The absorbed dose is the number of joules absorbed per kilogram of tissue.

Absorbed dose is measured in grays (Gy) where $1\,\text{Gy} = 1\,\text{J kg}^{-1}$.

Revision tip

Remember that absorbed dose calculations are based on the mass of tissue exposed. Therapeutic radiation may deliver an absorbed dose of, say, 5 Gy to a small mass of cells. However, a *whole body* dose of 5 Gy is likely to be fatal.

Key term

Effective dose: The effective dose in sieverts (Sv) is the dose in Gy multiplied by a quality factor depending on the type of radiation and the type of tissue irradiated.

  Worked example: Dose equivalent

1×10^{-13} mol of an alpha emitter is placed in 30 g of tissue for a period of 7 days.

Calculate the dose equivalent in sievert received by the tissue, assuming all the energy of the particles is transferred to the tissue.

Data: half-life of the emitter is 30 days, energy of emitted alpha particles = 5.2 MeV, number of particles mol^{-1} = 6.0×10^{23}, quality factor of alpha radiation = 20

This question includes ideas about decay and dose. Make sure you understand each step.

Step 1: Calculate the number of particles emitted during the week.

number of particles emitted =
number of undecayed nuclei at start of week – number of undecayed nuclei at end of week

As $N = N_0 e^{-\lambda t}$, the decay constant in day$^{-1} = \dfrac{\ln 2}{30}$

Number remaining after one week = 1×10^{-13} mol $\times e^{-6.93 \times \frac{7}{30}} = 8.5 \times 10^{-14}$ mol

Therefore, number of alpha particles emitted during the week =
1×10^{-13} mol $- 8.5 \times 10^{-14}$ mol $= 1.5 \times 10^{-14}$ mol $= 9.0 \times 10^9$ particles

Step 2: Energy absorbed = number of particles emitted × energy per particle

$= 5.2$ MeV $9.0 \times 10^9 = 4.68 \times 10^{16}$ eV $= 7.49 \times 10^{-3}$ J

Step 3: Dose in Gy $= \dfrac{\text{energy absorbed}}{\text{mass of tissue}} = \dfrac{7.49 \times 10^{-3}\,\text{J}}{0.03\,\text{kg}} = 0.25$ Gy

Step 4: Dose equivalent = dose in Gy × quality factor = 0.25 Gy × 20 = 5 Sv

Note that the dose may not be spread evenly throughout the sample.

Risk and radiation

Recent guidelines from the International Commission on Radiological Protection suggest that the incidence of cancer due to ionising radiation is about 5% per sievert. The average annual whole-body dose due to natural and artificial sources combined is around 2500 μSv.

Risk is estimated using the simple equation:

$$\text{risk} = \text{dose equivalent} \times \text{incidence per sievert}$$

Annual risk associated with background radiation (artificial and natural) $= 2500 \times 10^{-6}\,\text{Sv} \times 5\%\,\text{Sv}^{-1}$

$$= 0.0125\%$$

This shows that the likelihood of an individual developing cancer from background radiation is small. However, out of a population of 60 million, about 7500 will develop cancer each year due to background radiation $\left(60 \times 10^6 \times \dfrac{0.0125}{100}\right)$.

Revision tip

When you are calculating the likely number of incidences of cancer in a population, remember to use the probability per Sv rather than the percentage. A 5% chance is a probability of 0.05.

Summary questions

1 Explain the difference between energy absorbed, absorbed dose, and effective dose. *(2 marks)*

2 Calculate the dose in Gy when a beta source of constant activity $= 1.5 \times 10^3$ Bq is placed in 90 g of tissue for 24 hours. The average energy of the beta particles emitted $= 0.5$ MeV. *(3 marks)*

3 A chest X-ray gives a dose equivalent of about 0.1 mSv. If the risk of contracting cancer from ionising radiation is 5% per sievert, calculate an estimate for the number of cancers per million X-ray procedures. *(2 marks)*

4 Radium-223 is an alpha emitter with a half-life of 11.4 days. The alpha particles have energy $= 5.8$ MeV.
Calculate the dose equivalent absorbed by 40 g of cells over a period of 6 days. (initial activity $= 2.0$ kBq, quality factor $= 20$) *(4 marks)*

19.3 Stability and decay

Specification references: 6.2.2 (a) (ii), (b) (i), (c) (iv)

Nuclear stability

The stability of nuclei depends on the balance between the number of protons and the number of neutrons. Stable isotopes of low nucleon number elements tend to have equal numbers of protons and neutrons in their nuclei. Stable isotopes of higher nucleon number elements have more neutrons than protons in their nuclei.

The strong nuclear force acts between nucleons in the nucleus, overcoming the electrical repulsion of the protons. The strong nuclear force acts over a distance roughly the same as the diameter of a small nucleus. So, for large nuclei, more neutrons are required to dilute the effect of the electrical repulsion of the protons – which is exerted across a far greater distance.

Binding energy

Energy is required to pull apart the protons and neutrons in a stable nucleus. Therefore, the energy of the nucleus must be less than the energy of the separated particles. The rest energy of a nucleus is found from $E_{rest} = mc^2$, where m is the mass of the nucleus. The individual rest energies of all the protons and neutrons are subtracted from the rest energy of the nucleus. The resulting value is the binding energy of the nucleus. The more negative this value is, the more stable the nucleus is.

> ### 🖩 Worked example: Binding energy per nucleon
>
> The mass of the helium nucleus ($^4_2$He) is 4.0015 u. Use the data below to calculate the binding energy of the helium nucleus and the binding energy per nucleon.
>
> Data: proton mass = 1.007 28 u, neutron mass = 1.008 67 u
>
> **Step 1:** Calculate the difference in mass (Δm) between the mass of the nucleus and the masses of the individual nucleons, remembering that the nucleus comprises two protons and two neutrons.
>
> mass difference $\Delta m = 4.0015\ u - (2 \times 1.00728\ u) - (2 \times 1.00867\ u) = -0.0304\ u$
>
> **Step 2:** Convert the mass difference into kg.
>
> mass difference Δm in kg $= -0.0304 \times 1.660\ 56 \times 10^{-27}$ kg $= -5.048 \times 10^{-29}$ kg
>
> **Step 3:** Calculate the binding energy of the nucleus.
>
> binding energy $= \Delta mc^2 = -5.048 \times 10^{-29}$ kg $\times (3 \times 10^8$ m s$^{-1})^2 = -4.543 \times 10^{-12}$ J
>
> **Step 4:** Divide the value of the binding energy of the nucleus by the number of nucleons in the nucleus to find the binding energy per nucleon.
>
> binding energy per nucleon $= \dfrac{-4.543 \times 10^{-12}\ \text{J}}{4} = -1.136\ 10^{-12}$ J or -7.1 MeV

Unstable nuclei have less negative binding energies per nucleon. Spontaneous radioactive decay happens because nucleons tend towards lower, more negative energies.

The nuclear valley

Figure 1 shows how binding energy per nucleon varies with nucleon number. The plot resembles a deep, narrow valley. The lowest point and strongest binding is around the element iron $^{56}_{26}$Fe with binding energy -8.8 MeV per nucleon.

Note that on one side of the 'valley' nuclei show positron (β⁺) decay, which reduces the ratio of protons to neutrons in the nuclei. Nuclei on the other side of the 'valley' show electron (β⁻) decay, which increases the ratio of protons to neutrons in the nuclei. Make sure you understand the changes to nuclei produced by the decays as shown in the boxes.

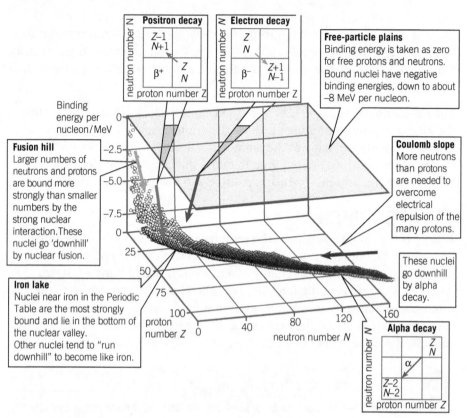

Positron decay

$Z-1$ $N+1$	
β^+	Z N

Electron decay

Z N	
β^-	$Z+1$ $N-1$

Free-particle plains
Binding energy is taken as zero for free protons and neutrons. Bound nuclei have negative binding energies, down to about −8 MeV per nucleon.

Fusion hill
Larger numbers of neutrons and protons are bound more strongly than smaller numbers by the strong nuclear interaction. These nuclei go 'downhill' by nuclear fusion.

Coulomb slope
More neutrons than protons are needed to overcome electrical repulsion of the many protons.

Iron lake
Nuclei near iron in the Periodic Table are the most strongly bound and lie in the bottom of the nuclear valley. Other nuclei tend to "run downhill" to become like iron.

These nuclei go downhill by alpha decay.

Alpha decay

	Z N
$Z-2$ $N-2$	α

▲ **Figure 1** *Stable nuclei lie along a narrow band in the nuclear valley*

Nuclei can exist in excited states of higher energy. When they fall from an excited state to a lower one the nuclei emit very high-energy photons. These are gamma rays with energy in the range 0.1 MeV to more than 5 MeV. This is the origin of the gamma rays emitted by radioactive materials.

Decay chains

The changes undergone by nuclei in alpha and beta decays are shown in Figure 1. These changes are accompanied by a release of energy, making the binding energy per nucleon of the resulting nucleus more negative. An unstable nucleus forms a decay chain when it goes through successive decays until it forms a stable nucleus. Figure 2 shows such a decay chain.

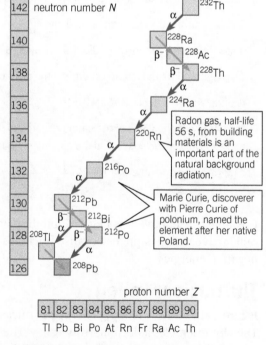

Radon gas, half-life 56 s, from building materials is an important part of the natural background radiation.

Marie Curie, discoverer with Pierre Curie of polonium, named the element after her native Poland.

proton number Z

81	82	83	84	85	86	87	88	89	90
Tl	Pb	Bi	Po	At	Rn	Fr	Ra	Ac	Th

▲ **Figure 2** *Decay chain from thorium-232*

Summary questions

proton mass = 1.007 28 u,
neutron mass = 1.008 67 u,
electron mass = 0.000 55 u,
1 u = 1.660 56 × 10⁻²⁷ kg

1 a $^{32}_{15}$P undergoes beta-minus decay to form sulfur (S). Write the nuclear equation for the decay. (*1 mark*)

   b Thorium, $^{230}_{90}$Th undergoes alpha decay to form radium, Ra. Write the nuclear equation for the decay. (*1 mark*)

2 Nitrogen-13 undergoes beta-plus decay as shown:
   $^{13}_{7}$N → $^{13}_{6}$C + $^{0}_{1}$e + $^{0}_{0}v$
   Use the data given to calculate the energy released in the decay. Assume that the neutrino has negligible mass.
   (mass of $^{13}_{7}$N nucleus = 13.001 89 u, mass of $^{13}_{6}$C nucleus = 13.000 05 u)
   (*3 marks*)

3 The mass of the $^{238}_{92}$U nucleus is 238.000 16 u. Calculate the binding energy per nucleon of the nucleus. Give your answer in J and MeV. (*4 marks*)

4 The binding energy of the $^{56}_{26}$Fe nucleus is −8.8 MeV. Using the masses of the individual protons and neutrons that make up the nucleus, calculate its mass in u and kg. (*4 marks*)

19.4 Fission and fusion

Specification references: 6.2.2 (a) (iii), b (ii), c(iv)

Nuclear fission

Figure 1 shows that the nuclei with the most number of nucleons, to the right of the graph, have less negative binding energies than those nearer (but more massive than) iron, Fe.

Key term

Nuclear fission: This is the splitting of heavy nuclei to form lighter nuclei, releasing energy.

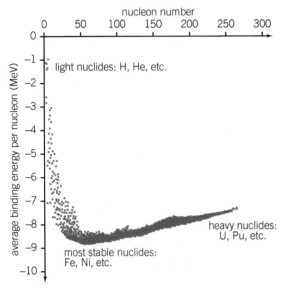

▲ **Figure 1** *Nuclear binding energy per nucleon against nucleon number*

In the process of nuclear fission, the first nucleus captures a neutron. The resulting nucleus breaks into two nuclei and a number of neutrons. Figure 2 shows that the average binding energy per nucleon becomes more negative by about 0.9 MeV in this process. This is the energy released in the fission event.

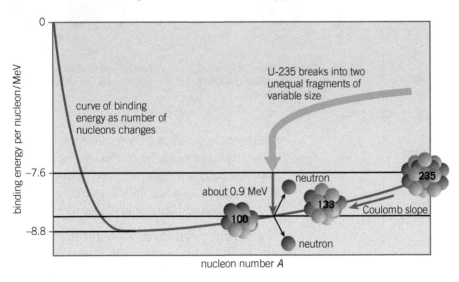

▲ **Figure 2** *Fission takes nucleons down the binding-energy valley*

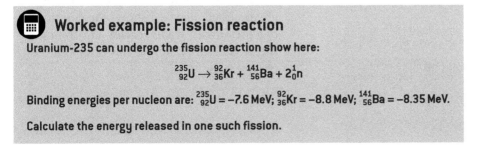

🖩 Worked example: Fission reaction

Uranium-235 can undergo the fission reaction show here:

$$^{235}_{92}U \rightarrow {}^{92}_{36}Kr + {}^{141}_{56}Ba + 2{}^{1}_{0}n$$

Binding energies per nucleon are: $^{235}_{92}U = -7.6$ MeV; $^{92}_{36}Kr = -8.8$ MeV; $^{141}_{56}Ba = -8.35$ MeV.

Calculate the energy released in one such fission.

Step 1: Find the total binding energies of each nucleus.

$^{235}_{92}U = 235 \times -7.6\,\text{MeV} = -1786\,\text{MeV}$; $^{92}_{36}Kr = 92 \times -8.8\,\text{MeV} = -809.6\,\text{MeV}$;

$^{141}_{56}Ba = 141 \times -8.35\,\text{MeV} = -1177.35\,\text{MeV}$

Step 2: Find the difference in binding energies between the original nucleus and the fission products. This is the energy released in the fission.

energy released $= -1786\,\text{MeV} - (-809.6\,\text{MeV}) - (-1177.35\,\text{MeV}) = 200\,\text{MeV}$ (2 s.f.)

Power from fission

Figure 3 is a representation of a fission chain reaction in which neutrons released from one fission event go on to induce further fissions. A critical mass of fuel is required for a sustainable chain reaction, in which (on average) one neutron from each fission event induces a subsequent fission.

Critical chain reaction

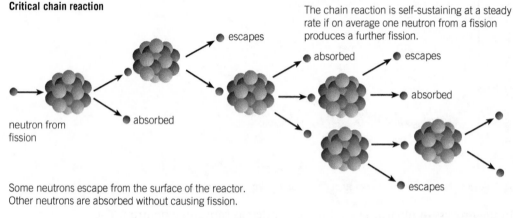

The chain reaction is self-sustaining at a steady rate if on average one neutron from a fission produces a further fission.

neutron from fission

Some neutrons escape from the surface of the reactor. Other neutrons are absorbed without causing fission.

Sub-critical mass

All chains die out as neutrons are absorbed or escape.

Critical mass

One new fission follows each fission, on average. Reaction goes at steady rate.

Super-critical mass

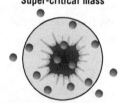

Several new fissions follow each fission – reaction grows rapidly.

▲ **Figure 3** *Chain reaction and critical mass*

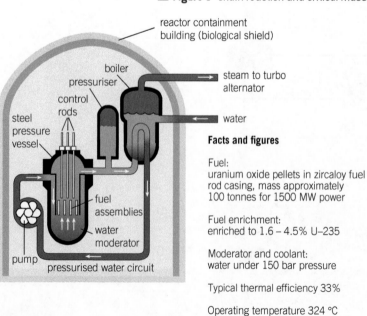

reactor containment building (biological shield)

boiler

pressuriser

control rods

steel pressure vessel

steam to turbo alternator

water

fuel assemblies

water moderator

pump

pressurised water circuit

Facts and figures

Fuel:
uranium oxide pellets in zircaloy fuel rod casing, mass approximately 100 tonnes for 1500 MW power

Fuel enrichment:
enriched to 1.6 – 4.5% U–235

Moderator and coolant:
water under 150 bar pressure

Typical thermal efficiency 33%

Operating temperature 324 °C

Neutrons released in fission move too quickly to be captured easily by nuclei. A moderator (often water) is a material which slows down the neutrons, making their capture by nuclei more likely, producing more fission events.

If too many neutrons produce further fission events the chain reaction can grow very quickly. To avoid this, control rods are used to absorb neutrons. The further the rods are lowered into the fuel, the more neutrons are absorbed. Figure 4 shows the design of a pressurised water reactor, illustrating the moderator (water, in this case) and the control rods.

▲ **Figure 4** *The design of a pressurised water reactor*

- A typical reactor might require sufficient nuclear fuel to produce a power of 1500 MW.
- Each fission event produces about 200 MeV (see the Worked example above) or 3.2×10^{-11} J.
- Number of fissions required per second $= \dfrac{1500 \times 10^6 \, \text{J s}^{-1}}{3.2 \times 10^{-11} \, \text{J}} = 4.7 \times 10^{19} \, \text{s}^{-1}$
- Mass of uranium used per second = mass of uranium-235 atom $4.7 \times 10^{19} \, \text{s}^{-1} = 1.9 \times 10^{-5} \, \text{kg s}^{-1}$
- This is about 600 kg of uranium-235 nuclei per year.

The fuel used in reactors is enriched uranium which is about 3% uranium-235 and 97% non-fissile uranium-238. So, about 20 000 kg of uranium is used in such a reactor per year.

Nuclear fusion

Figure 5 represents the process of fusion in the Sun. High temperatures are needed to give the colliding nuclei sufficient energy to come close together against the electrical potential barrier. You can see that, at the moment of fusion a proton must decay into a neutron. This requirement makes fusion in the Sun a very slow process, which has helped keep the energy output of the Sun constant for billions of years, allowing life to develop on Earth.

> **Key term**
>
> **Nuclear fusion:** This is the fusing of two light nuclei to form a more massive nucleus. The binding energy per nucleon of the resulting, larger nucleus is more negative than the average binding energy per nucleon of the original nuclei.

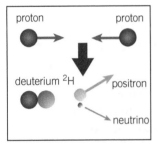 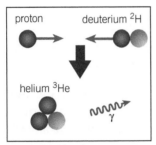 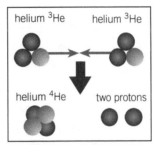

Two protons fuse, converting one to a neutron, to form deuterium ^{2}H.

Deuterium ^{2}H captures another proton to form ^{3}He.

Two ^{3}He nuclei fuse, giving ^{4}He and freeing two protons.

▲ **Figure 5** *Nuclear fusion in the Sun, a three-stage process*

Summary questions

1 a Explain how a fission reaction releases energy by referring to the binding energies per nucleon of the original nucleus and the nuclei produced. *(1 mark)*

   b Explain how a fusion reaction releases energy by referring to the binding energies per nucleon of the original particles and the nucleus produced. *(1 mark)*

2 Calculate the energy released in the fission event given below:

$$^{236}_{92}\text{U} \rightarrow {}^{146}_{57}\text{La} + {}^{87}_{25}\text{Br} + 3\,{}^{1}_{0}\text{n}$$

(binding energies per nucleon: $^{236}_{92}\text{U} = -1.21 \times 10^{-12}$ J; $^{146}_{57}\text{La} = -1.35 \times 10^{-12}$ J; $^{87}_{25}\text{Br} = -1.37 \times 10^{-12}$ J) *(3 marks)*

3 Experimental fusion reactors make use of the following reaction:

$$^{2}_{1}\text{H} + {}^{3}_{1}\text{H} \rightarrow {}^{4}_{2}\text{He} + {}^{1}_{0}\text{n}$$

Calculate the energy released in one such reaction.

(masses of particles: $^{2}_{1}\text{H} = 2.0136$ u; $^{3}_{1}\text{H} = 3.0155$ u; $^{4}_{2}\text{He} = 4.0015$ u; $^{1}_{0}\text{n} = 1.008\,67$ u) *(3 marks)*

> **Revision tip**
>
> Notice that you can be asked to calculate the energy released in nuclear reactions by considering the mass difference between the original particles and the products or by considering the difference in average binding energies. Make sure that you are confident in using both approaches.

1   Here are three sub-atomic particles:

1 neutrino   2 positron   3 up quark

a   Which of the particles is/are fundamental particle(s)?   *(1 mark)*

   A 1, 2, and 3   **B** 1 and 2   **C** 2 and 3   **D** 1

b   Which of the particles is/are positively charged?   *(1 mark)*

   A 1, 2, and 3   **B** 1 and 2   **C** 2 and 3   **D** 1

c   Which of the particles is/are lepton(s)?   *(1 mark)*

   A 1, 2, and 3   **B** 1 and 2   **C** 2 and 3   **D** 1

2   An alpha particle of energy 6 MeV makes a head-on approach to a silver nucleus $^{108}_{47}Ag$. What is the distance of closest approach? (charge on a proton = 1.6×10^{-19} C)   *(1 mark)*

   A 1.7×10^{-14} m   **B** 2.3×10^{-14} m   **C** 2.9×10^{-14} m   **D** 5.2×10^{-14} m

3   The rest mass of an electron is 0.51 MeV. An electron is accelerated through a potential difference of 600 kV.

a   Calculate the relativistic factor γ of the accelerated electron.   *(2 marks)*

b   Calculate the velocity v of the electron.   *(2 marks)*

c   The momentum of the electron is given by γmv. The rest mass of an electron is 9.1×10^{-31} kg. Calculate the de Broglie wavelength of the accelerated electron.   *(2 marks)*

4   The risk of developing cancer due to radiation exposure is about 5% per sievert. The maximum permitted dose to radiation workers is 20 mSv per year. Calculate an estimate for the risk of developing cancer over a 40-year career in the nuclear industry.   *(2 marks)*

5   This question is about strontium-90, a beta emitter.

a   Copy and complete the decay equation.

   $$^{90}_{38}Sr \rightarrow {}^{90}_{39}Y + {}^{0}_{::}e + {}^{0}_{0}\bar{v}$$ *(1 mark)*

b   The anti-neutrino is required to conserve a number of quantities. State one of these quantities.   *(1 mark)*

c   A source is kept in a lead-lined case. Explain why such a case is used.   *(3 marks)*

d   The source is used in a laboratory test and is removed from the case for 5 minutes and placed in the centre of a 2.0 g collection of cells. The activity of the source is 1.2×10^5 Bq. The average energy of the beta particles emitted is 0.14 MeV.

   i   Calculate the total energy released by the source in 5 minutes.   *(2 marks)*

   ii   Calculate the dose given to the cells. Assume that all the beta particles are absorbed by the cells. (quality factor of beta radiation = 1)   *(2 marks)*

6   The intensity of gamma radiation travelling through air varies with $\frac{1}{r^2}$ where r is the distance between the point source of radiation and the detector.

a   The count rate from a gamma source at a distance of 0.40 m is 500 counts s^{-1}.

   i   What is the expected count rate at a distance of 1.0 m from the source?   *(2 marks)*

   ii   Why might the actual count rate be different from your calculated answer?   *(1 mark)*

b The half-life of the source is 40 minutes. What is the expected count rate at a distance of 1.2 m from the source after 80 minutes? *(3 marks)*

7 Figure 1 represents the path of an alpha particle near a positively charged nucleus.

State and explain:

a the point of the path at which the acceleration of the alpha particle is the greatest *(2 marks)*

b the point of the path at which the velocity of the alpha particle is the smallest. *(2 marks)*

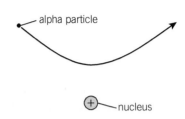

▲ **Figure 1**

8 This question is about energy from nuclear power.

a One fission reaction involving uranium-235 is:

$$^{235}_{92}U + ^1_0n \rightarrow ^{98}_{40}Zr + ^{135}_{52}Te + 3\,^1_0n$$

i Explain how this process can set up a chain reaction and suggest why a minimum mass of uranium-235 is required for such a chain reaction to occur. *(3 marks)*

ii Use the data below to calculate the energy released in the reaction.

nuclear masses: $^{235}_{92}U$: 235.0349 u, $^{98}_{40}Zr$: 97.9127 u,

$^{135}_{52}Te$: 134.9165 u, ^1_0n: 1.0087 u, 1 u = 1.661×10^{-27} kg *(3 marks)*

b It is thought that there is about 5.9×10^9 kg of recoverable uranium available. Current usage of uranium is about 6.6×10^7 kg per year.

i Using suggested estimates, calculate how long uranium will remain a source of energy. *(2 marks)*

ii Suggest and explain why this can only be a rough estimate of the length of time uranium will remain a source of energy. *(2 marks)*

c Nuclear fusion is being considered as a possible energy source. One suggested reaction is:

$$^2_1H + ^3_1H \rightarrow ^4_2He + ^1_0n$$

Calculate the energy released in this reaction.

rest energies: ^1_0n: 942 MeV, ^2_1H: 1.88 GeV, ^3_1H: 2.82 GeV,

^4_2He: 3.74 GeV *(2 marks)*

d The reactants must approach to about 10^{-14} m of one another for fusion to occur. Calculate the electrical potential energy of the two nuclei at this separation, explain why this gives a measure of the kinetic energy of the particles required for fusion to occur and make an estimate of the temperature required for the reactants to fuse. *(6 marks)*

Answers to practice questions

Chapters 1 and 2

1 a $-4.00\,\text{D}$ [1]

  b $-1.25\,\text{D}$ [1]

  c As Annie can focus objects at 80 cm, her eye lens can add $+1.25\,\text{D}$ to the curvature of waves at her eye. [1]

    To get a focused image at 25 cm requires the eye lens to add $+4.00\,\text{D}$ to the curvature of the waves, [1]

    $1.25\,\text{D} + 2.75\,\text{D} = 4.00\,\text{D}$ [1]

2 $2.7 = \dfrac{v}{u} = \dfrac{v}{0.3\,\text{m}} \therefore v = 0.81\,\text{m}$ [1]

  $\dfrac{1}{f} = \dfrac{1}{0.81} - \left(-\dfrac{1}{0.3}\right) = 4.56...\,\text{m}^{-1}$ [1]

  $f = 0.22\,\text{m}$ (2 s.f.) [1]

3 Number of pixels on 6 km length =
$\sqrt{1.8\times10^{9}} = 42\,425.4...$ [1]

  Length per pixel $= \dfrac{6000\,\text{m}}{42\,425.4...}$ [1]

  Length per pixel $= 0.14\,\text{m}$ (2 s.f.) [1]

4 a Points plotted correctly. [1]

    Straight line drawn with ruler to intercept on x-axis. [1]

  b intercept $= 0.2\,\text{m}$ [1]

    At the focal point, all (parallel) rays are focused to a point [1]

    so image size will be zero (in theory). [1]

  c When $v = 0.4\,\text{m}$ and $f = 0.2\,\text{m}$, $u = \dfrac{1}{0.4\,\text{m}} - \dfrac{1}{0.2\,\text{m}}$ [1]

    $u = -0.4\,\text{m}$ [1]

    magnification $= \dfrac{0.4\,\text{m}}{-0.4\,\text{m}} = (-)\,1$ hence image size = object size [1]

5 a Focal length $= 0.0045\,\text{m}$ [1]

  b Use lens equation to show that when $u = -1.0\,\text{m}$, $v = 0.0045...\,\text{m}$ [1]

    Use lens equation to show that when $u = -0.1\,\text{m}$, $v = 0.0047...\,\text{m}$ [1]

    When $u = -1.0\,\text{m}$, image is focused on the light-sensitive surface whilst the image is focused behind the surface when $u = -0.1\,\text{m}$ [1]

  c Bits needed per pixel $= \log_2 256 = 8$ [1]

    Number of bits per image $= 1200 \times 1000 \times 3 \times 8 = 2.88\times10^{7}$ [1]

    Number of images that can be stored $= \dfrac{4.5\times10^{9}}{2.88\times10^{7}} = 156$ [1]

6 a Bit rate = number of bits per image number of images transmitted per second
$3.6\times10^{5}\times24\times18$ [1]
$= 156\times10^{6}\,\text{bit s}^{-1}$ [1]

  b Bit rate = number of bits per image number of images transmitted per second
$1.2\times10^{6}\,\text{bit s}^{-1}$ [1]

  c Highest frequency that can be accurately sampled $= 10\,000\,\text{Hz}$ [1]

    Sampling higher frequencies will produce lower frequency notes (aliases) which are not present in the original signal. [1]

7 a $0.03\,\text{m}$ [1]

  b i The amplitude of the received signal rises and falls as the grille is rotated. [1]

    Starting from maximum amplitude, the amplitude falls to a minimum at a 90° rotation, rises to a maximum at 180° rotation and falls to a minimum at 270°. [1]

    ii This is a demonstration of polarisation and only occurs with transverse waves. [1]

    The microwaves are polarised [1]

    which means that they are emitted with the transverse oscillations of the electric (or magnetic) field in a single plane. [1]

    The waves are absorbed by the bars of the grille when the bars are parallel to the direction of the oscillation of the electric field. [1]

8 a From the graph, 10 samples in 225 μs give time between samples $= 22.5\,\mu\text{s}$ [1]

    sampling rate $= \dfrac{1}{22.5\,\mu\text{s}} = 44.4\,\text{kHz}$ [1]

  b $\dfrac{12\,\text{mV}}{64\,000} = 1.9\times10^{-7}$ [1]

  c Number bits required $= \log_2 64\,000$ [1]
    number bits required $= 16$ [1]

  d The following points should be included in a complete, high-level answer [6]

- Higher sampling rate allows higher frequencies to be sampled without risk of aliasing.
- More quantisation levels means more accurate recording of the original sound (or signal).
- Increasing either the sampling rate or number of quantisation levels increases the bit rate of the system.
- Bit rate for CD quality sound $= 44.1\times10^{3} \times 16 \times 2\,\text{bit s}^{-1}$
- Bit rate for CD quality sound $= 1.4\,\text{Mbit s}^{-1}$
- Bit rate for CD playback is about 8.8 times that of streaming.
- The streamed system will either have few samples per second (leading to problems with aliasing or requiring filtering of the original sound) OR...
- ... few quantisation levels (leading to a less accurate representation of the amplitude of the waveform) OR....
- ... some 'compression' of the original recording is used to reduce the required bit rate.

For a level of response question such as this you will only gain higher marks if you include all aspects of the answer in your response and set out your answer in a logical manner. You do not have to phrase your answer to match the mark scheme, but the physics must be clear and cover the same ground.

Chapter 3

1 B $1.3\,\Omega$ *[1]*

2 A $3.7\,V$ *[1]*

3 B $0.64\,\Omega$ *[1]*

4 C $\varepsilon = 2.8\,V$, $r = 0.16\,\Omega$ *[1]*

5 **a** Charge $Q = 5.0 \times 10^{-3}\,A \times 60\,s = 0.30\,C$ *[1]*

number of electrons $= \dfrac{Q}{e} = \dfrac{0.30\,C}{1.6 \times 10^{-19}\,C}$

$= 1.9 \times 10^{18}$ *[1]*

b $P = IV = 5.0 \times 10^{-3}\,A \times 12\,000\,V = 60\,W$ *[1]*

$E = Pt = 60\,W \times 60\,s = 3600\,J$ *[1]*

6 At $50\,°C$:

$R_{wire} = \dfrac{V}{I} = \dfrac{6.0\,V}{0.44\,A}$ *[1]*

(allow $0.43\,A \le I \le 0.45\,A$)

$R_{wire} = 13.6\,\Omega$ ($0.43\,A \Rightarrow 14.0\,\Omega$, $0.45\,A \Rightarrow 13.3\,\Omega$) *[1]*

($0.43\,A \Rightarrow 14.0\,\Omega$, $0.45\,A \Rightarrow 13.3\,\Omega$)

$V_{wire} = 6.0\,V \times \dfrac{R_{wire}}{R_{total}} = 6.0\,V \times \dfrac{13.6\,\Omega}{(13.6\,\Omega + 22\,\Omega)}$ *[1]*

$V_{wire} = 2.29\,V = 2.3\,V$ (2 s.f.) *[1]*

($13.3\,\Omega \Rightarrow 2.27\,V = 2.3\,V$, $14.0\,\Omega \Rightarrow 2.33\,V = 2.3\,V$)

7 **a** Cross-sectional area of one copper wire $=$

$\pi \times \left(\dfrac{0.64 \times 10^{-3}\,m}{2}\right)^2 = 3.22 \times 10^{-7}\,m^2$

total cross-sectional area $= 10 \times 3.22 \times 10^{-7}\,m^2$

$= 3.22 \times 10^{-6}\,m^2$ *[1]*

total length in circuit $= 2 \times 25\,m = 50\,m$

$R = \dfrac{\rho L}{A} = \dfrac{1.6 \times 10^{-8}\,\Omega\,m \times 50\,m}{3.22 \times 10^{-6}\,m^2}$

$= 0.249\,\Omega$ (about $\frac{1}{4}\,\Omega$) *[1]*

b R of heater $= \dfrac{V^2}{P} = \dfrac{(230\,V)^2}{2000\,W} = 26\,\Omega$ *[1]*

This is much larger than $0.249\,\Omega$ so the p.d. across the heater is close to $230\,V$. *[1]*

c $P = I^2R = \left(\dfrac{2000\,W}{230\,V}\right)^2 \times 0.249\,\Omega = 19\,W$ *[1]*

The heat needs to dissipate into the environment to prevent the wire overheating: if it were not unrolled, the insulation may melt. *[1]*

8 Graph as shown in Figure 1 in the text. Axes correctly labelled, including units, and sensible scale chosen. *[1]*

All points correctly plotted *[2]*

[If one point misplotted only award 1 mark.]

Best fit curve *[1]*

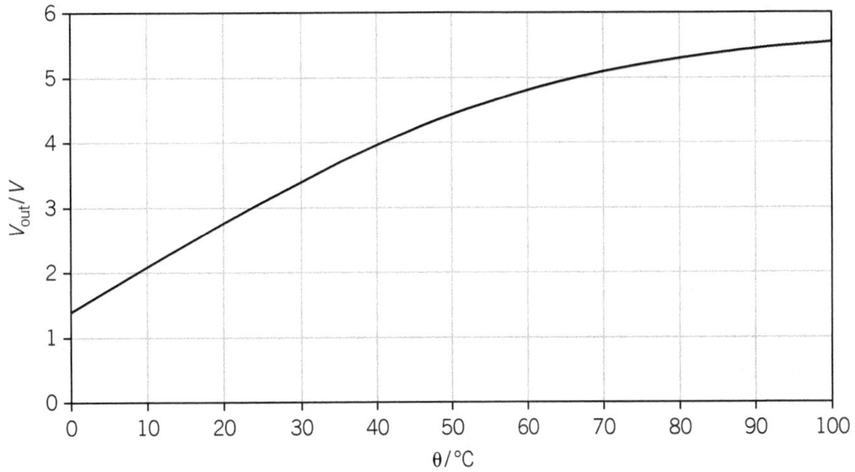

▲ Figure 1

b Mean sensitivity $= \dfrac{(48\,V - 44\,V)}{10\,°C}$ (allow $\pm 1\,V$ on each p.d. reading) *[1]*

mean sensitivity $= 0.4\,V\,°C^{-1}$ (including unit) *[1]*

c Sensitivity $=$ graph gradient is greater at lower temperature *[1]*

which means that it is better for a bedroom. *[1]*

(Kettle would not switch off necessarily at $100\,°C$)

Chapters 4 and 5

1 A *[1]*

2 D *[1]*

3 **a** Number of copper atoms in $1\,m^3 =$

$8.45... \times 10^{28}\,m^{-3}$ *[1]*

Assuming that copper atoms are cubic: *[1]*

Length of one side $= \sqrt[3]{\dfrac{1}{8.45 \times 10^{28}\ m^{-3}}} =$

$2.3 \times 10^{-10}\,m$ *[1]*

b Number of dislocations $= \dfrac{2.0 \times 10^{-3}\,m}{2.3 \times 10^{-10}\,m}$ *[1]*

Number of dislocations $= 8.7 \times 10^6$ dislocations *[1]*

4 **a** $\dfrac{E}{volume} = \dfrac{1}{2}\dfrac{F\,x}{volume}$ *[1]*

$\dfrac{E}{L \times A} = \dfrac{1}{2}\dfrac{F\,x}{L \times A} = \dfrac{1}{2}\dfrac{F}{A} \times \dfrac{x}{L} = \dfrac{1}{2} \times$ stress $\times$ strain *[1]*

b $J = N\,m$ $\therefore$ energy per unit volume $= N\,m \times m^{-3}$

$= N\,m^{-2} = Pa$ *[1]*

c Stress $= 1.4 \times 10^8\,Pa\,s$ *[1]*

Energy stored per unit volume $=$

$\dfrac{1}{2}$stress$\times$strain $= \dfrac{1}{2}$stress$\times\dfrac{\text{stress}}{E} = \dfrac{1}{2} \times \dfrac{(1.4 \times 10^8\,Pa)^2}{1.8 \times 10^{11}\,Pa}$ *[1]*

Energy stored per unit volume $= 5.4 \times 10^4\,J\,m^{-3}$ *[1]*

5 **a** Energy stored $= \dfrac{1}{2} \times 19\,N \times 1.5 \times 10^{-3}\,m$ *[1]*

Energy stored $= 1.4 \times 10^{-2}\,J$ *[1]*

b $E = \dfrac{\text{stress}}{\text{strain}} = \dfrac{FL}{Ax}$

$E = \dfrac{20\,N \times 2.0\,m}{(1.26 \times 10^{-7}\,m^2 \times 1.6 \times 10^{-3}\,m)}$ *[1]*

$E = 2.0 \times 10^{-11}\,m$ *[1]*

c Force = stress × area =
3.7 × 10^8 N m^{-2} × 1.26 × 10^{-7} m^2 *[1]*
force = 47 N   *[1]*

6 The following points are each worth 1 mark.   *[6]*

Macroscopic effects:

Alloying makes the metal harder / less ductile.
This will also make the metal more brittle.

Microscopic explanation:

Crystalline structure of metal has mobile
dislocations.
These allow layers of atoms to move over one
another by breaking one bond at a time.

This movement produces plastic deformation
where work is done permanently deforming the
material.

Alloying atoms 'pin' dislocation – stopping them
travelling through structure.

Less plastic deformation gives a harder material
but stress concentrations can occur making the
material more brittle.

For a level of response question such as this you will
only gain higher marks if you include all aspects of the
answer in your response and set out your answer in a
logical manner. You don't have to phrase your answer
to match the mark scheme, but the physics must be
clear and cover the same ground.

7 Polythene will stretch more easily / be less stiff
than polystyrene   *[1]*
and will behave elastically (for small strains)   *[1]*
because the chains will unwind under stress   *[1]*
(which will coil up when the stress is removed).
Polystyrene will be stiffer because the side arms
stop the molecule uncoiling.   *[1]*

8 a The point at which plastic deformation begins   *[1]*
b $2.0 \times 10^{11} \, \text{N m}^{-2} = \dfrac{58 \times 10^8 \, \text{N m}^{-2}}{\varepsilon}$ *[1]*

extension = $\varepsilon L = 75 \, \text{m} \times \dfrac{58 \times 10^8 \, \text{N m}^{-2}}{2.0 \times 10^{11} \, \text{N m}^{-2}}$ *[1]*
extension = 0.33 m   *[1]*

c Paul thinks that the cross-sectional area
of the wire must be doubled.
The breaking stress does not depend on the
length of the cable when the weight of the
cable is ignored.
Assuming that doubling the length of the
cable does not double the total weight
supported by the cable,
the diameter will not need to be doubled.
Ameena has not considered the increase
in weight of cable, so Jack is correct.
However, the difference in total weight
may be very small,
so the extra diameter required could be
insignificant.   *[6]*

9 a Extension of steel = 0.011 m (2 s.f.)   *[1]*
Extension of nylon = 0.64 m   *[1]*
b Energy stored in steel = 8.3 J (2 s.f.)   *[1]*
Energy stored in nylon = 480 J   *[1]*
c Steel is relatively stiff   *[1]*
So will not stretch under a load.   *[1]*
Nylon is less stiff so will exert a decelerating
force on a climber   *[1]*
Over a larger distance   *[1]*
(decreasing the average force on the climber).

10 a $h = \dfrac{4 \, r^3}{3R^2}$ *[1]*
$h = 2.1 \times 10^{-9} \, \text{m}$ *[1]*

b The calculation gives the height of an oil
molecule if the disc is one molecule thick.   *[1]*

c Maximum size of molecule = $5.6 \times 10^{-9} \, \text{m}$ *[1]*
Minimum size = $7.4 \times 10^{-10} \, \text{m}$ *[1]*

Ratio of maximum/minimum = 7.6   *[1]*
This is greater than seven times.

11 a Breaking stress $= \dfrac{F}{A} = \dfrac{0.58}{(\pi \times (2.5 \times 10^{-5} \, \text{m})^2}$ *[1]*
Breaking stress = $3.0 \times 10^8 \, \text{Pa}$ (2 s.f.)   *[1]*

b Number of hairs $= 75 \, \text{kg} \times \dfrac{9.8 \, \text{N kg}^{-1}}{0.58}$ *[1]*
Number of hairs = 1300 (2.f.)   *[1]*

Chapters 6 and 7

1 Time period $= \dfrac{1}{80 \, \text{Hz}}$ *[1]*
Time period = 0.0125 s   *[1]*

2 a Diagram showing:
one loop between ends of the wire   *[1]*
labelled nodes (N) at both ends and antinode
(A) in the middle of the string   *[1]*
length between ends of string labelled as
0.6 m.   *[1]*

b 264 m s^{-1} *[1]*

c 311 Hz   *[1]*

3 a The angle is more difficult to measure   *[1]*
because the ray from the light source is
broader when it leaves the transparent block.   *[1]*

b In questions such as this you will be marked on:
correctly labelled axes   *[1]*
accuracy of plotting   *[1]*
and use of uncertainty bars to find the best
fit line.   *[1]*

c Showing calculation of gradient, for example,
by a clear triangle on the graph   *[1]*
gradient = 1.5 (2 s.f.)   *[1]*
uncertainty ± 0.1   *[1]*

d $2.0 \times 10^8 \, \text{m s}^{-1}$ *[1]*

4 Initial set-up: path difference TMR – TR = whole
number of wavelengths   *[1]*

As the reflecting surface is moved back the path
difference is increased until it becomes $\left(n + \tfrac{1}{2}\right)$

wavelengths (where n is an integer). *[1]*
At this position the waves reaching the receiver directly from the transmitter are in antiphase with those which have travelled to the detector having been reflected. *[1]*
This forms a (superposition) minimum. *[1]*
When the reflecting surface is moved further back the path difference becomes a whole number of wavelengths again and the waves from the two paths meet in phase *[1]*
producing a maximum. *[1]*

b Extra distance travelled between one maximum and the next = one wavelength *[1]*

Difference in path differences = final length TMR – initial length TMR

Difference in path differences = $(2 \times (0.24^2 + 0.4^2)^{0.5}) - (2 \times (0.21^2 + 0.4^2)^{0.5})$ = wavelength *[1]*

Difference in path differences = 0.029 m *[1]*

c If the absolute uncertainty in the measurement of length MP does not change *[1]*
the percentage uncertainty in the measurement will decrease as length MP is increased. *[1]*
However, the amplitude of the maxima will decrease as MP increases, making it harder to detect the exact position of the maximum. *[1]*

5 a Grating spacing = $\dfrac{1}{6 \times 10^5\,\text{m}} = 1.7 \times 10^{-6}\,\text{m}$ *[1]*

b $\sin\theta = \dfrac{5.9 \times 10^{-7}\,\text{m}}{1.7 \times 10^{-6}\,\text{m}} = 0.354$ *[1]*
$\theta = 21°$ *[1]*

c Greatest value of $\sin\theta = 1$. Therefore
$1 = n_{max} \times \dfrac{5.9 \times 10^{-7}\,\text{m}}{1.7 \times 10^{-6}\,\text{m}}$ *[1]*

$n_{max} = \dfrac{1.7 \times 10^{-6}\,\text{m}}{5.9 \times 10^{-7}\,\text{m}} = 2.88$ *[1]*

Therefore, 2 orders of maxima are possible. *[1]*

6 Wavelength = $\dfrac{5.0 \times 10^{-4}\,\text{m} \times 4.0 \times 10^{-3}\,\text{m}}{2.8\,\text{m}}$ *[1]*

Wavelength = $7.1 \times 10^{-7}\,\text{m}$ *[1]*

7 a Energy of incident photon = $\dfrac{hc}{\lambda} = 4.2 \times 10^{-19}\,\text{J}$ *[1]*

Work function = $4.2 \times 10^{-19}\,\text{J} - 0.3 \times 10^{-19}\,\text{J}$ = $3.9 \times 10^{-19}\,\text{J}$ *[1]*

b At longest wavelength, photon energy = work function. *[1]*
$\lambda = \dfrac{hc}{E} = 5.1 \times 10^{-7}\,\text{m}$ *[1]*

8 a Use $\sin\theta = \dfrac{n\lambda}{d}$ to show that a maximum is found at 17.1°. *[1]*

Photon energy = $\dfrac{hc}{\lambda} = 4.0 \times 10^{-19}\,\text{J}$ *[1]*

Kinetic energy max = $4.04.. \times 10^{-19}\,\text{J} - 3.7 \times 10^{-19}$ *[1]*
= $3.41... \times 10^{-20}\,\text{J}$ *[1]*

b Showing that 34° is the angle of the second order maximum. *[1]*

As the metal surface is moved up to 34° the maximum energy of the photoelectrons does not change *[1]*
but the rate of emission falls to a minimum at the point of minimum in the interference pattern *[1]*
and rises again to a second maximum at 34°. *[1]*
Explanation that the more photons arrive per unit time at positions of maxima *[1]*
so more electrons are emitted.

c Interference patterns cannot be explained by the simple particle model *[1]*
and the photoelectric effect can't be explained by the simple wave model. *[1]*
Therefore, this experiment cannot be explained by either of the models alone.

9 a $p^2 = m^2v^2$
$\dfrac{m^2v^2}{2m} = \frac{1}{2}mv^2$ *[1]*

b $\lambda = \dfrac{h}{mv} = \dfrac{h}{\sqrt{2mE_k}}$ *[1]*

$\lambda = \dfrac{6.6 \times 10^{-34}\,\text{J s}}{\sqrt{2 \times 9.1 \times 10^{-31}\,\text{kg} \times 500\,\text{J C}^{-1} \times 1.6 \times 10^{-19}\,\text{C}}}$ *[1]*

$\lambda = 5.5 \times 10^{-11}\,\text{m}$ *[1]*

c The spacing is about three times the wavelength of the electrons. *[1]*
(If electrons were passing through two slits of this spacing) the angle to the first minimum

would be $\sin^{-1}\left(\dfrac{5.5 \times 10^{-11}\,\text{m}}{1.4 \times 10^{-10}\,\text{m}}\right)$ *[1]*

angle to first minimum = 23° *[1]*
so diffraction effects would be observed. (N.B. the structure of graphene would not produce a pattern of dark and bright fringes, but a more complicated pattern reflecting its structure.)

d Your answer should include:

Electrons exploring both paths through the slits. *[1]*

When the phasors meet in phase the phasor amplitudes combine to give a larger amplitude than that of a single phasor. *[1]*

When the phasors meet in antiphase the phasor amplitudes combine to give minimum amplitude. *[1]*

Probability of an electron arriving at a particular point on the screen is proportional to the combined phasor amplitude squared. *[1]*

Chapter 8

1 D *[1]*

2 A *[1]*

3 C *[1]*

4 A *[1]*

5 a $s = ut + \frac{1}{2}at^2$ where $s = 25\,\text{m}$, $a = 9.8\,\text{m s}^{-2}$ and $t = 1.3\,\text{s}$

$25\,\text{m} = u \times 1.3\,\text{s} + \frac{1}{2} \times 9.8\,\text{m s}^{-2} \times (1.3\,\text{s})^2$ [1]

$= u \times 1.3\,\text{s} + 8.28\,\text{m}$

$u = \dfrac{(25\,\text{m} - 8.28\,\text{m})}{1.3\,\text{s}} = 13\,\text{m s}^{-1}$ [1]

b $v^2 = u^2 + 2as$ where $v = 0$, $s = 34\,\text{m}$ and $a = -9.8\,\text{m s}^{-2}$ [1]

$0 = u^2 + 2 \times (-9.8\,\text{m s}^{-2}) \times 34\,\text{m} = u^2 - 666.4\,\text{m}^2\text{s}^{-2}$

$u = \sqrt{(666.4\,\text{m}^2\text{s}^{-2})} = 26\,\text{m s}^{-1}$ [1]

6 a distance $= \sqrt{\{(200\,\text{km})^2 + (300\,\text{km})^2\}} = 360\,\text{km}$ [1]

speed $= \dfrac{360\,000\,\text{m}}{(35 \times 60\,\text{s})} = 170\,\text{m s}^{-1}$ [1]

direction $= \text{E arctan}\left(\dfrac{300}{200}\right) \text{S} = \text{E } 56°\,\text{S}$ / bearing 146° [1]

b Resolve into east–west and north–south directions.

The east–west component of velocity v_{EW} of the plane relative to the air needs to be $25\,\text{m s}^{-1}$ due east to 'cancel out' the wind and leave the plane with the north–south component v_{NS} only. [1]

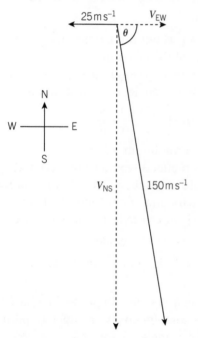

▲ **Figure 1**

$25\,\text{m s}^{-1} = 150\,\text{m s}^{-1} \times \cos\theta$ [1]

$\cos\theta = \dfrac{25\,\text{m s}^{-1}}{150\,\text{m s}^{-1}} = \dfrac{1}{6} = 0.166 \Rightarrow \theta = 80°$

The plane needs to be steered in the direction E 80° S (bearing 170°). [1]

7 a Graph as shown in Figure 2.
Axes correctly labelled [1]
and all points correctly plotted (to nearest half-square) [1]

[Allow 1 mark if one error made in labelling axes or plotting points]

Smooth best-fit curve [1]

Gradient lines drawn as tangents to $t = 0.40\,\text{s}$ and $0.60\,\text{s}$ (shown in Figure 1 as dashed line and solid line respectively). [Do not give this mark if either gradient is calculated over a time interval of less than 0.2 s.] [1]

velocity at $0.40\,\text{s}$ = gradient $= \dfrac{(3.45\,\text{m} - 0.75\,\text{m})}{(0.8\,\text{s} - 0\,\text{s})}$

$= 3.38\,\text{m s}^{-1}$ [1]

velocity at $0.60\,\text{s} = \dfrac{(4.0\,\text{m} - 0\,\text{m})}{(0.8\,\text{s} - 0.02\,\text{s})} = 5.13\,\text{m s}^{-1}$ [1]

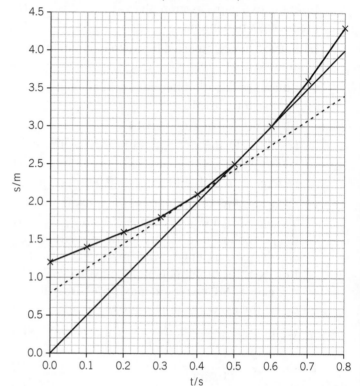

▲ **Figure 2**

b Acceleration $a = \dfrac{\Delta v}{\Delta t} = \dfrac{(5.13\,\text{m s}^{-1} - 3.38\,\text{m s}^{-1})}{0.20\,\text{s}}$ [1]

Acceleration $a = 8.8\,\text{m s}^{-2}$ [1]

8 a Answers are given in bold in Table 1. [2]
Any two correct = 1 mark; all three correct = 2 marks

▼ **Table 1**

t / s	a / m s^{-2}	v / m s^{-1}	s / m
(0.2)	**8.33**	**1.96**	**0.098**

b i Any two from: real graph should be a smooth curve / this graph has sudden jumps [1]
v stays at 0 for 0.1 s while in reality it starts moving immediately [1]
v is constant during each Δt interval whereas it really increases [1]

ii Use a smaller time interval Δt [1]

Chapter 9

1 D $40\,\text{m s}^{-1}$ [1]

2 C $180\,\text{m s}^{-1}$ [1]

3 B $48\,000\,\text{J}$ [1]

4 D 9.7, 7.1 [1]

5 **a** Impulse = momentum change =
$0.28\,kg \times 8.0\,ms^{-1} - 0.28\,kg \times (-14\,ms^{-1}) =$
$2.24\,Ns - (-3.92\,Ns) =$ [2]

[If one error in relative signs, give one mark for
the above]

impulse = $6.16\,Ns = 6.2\,Ns$ [1]

b Impulse = $F\Delta t \Rightarrow F = \dfrac{impulse}{\Delta t}$ [1]

$F = \dfrac{6.16\,Ns}{0.32\,s} = 19\,N$ [1]

6 **a** Roughly half the peak value: allow
between 12 N and 17 N [1]

b Impulse = answer to **a** × 0.64 s = 7.7 to 11 N s [1]

momentum gain = impulse, so $v = \dfrac{impulse}{0.42\,kg} =$
18 to 26 m s^{-1} [1]

7 **a** Vertical component of velocity =
$15\,ms^{-1} \times \sin 18° = 4.64\,ms^{-1}$ [1]

Rate of increase of g.p.e. =
weight × vertical component of velocity [1]

$= 2100\,kg \times 9.8\,Nkg^{-1} \times 4.64\,ms^{-1} = 95\,400\,W =$
96 kW [1]

b Total power delivered = $Fv = 42\,000\,N \times 15\,ms^{-1} =$
630 000 W = 630 kW [1]

Efficiency = $\dfrac{96\,kW}{630\,kW} \times 100\% = 15\%$ [1]

e.c.f. power values from **a** and **b**

c Decelerating force down slope = component of
weight + friction [1]

$= (2100\,kg \times 9.8\,Nkg^{-1}) \times \sin 18° + 20\,000\,N =$
26 360 N [1]

Deceleration $a = \dfrac{26\,360\,N}{2100\,kg} = 12.5\,ms^{-2}$ [1]

$a = \dfrac{\Delta v}{\Delta t} \Rightarrow \Delta t = \dfrac{\Delta v}{a} = \dfrac{15\,ms^{-1}}{12.5\,ms^{-2}} = 1.2\,s$ [1]

8 **a** 30–32 m (actual value: 30.7 m) [1]

b $\tan\theta \approx \dfrac{(y_1 - y_0)}{(x_1 - x_0)} = \dfrac{20\,m}{31.5\,m}$ [1]

$\tan\theta = 0.635 \Rightarrow \theta = 32°$ [1]

Gradient drops continually until object reaches
the maximum height, so initial angle is greater
than 32° (actual value = 37.8°). [1]

c x values are equally spaced [1]
so horizontal component of velocity is not
dropping. [1]

OR

y values are symmetrical (about 2.5 s) [1]
so vertical component of velocity is not of
smaller magnitude during the fall than at the
equivalent point during the rise. [1]

d Peak is lower. [1]

Peak occurs at a smaller value of x. [1]

x-distance travelled after the peak is less than
that travelled before the peak. [1]

Chapter 10

1 **a** $2.85... \times 10^{15}$ atoms [1]

b decay constant = $\dfrac{activity}{number\ of\ nuclei} = \dfrac{167 \times 10^6}{2.85...}$ [1]

decay constant = $5.8 \times 10^{-8}\,s^{-1}$ [1]

c half-life = $\dfrac{\ln 2}{5.8 \times 10^{-8}\,s^{-1}} = 11.9...\times 10^6\,s$ [1]

half-life = 138 days [1]

2 **a** The chance/probability [1]
of a <u>nucleus</u> [1]
decaying in <u>one second</u> (or unit time) [1]
is 1×10^{-4} s.

b **i** There are twice as many atoms of
isotope B as isotope A. [1]

ii This will occur after two half-lives of
radioisotope A (or one half-life of B) [1]

$= \dfrac{\ln 2}{1 \times 10^{-4}\,s^{-1}} = 6930\,s$ [1]

3 The activity will fall to $\dfrac{1}{16}$ of the original value
after 4 half-lives [1]
so half-life = $\dfrac{20}{4} = 5$ hours. [1]

OR

Fraction remaining = $\dfrac{1}{2^n}$ where n is the number of
half-lives

$2^n = 16$ therefore $n = \log_2 16 = 4$ [1]

so half-life = $\dfrac{20}{4} = 5$ hours [1]

4 **a** Decay constant = $\dfrac{0.693}{12.5\,h^{-1}}$ [1]
(or, calculated in s^{-1} = $1.54 \times 10^{-5}\,s^{-1}$)

$A = 100 \times 10^3 \times e^{-\left(0.693 \times \frac{1}{12.5}\right)}$ [1]
$A = 94.6\,kBq$ [1]

b $10 = 100 \times e^{-\left(\left(\frac{0.693}{12.5}\right)t\right)}$ therefore: $\ln 0.1 =$

$-\left(\dfrac{0.693}{12.5}\right)t$ [1]

$t = -\dfrac{2.3}{(-0.693/12.5)} = 41.5$ hours [1]

5 **a** 4.5 V [1]

b 22 mJ [1]

c 9.2(4) s [1]

d $\ln 0.25 = \dfrac{-t}{9.24}$ [1]
$t = -\ln 0.25 \times 9.24$ [1]
$t = 12.8\,s$ [1]

e Energy stored is proportional to V^2 so energy will
have fallen to 0.25 of its original value when p.d.
across capacitor is 2.25 V. [1]

$2.25 = 4.5 \times e^{-t/RC}$

$\ln 0.5 \times -9.2... = -t$ [1]

$t = 6.4\,s$ [1]

f This is not correct. If the resistance of the
voltmeter was lower the effective load resistance
would decrease. [1]
This will reduce the time constant [1]
so decay will be quicker. [1]

6 **a** 1.25×10^9 years *[1]*

  b $0.4 = e^{-\lambda t}$ *[1]*

  $\ln 0.4 = -\left(\dfrac{0.693}{12.5 \times 10^9}\right) t$

  $t = 1.65 \times 10^9$ years *[1]*

7 $Q_0 = 21.1..\,\text{mC}$ *[1]*

  $RC = 103.4\,\text{s}$ *[1]*

  $Q = 21.1\left(1 - e^{-\left(\frac{75}{103.4}\right)}\right) = 10.9\,\text{C}$ *[1]*

Chapter 11

1 C $1.2\,\text{s}$ *[1]*

2 D $790\,\text{m s}^{-1}$ *[1]*

3 D $16 E_1$ *[1]*

4 **a** Time period on Moon = $2.0\,\text{s} \times \sqrt{6}$ *[1]*

  $= 4.9\,\text{s}$ *[1]*

  (You can do this by substitution into the equation for time period of a pendulum.)

  b $L = \dfrac{gT^2}{4\pi^2}$ *[1]*

  where $g = \dfrac{9.8}{6}\,\text{N kg}^{-1}$. $L = 0.17\,\text{m}$ *[1]*

5 **a** Velocity = $330\,\text{Hz} \times 1.3\,\text{m}$ *[1]*

  Velocity = $429\,\text{m s}^{-1}$ *[1]*

  b **i** (magnitude of) maximum velocity of string = $2\pi f A$

  (magnitude of) maximum velocity of string = $2\pi \times 330\,\text{Hz} \times 8.0 \times 10^{-4}\,\text{m}$ *[1]*

  (magnitude of) maximum velocity of string = $1.7\,\text{m s}^{-1}$ *[1]*

  ii (magnitude of) maximum acceleration = $4\pi^2 f^2 A$

  (magnitude of) maximum acceleration = $4\pi^2 \times 330^2\,\text{Hz}^2 \times 8.0 \times 10^{-4}\,\text{m}$ *[1]*

  (magnitude of) maximum acceleration = $3440\,\text{m s}^{-2}$ *[1]*

  c **i** $\ln 0.5 = -0.007n$ *[1]*

  $n = -\dfrac{0.693}{(-0.007)}$ *[1]*

  $n = 99$ oscillations *[1]*

  ii Energy is proportional to amplitude squared so if energy is halved, amplitude will decrease by a factor of $\sqrt{2}$.

  new amplitude = $\dfrac{0.8\,\text{mm}}{\sqrt{2}}$ *[1]*

  new amplitude = $0.57\,\text{mm}$ *[1]*

  d Both strings will oscillate 100 times before they cannot be heard. *[1]*

  The frequency of the higher string is about four times that of the lower string *[1]*

  so it will take the lower string four times as long to become inaudible. *[1]*

6 **a** $f = \dfrac{1}{2\pi}\sqrt{\dfrac{23\,\text{N m}^{-1}}{0.3\,\text{kg}}}$ *[1]*

  $f = 1.4\,\text{Hz}$ *[1]*

  b Force constant of the system doubles *[1]*

  so frequency increases by a factor of $\sqrt{2}$.

  new frequency = $2.0\,\text{Hz}$ *[1]*

  c Driving frequency = natural frequency *[1]*

  so resonance occurs *[1]*

  d Total energy = maximum kinetic energy = $\frac{1}{2}m \times (2\pi f A)^2$ *[1]*

  Total energy = $8.5 \times 10^{-4}\,\text{J}$ *[1]*

  Using $E = \frac{1}{2}kA^2$ gives the value $8.3 \times 10^{-4}\,\text{J}$. The difference between the two values is due to intermediate rounding. Both are acceptable.

Chapters 12 and 13

1 D $5.8 \times 10^{-3}\,\text{m s}^{-2}$ *[1]*

2 B F *[1]*

3 C $1.2\,W$ *[1]*

4 B *[1]*

5 Assume speed of light constant throughout journey. *[1]*

  distance = $3 \times 10^8\,\text{m s}^{-1} \times 25.1\,\text{s}$ *[1]*

  distance = $7.5 \times 10^9\,\text{m}$ *[1]*

6 **a** The force acts towards the Sun *[1]*

  at right angles to the direction of motion of the planet. *[1]*

  b $\dfrac{mv^2}{r} = \dfrac{GMm}{r^2}$ *[1]*

  $v = \dfrac{2\pi r}{r} \therefore \dfrac{m4\pi^2 r^2}{T^2 r} = \dfrac{GMm}{r^2}$ *[1]*

  $\therefore M = \dfrac{4\pi^2 r^3}{GT^2}$

  c $M = \dfrac{4\pi^2 \times \left(2.3 \times 10^{11}\,\text{m}\right)^3}{6.7 \times 10^{-11}\,\text{N m}^2\,\text{kg}^{-1} \times \left(6.0 \times 10^7\,\text{s}\right)^2}$ *[1]*

  $M = 2.0 \times 10^{30}\,\text{kg}$ *[1]*

7 **a** Work done = force × distance, *[1]*

  no component of force along equipotential line *[1]*

  b Equipotentials with equal potential differences get further apart with distance from planet. *[1]*

  c Line at right angles to equipotential line at X *[1]*

  pointing towards planet *[1]*

  d Energy required for $1\,\text{kg} = (+)6.3 \times 10^7\,\text{J}$ *[1]*

  Initial velocity = $v = \sqrt{2 \times 6.3 \times 10^7\,\text{J kg}^{-1}}$ *[1]*

  $v = 1.1 \times 10^4\,\text{m s}^{-1}$ *[1]*

  e $\dfrac{\text{potential at surface}}{\text{potential at X}} = \dfrac{-\dfrac{GM}{rs}}{-\dfrac{GM}{rx}}$ *[1]*

  $\therefore r_x = \dfrac{6.3 \times 10^7\,\text{J kg}^{-1}}{9.6 \times 10^6\,\text{J kg}^{-1}} \times 6.4 \times 10^6\,\text{m}$ *[1]*

  $r_x = 4.2 \times 10^7\,\text{m}$ *[1]*

8 The gravitational field strength g gives the magnitude and direction of the force on a mass of one kilogram at a point in a gravitational field. *[1]*
It is not the same as gravitational force, which is equal to mg. *[1]*
Gravitational potential is the energy required per kg to move a mass from a point in a gravitational field to infinity. *[1]*
It varies with $\frac{1}{\text{distance}}$. *[1]*
You can find change in potential from the area under the line of a field strength versus distance graph. *[1]*

9 $t = \dfrac{17 \times 10^{-6}\,\text{s}}{\sqrt{1 - \dfrac{(0.85c)^2}{c^2}}}$ *[1]*

$t = 32\,\mu\text{s}$ *[1]*

10 a Galaxies moving away show redshift *[1]*
where lines in the spectrum are shifted towards longer wavelength.
The bigger the shift, the greater the velocity. *[1]*

b Galaxies are (nearly) all moving away from each other *[1]*
so at some time in the past they must have been much closer together. *[1]*

c i Units of Mpc^{-1} are equivalent to km^{-1} (both are distances), so the units of km and Mpc^{-1} cancel, leaving s^{-1}. *[1]*

ii $2.17 \times 10^{-18}\,\text{s}$ *[1]*

d Age in seconds $= 4.61 \times 10^{17}\,\text{s}$ *[1]*
Age in years $= 1.4 \times 10^{10}$ years *[1]*

11 a Acceleration $= \dfrac{(20\,\text{m s}^{-1})^2}{25\,\text{m}}$ *[1]*
Acceleration $= 16\,\text{m s}^{-2}$ *[1]*

b Centripetal force $= 4800\,\text{N}$ *[1]*

c The centripetal force required for the turn is provided by the friction between the tyres and the road. *[1]*
This reduces in wet conditions. *[1]*
Travelling slower reduces the centripetal force required. *[1]*

Chapters 14 and 15

1 A $P/2$ *[1]*

2 D $350\,\text{m s}^{-1}$ *[1]*

3 B $310\,\text{m s}^{-1}$ *[1]*

4 a Rate of rise of temperature $= \dfrac{1400\,\text{W}}{(4200\,\text{J kg}^{-1}\,\text{K} \times 1.2\,\text{kg})}$ *[1]*
Rate of rise of temperature $= 0.28\,\text{K s}^{-1}$ *[1]*

b Expect the rate to decrease *[1]*
because when the water is hotter than its surroundings it will transfer energy to those surroundings. *[1]*

5 $p = \dfrac{nRT}{V} = \dfrac{0.7\,\text{mol} \times 8.31\,\text{J mol}^{-1}\,\text{K}^{-1} \times 298\,\text{K}}{4.4 \times 10^{-3}\,\text{m}^3}$ *[1]*

$p = 3.9 \times 10^5\,\text{Pa}$ *[1]*

6 $nRT = \dfrac{1}{3}Nmc^2 \ \therefore\ c_{rms} = \sqrt{\dfrac{3RT}{M_m}}$ where M_m is the mass of one mole of gas *[1]*

$c_{rms} = \sqrt{\dfrac{3 \times 8.31\,\text{J mol}^{-1}\,\text{K}^{-1} \times 293\,\text{K}}{0.004\,\text{kg mol}^{-1}}}$ *[1]*

$c_{rms} = 1400\,\text{m s}^{-1}$ ($1350\,\text{m s}^{-1}$ to 2 s.f.) *[1]*

7 a $8.3 \times 10^{-20}\,\text{J}$ *[1]*

b $f = e^{\frac{8.3 \times 10^{-20}\,\text{J}}{1.38 \times 10^{-23}\,\text{J K}^{-1} \times 298\,\text{K}}}$ *[1]*

$f = 1.7 \times 10^{-9}$ *[1]*

8 a Mass of one molecule $m = 2.666.. \times 10^{-25}\,\text{kg}$ *[1]*
$\dfrac{1}{2}m\overline{c^2} = \dfrac{3}{2}kT \ \therefore\ c_{rms} = \sqrt{\dfrac{3kT}{m}} = 213\,\text{m s}^{-1}$
$= 210\,\text{m s}^{-1}$ (2 s.f.) *[1]*
(You must show your own answer.)

b Number of steps taken (that is, number of collisions) $N = \left(\dfrac{d}{x}\right)^2 = 4 \times 10^{12}$ *[1]*
Total distance travelled $= 4 \times 10^{12} \times 1.0 \times 10^{-7}\,\text{m} = 4 \times 10^5\,\text{m}$ *[1]*
Time taken $= \dfrac{\text{distance}}{\text{speed}} = \dfrac{4 \times 10^5\,\text{m}}{210\,\text{m s}^{-1}} = 1900\,\text{s} = 32$ minutes *[1]*

c You can tackle this question by repeating the calculation from the beginning:
Calculate c_{rms} (oxygen) $= 476.9..\,\text{m s}^{-1}$ *[1]*
The oxygen will make more collisions (take more steps) in 30 minutes because it spends less time between collisions as it is moving faster. The average number of steps an oxygen molecule will make = number of steps made by bromine molecule
$\times \dfrac{\text{rms speed of oxygen}}{\text{rms speed of bromine}} = 8.95... \times 10^{12}$ *[1]*
displacement $= x\sqrt{N} = 1.0 \times 10^{-7}\,\text{m} \times \sqrt{8.95...\times 10^{12}} = 0.3\,\text{m}$ *[1]*

OR

You can tackle this by realising that as the kinetic energy of the oxygen molecules is the same as the kinetic energy of the bromine at the same temperature, $v_{\text{oxygen}} = \sqrt{5}\,v_{\text{bromine}}$

So, in the same time the oxygen will make $\sqrt{5}$ as many collisions as the bromine. Therefore, the displacement of the oxygen after the same time will be:

$x\sqrt{\sqrt{5}N} = x\sqrt[4]{5}\ \sqrt{N} = 1.0 \times 10^{-7}\,\text{m} \times \sqrt[4]{5} \times \sqrt{4 \times 10^{12}}$
$= 0.3\,\text{m}$

9 $Q_{hot\ liquid} = -Q_{cold\ liquid}$

$\therefore mc\,\theta_{hot\ liquid} = mc\,\theta_{cold\ liquid}$

$\therefore 0.25\,\text{kg} \times (-20\,^{\circ}\text{C}) = m_{cold\ liquid} \times 55\,^{\circ}\text{C}$ *[1]*

mass of cold liquid = 0.091 kg   *[1]*

10 a   Energy = $\dfrac{2.3 \times 10^6\,\text{J}}{6.0 \times 10^{23}\,\text{mol}^{-1} \times \left(\frac{1}{0.018}\right)\text{mol}}$ *[1]*

    $= 6.9 \times 10^{-20}\,\text{J}$ *[1]*

  b $f = e^{-6.9 \times 10^{-20}\,\text{J}/(1.4 \times 10^{-23}\,\text{J K}^{-1} \times 293\,\text{K})}$ *[1]*

    $= 5.0 \times 10^{-8}$ *[1]*

  c   Calculate f at 303 K = 9.6×10^{-8} *[1]*

    As the Boltzmann factor gives the fraction of particles with sufficient energy to evaporate   *[1]*

    the number evaporating per second will be proportional to the Boltzmann factor. As the Boltzmann factor has roughly doubled, so will rate of evaporation.   *[1]*

11 You must clearly state what you expect to observe, explain the behaviour in terms of kinetic theory, and describe how to use the apparatus to determine absolute zero. The following points are all important to include in your answer.   *[6]*

- Expect to observe that pressure is proportional to temperature in K (absolute or thermodynamic temperature).

Kinetic explanation can include:

- As T increases so does mean square speed of particles.
- More collisions with walls per second increases force on walls
- Higher velocity collisions with walls increases force on walls
- Linking force to rate of change of momentum
- Linking $pV = \dfrac{1}{3}N m\overline{c^2}$ and $pV = NkT$ to show relationship in the first bullet point.

Experimental determination explanation can include:

- Plotting graph of p vs. temperature (in °C or K)
- Extrapolating back to zero pressure

12 a   Correct graph: p vs. $\dfrac{1}{V}$ OR V vs. $\dfrac{1}{p}$ Or log V vs. log p *[1]*

    Statement: either of the first two graphs will be a straight line through origin.   *[1]*

    Log–log graph will be a straight line of gradient −1.   *[1]*

  b   Graph is inverse curve above initial line.   *[1]*

    Explanation, e.g., at a higher temperature the same mass of gas will exert a greater pressure in a given volume *because* $pV = nRT$ so if V, R and n are constant, when temperature increases so does pressure.   *[1]*

    (or a similar argument based on constant p).

    Remember, you have to explain your reasoning not just describe your line.

13 a $\dfrac{E}{kT} = 26$ *[1]*

  b $f = 5.1 \times 10^{-12}$ *[1]*

  c   •   Easily detectable shows that, at any instant, there are many ions present.

     •   Although the Boltzmann factor is a small proportion, there are many atoms in the Sun   *[1]*

       so a small proportion of a very large number is still a large number.   *[1]*

     •   Numerical example, e.g., 5×10^{-12} of one mole $= 3 \times 10^{12}$ ions   *[1]*

     •   Many collisions per second so many chances to 'get lucky'.   *[1]*

Chapter 16

1   B 2.7×10^{-2} Wb m^{-2} *[1]*

2   A 18.6 V, 0.41 A   *[1]*

3 a   Maximum flux linkage = 0.648 Wb or Wb turns   *[1]*

  b   Maximum rate of change of flux linkage (and hence maximum e.m.f.) occurs when flux linkage is zero.   *[1]*

    Maximum e.m.f. evaluated from gradient of graph in range 17 V to 20 V.   *[1]*

  c   The maximum e.m.f. will increase by a factor of four.   *[1]*

    Doubling the frequency doubles the maximum rate of change of flux.   *[1]*

    Doubling the number of turns doubles the maximum flux linkage.   *[1]*

4 a   Flux linkage = $N\phi \cos(35^{\circ})$

    Flux linkage = 260×0.045 Wb m$^{-2} \times \pi \times (0.05\,\text{m}^2) \times \cos(35^{\circ})$ *[1]*

Flux linkage = 0.0753 Wb (turns) ≈ 0.08 Wb *[1]*

Note that in 'show that' questions you must always include your calculated answer.

b Magnitude of average e.m.f. induced = $-N\dfrac{\Delta\phi}{\Delta t}$ =

$\dfrac{(260\times0.045\,\text{Wb m}^{-2}\times\pi\times(0.05\,\text{m}^2))\,\text{Wb}}{0.18\,\text{s}}$ *[1]*

Magnitude of average e.m.f. induced = 0.51 V *[1]*

This is an average value because the rate of change of flux linkage is not constant. *[1]*

c Frequency = $\dfrac{1}{(0.18\,\text{s}\times4)}$ = 1.39 Hz *[1]*

Maximum e.m.f. = 2 × π × 1.39 Hz × 260 × 0.045 Wb m^{-2} × π × (0.05 m)^2 *[1]*

Maximum e.m.f. = 0.80 V *[1]*

5 An e.m.f. is induced when a change of flux linkage occurs. *[1]*

As flux linkage = magnetic flux density × number of turns × area of coil, when the area is reduced there is a change of flux linkage. *[1]*

6 a Force on the wire = 0.086 N *[1]*

b Work done = 0.086 N × 0.24 m *[1]*
work done = 0.021 J *[1]*

c Flux cut = 0.24 m × 0.12 m × 0.090 Wb m^{-2} *[1]*
flux cut = 0.0026 Wb *[1]*

d Induced e.m.f. = $\dfrac{0.0026\,\text{Wb}}{0.26\,\text{s}}$ = 0.01 V *[1]*

7 There is an e.m.f. induced across the coil as it rotates. *[1]*

The faster the coil rotates, the larger the e.m.f. induced. *[1]*

The induced e.m.f. acts in a direction to oppose the current in the coil or (alternative answer) acts against the e.m.f. driving the current in the coil (from Lenz's law). *[1]*

8 a e.m.f. = 250 m s^{-1} × 55 m × 1.6 × 10^{-4} T *[1]*
e.m.f. = 2.2 V *[1]*

b e.m.f. = rate of change of flux *[1]*

Either: nearer the poles the field strength is greater so the rate of change of flux (or rate of cutting of flux) is greater *[1]*

Or: the vertical component of the magnetic field is larger nearer the poles than nearer the equator. *[1]*

Chapter 17

1 a A N C^{-1} *[1]*

b C Wb s^{-1} *[1]*

c B Wb m^{-2} *[1]*

2 B 0.58r *[1]*

3 C radial distance from point charge r/m, potential/V *[1]*

4 $k=\dfrac{Fr^2}{Qq}$ units: $\dfrac{Fm^2}{C^2}$ or F m^2 C^{-2} *[1]*

5 6.8 × 10^6 *[1]* V m^{-1} *[1]*
(unit N C^{-1} accepted)

6 a Velocity = $\sqrt{\dfrac{2\times1.6\times10^{-19}\,C\times180\,V}{9.1\times10^{-31}\,kg}}$ *[1]*

velocity = 8.0 × 10^6 m s^{-1} *[1]*

b Either: equate $qvB = \dfrac{Vq}{d}$ *[1]*

∴ $V = Bvd$ *[1]*
$V = 0.26\,T\times8.0\times10^6\,\text{m s}^{-1}\times0.28\,\text{m} = 5.8\times10^5\,V$ *[1]*

Or: calculate force due to B-field as 3.3 × 10^{-13} N *[1]*

$\dfrac{Vq}{d} = 3.3\times10^{-13}\,N$ *[1]*

which evaluates to V = 5.8 × 10^5 V *[1]*

7 a kinetic energy of accelerated electron, $E_k = eV$ *[1]*

velocity = $\sqrt{\dfrac{2E_k}{m}}$ *[1]*

velocity = $\sqrt{\dfrac{2eV}{m}}$

b $\dfrac{mv^2}{r} = evB$ *[1]*

∴ $r = \dfrac{mv}{eB}$ *[1]*

$r = \dfrac{m\sqrt{\dfrac{2eV}{m}}}{eB}$ *[1]*

$r = \dfrac{1}{B}\sqrt{\dfrac{2mV}{e}}$

c i Radius = 0.049 m *[1]*

ii Radius of path ∝ $\sqrt{m}$ as accelerating potential V the same for same energy, and magnitude of charge is the same *[1]*

$\sqrt{1800}$ = 42 *[1]* so radius will be 42 times that of the electron radius.

Chapters 18 and 19

1 a A 1, 2, and 3 *[1]*

b C 2 and 3 *[1]*

c B 1 and 2 *[1]*

2 B 2.3 × 10^{-14} m *[1]*

3 a $\gamma = \dfrac{0.51\,\text{MeV} + 0.60\,\text{MeV}}{0.51\,\text{MeV}}$ *[1]*

γ = 2.2 *[1]*

b $2.2 = \dfrac{1}{\sqrt{1-\dfrac{v^2}{c^2}}} \quad \therefore v^2 = c^2\left(1 - \dfrac{1}{2.2^2}\right)$ *[1]*

$v = 2.7 \times 10^8 \, \text{m s}^{-1}$ *[1]*

c Wavelength =

$\dfrac{6.6 \times 10^{-34} \, \text{J s}}{(2.2 \times 9.1 \times 10^{-31} \, \text{kg} \times 2.7 \times 10^8 \, \text{m s}^{-1})}$ *[1]*

Wavelength = $1.2 \times 10^{-12} \, \text{m}$ *[1]*

4 Total exposure = $0.8 \, \text{Sv}$ *[1]*
risk of contracting cancer = 4% *[1]*

5 a $_{0}^{0}\text{e}$ *[1]*

b Lepton number / mass-energy / momentum *[1]*

c Beta radiation is ionising *[1]*

and can cause damage to cells. *[1]*

Beta radiation will not pass through lead. *[1]*

d i Total energy released in 5 min =
$1.2 \times 10^5 \times 5 \times 60 \times 0.14 \times 10^{-13}$ *[1]*

Total energy released in 5 min = $5.0 \times 10^{-7} \, \text{J}$ *[1]*

ii Dose given to cells = $\dfrac{1 \times (5.0 \times 10^{-7} \, \text{J})}{2.0 \times 10^{-3} \, \text{kg}}$ *[1]*

Dose given to cells = $250 \times \mu\text{Sv}$ *[1]*

6 a i Counts at 1.0 m = $500 \times \left(\dfrac{0.4^2}{1^2}\right)$ *[1]*

Counts at 1.0 m = $80 \, \text{counts s}^{-1}$ *[1]*

ii Decay is a random process. *[1]*

b After 80 minutes, count rate at 0.4 m will be
125 counts s⁻¹. *[1]*

Counts at 1.2 m = $125 \times \left(\dfrac{0.4^2}{1.2^2}\right)$ *[1]*

Counts at 1.2 m = $14 \, \text{counts s}^{-1}$ *[1]*

7 a Acceleration is the greatest at point of closest approach *[1]*

because at this point force between particles is the greatest. *[1]*

b Velocity is the minimum at point of closest approach *[1]*

because at this point the greatest amount of kinetic energy has been transferred to electrical potential energy. *[1]*

8 a i More than one *[1]* neutron can be captured by a uranium-235 nucleus producing further fissions. *[1]*

If the mass (and volume) of the uranium is below a certain value too many neutrons will escape the uranium before producing further fissions. *[1]*

ii Mass change = $0.1883 \, \text{u}$ *[1]*

Mass change = $3.12... \times 10^{-28} \, \text{kg}$ *[1]*

$E = mc^2$ gives $2.8 \times 10^{-11} \, \text{J}$ *[1]*

b i Time uranium reserves = remaining uranium/ mass of uranium required each year

$\dfrac{5.9 \times 10^9}{6.6 \times 10^7 \, \text{kg yr}^{-1}}$ *[1]*

= 89 years (2 s.f.) *[1]*

ii Suggestion / explanation pairs, e.g.:

Demand may increase *[1]*

as population (or industrialisation) increases. *[1]*

New sources of uranium may be found *[1]*

as detection techniques improve. *[1]*

c Energy released = (1.88 GeV + 2.82 GeV) − (3.74 GeV + 0. 942 MeV) *[1]*

Energy released = 0.018 GeV *[1]*

d Potential energy = $\dfrac{k \times (1.6 \times 10^{-19} \, \text{C})^2}{1.0 \times 10^{-14} \, \text{m}}$ *[1]*

Potential energy = $2.3 \times 10^{-14} \, \text{J}$ *[1]*

At great separation the potential energy tends to zero *[1]*

so the value is the work required to bring the particles together. *[1]*

$E \sim kT$; energy of each particle in a collision = $1.65 \times 10^{-14} \, \text{J}$ *[1]*

$E = 800 \times 10^6 \, \text{K}$ *[1]* although fusions will occur at lower temperatures due to the distribution of energies in a group of particles.

Answers to summary questions

1.1

1 Radius $= \dfrac{1}{280\,\mathrm{m^{-1}}}$ [1]

Radius $= 3.57 \times 10^{-3}\,\mathrm{m}$ [1]

2 Curvature $= \dfrac{1}{6.4 \times 10^6\,\mathrm{m}}$ [1]

Curvature $= 1.57 \times 10^{-7}\,\mathrm{m^{-1}}$ [1]

3 Focal length $= \dfrac{1}{16.0\,\mathrm{D}}$ [1]

Focal length $= 62.5\,\mathrm{mm}$ [1]

4 The first diagram should be similar to the wave-front diagram in Figure 3. [1]

The second diagram should have the same wavelength waves [1] but half the focal length. [1] Focal lengths should be marked on both diagrams. [1]

1.2

1 Magnification $= \dfrac{v}{u} = \dfrac{3.7\,\mathrm{m}}{0.07\,\mathrm{m}}$ [1]

Magnification $= 53$ (2 s.f.) [1]

2 $\dfrac{1}{u} = \dfrac{1}{0.090\,\mathrm{m}} - \dfrac{1}{0.038\,\mathrm{m}} = -\dfrac{2600}{171}\ (= -15.2\ldots)\,\mathrm{m^{-1}}$ [1]

$u = \dfrac{171}{2600} = -0.066\,\mathrm{m}$ [1]

3 $\dfrac{1}{v} = \dfrac{1}{-0.065} + \dfrac{1}{0.064} = 0.240\,\mathrm{m^{-1}}$ [1]

$v = 4.16\,\mathrm{m}$ [1]

$m = \dfrac{v}{u} = \dfrac{4.16}{-0.065} = 64$ [1]

1.3

1 Bits $= 1024 \times 512 \times 8 = 4\,194\,304$ bits [1]

bytes $= \dfrac{4\,194\,304}{8} = 524\,288$ [1]

2 $N = 2^{10} = 1024$ [1]

3 Resolution $= \dfrac{0.2\,\mathrm{m}}{512} = 3.9 \times 10^{-4}\,\mathrm{m\,pixel^{-1}}$

$(0.39\,\mathrm{mm\,pixel^{-1}})$ [1]

4 $N = \log_2 (2 \times 10^6)$ [1]

$N = 21$ bits [1]

5 Number of images $= \dfrac{2 \times 8 \times 10^9}{(8 \times 10^6 \times 24)}$ [1]

Number of images $= 83$ [1]

6 The 'noisy' pixel will have a value much different from its neighbours [1], taking the median will replace the value with one in the range of values of its neighbours. Limitation: [1]

- If the bright dot extends over many pixels the noise will not be (fully) removed
- The method may also remove very fine detail.

1.4

1 $f = \dfrac{3.0 \times 10^8\,\mathrm{m\,s^{-1}}}{690 \times 10^{-9}\,\mathrm{m}} = 4.3 \times 10^{14}\,\mathrm{Hz}$ [1]

2 a $\sqrt{\mathrm{m\,s^{-2} \times m}} = \sqrt{\mathrm{m^2\,s^{-2}}} = \mathrm{m\,s^{-1}}$ [1]

b Wavelength calculated to $64.11\ldots\,\mathrm{m}$ [1]

Frequency $= \dfrac{v}{\lambda} = 0.16\,\mathrm{Hz}$ [1]

(Or, solve for f: $f = \dfrac{g}{2\pi v}$, substitute and evaluate to $0.16\,\mathrm{Hz}$)

3
- Polarising lenses only transmit the component of light oscillating in one plane. [1]
- When this plane is as right angles to the oscillation of the light reflected from the sunlight (the glare) the lens will not transmit the reflected light [1]

  so the glare will not reach the eye. [1]
- If the glasses are turned through 90° (from horizontal to vertical) the observer will see the glare increase [1]

  as the lenses will transmit the reflected glare. [1]

2.1

1 a 9 [1]

b 10 (calculator answer of 9.97 rounds up to 10) [1]

2 Resolution $= \dfrac{10.00\,\mathrm{V}}{7}$ [1]

Resolution $= 1.43\,\mathrm{V}$ [1]

3 a Resolution $= \dfrac{24.0\,\mathrm{V}}{63}$ [1]

Resolution $= 0.032\,\mathrm{V}$ [1]

b Half the resolution will require twice as many bits. [1]

4 Maximum number of levels

$= \dfrac{(126.0\,\mu\mathrm{V} + 2.0\,\mu\mathrm{V})}{2.0\,\mu\mathrm{V}} = 64$ [1]

Maximum number of bits $= \log_2 64 = 6$ [1]

2.2

1 Memory $= 0.16 \times 3.5 \times 60$ bits [1]

Memory $= 1.26 \times 10^8$ bits [1]

Memory $= 1.575 \times 10^8$ bytes [1]

2 If the sampling rate (number of samples per second) increases this will lead to more high frequency [1] detail [1] in the signal.

3 Amount of data in one page of text $= 3000 \times 8$ bits $= 2.4 \times 10^4$ bits [1]

Duration of signal $= \dfrac{2.4 \times 10^4\,\mathrm{bits}}{(10^6\,\mathrm{bits\,s^{-1}})} = 0.024\,\mathrm{s}$ [1]

3.1

1 a 8.4 C (2 s.f.) [2]

  b 13 J (2 s.f.) [2]

2 a 9.1 A (2 s.f.) [2]

  b 2800 C (2 s.f.) [2]

  c 660 kJ (2 s.f.) [2]

3 a 350 MJ [3]

  b $\dfrac{8.75 \times 10^{11}\,W}{4.0 \times 10^{9}\,W}$ = 220 times as great as Drax [2]

3.2

1 0.41 mA [2]

2 0.15 Ω, 6.7 S (2 s.f.) [3]

3 0.25 S [3]

4 6.5 Ω [3]

5 All parallel: 20 Ω, 50 mS

  All series: 180 Ω, 5.6 mS

  Two in parallel with the third connected in series with their combination: 90 Ω, 11 mS

  Two in series with the third in parallel with their combination: 40 Ω, 25 mS [7]

6 350 Ω [2]

7 The component is approximately ohmic with $R \approx 40\,\Omega$, $G \approx 0.025\,S$ up to a p.d. of about 4 V, but the resistance increases/conductance decreases as the p.d. increases beyond that. [8]

3.3/3.4

1 a 13 Ω (2 s.f.) [2]

  b 0.076 S (2 s.f.) [1]

2 a 1.9 m (2 s.f.) [4]

  b At the higher temperature the resistivity will be larger, increasing the resistance and so decreasing the current. This means that $P = IV$ will be less. [2]

3 0.17 mA [4]

3.5

1 1.9 V across 330 Ω, 2.6 V across 470 Ω (2 s.f.) [2]

2 The resistance of the LDR would increase and the resistance of the thermistor would increase. This would increase the p.d. across the thermistor and reduce the p.d. across the LDR (but they would still add to 6.0 V). [2]

3 a 0.26 V and 2.1 V (2 s.f.) [2]

  b 1.9 V and 5.0 V (2 s.f.) [1]

  c 4.9 V and 5.9 V (2 s.f.) [1]

3.6

1 a 0.68 A (2 s.f.) [2]

  b 1.4 V (2 s.f.) [1]

2 9.1 V

  0.40 Ω

3 0.28 Ω (2 s.f.) [6]

4.1

1 Suitable polymer chosen [1] with correct mechanical properties [1] applied to context.

  Example answer: Polythene [1] is tough and strong [1] used for packaging such as shopping bags where the material must be strong enough to support the load and take the shape of the shopping. [1]

2 Brittleness refers to the manner in which the material fractures [1]

  not the force required for fracture. [1]

3 These materials are tough [1]

  so will not shatter on impact. [1]

  They are unsuitable for lenses because they are not hard enough, they would scratch easily. [1]

  Other point, e.g., transparent so the liquid inside the bottle can be viewed, can be moulded into many shapes. [1]

4.2

1 $F = 40\,N\,m^{-1} \times (0.145 - 0.120)$ [1]

  $F = 1.0\,N$ [1]

2 a Graph is a straight line [1]

    through the origin. [1]

  b Energy = $\dfrac{1}{2} \times 4.2\,N \times 0.06\,m$ [1]

    energy = 0.13 J (2 s.f.) [1]

  c Straight line starting at the origin with half the gradient of the first line [1]

    after 0.06 m the line curves and becomes less steep. [1]

3 a $k = \dfrac{F}{x} = \dfrac{160\,N}{0.01\,m}$ [1]

    $k = 1.6 \times 10^{4}\,N\,m^{-1}$ [1]

  b total weight in car = 1920 N [1]

    weight of three passengers = 1920 N − 640 N = 1280 N [1]

4.3

1 a Steel; the line has the greatest initial gradient. [1]

  b Steel [1]

  c Glass shows little plastic deformation before breaking. [1]

2 $\sigma = \dfrac{F}{A} \therefore F = \sigma A = 3.4 \times 10^9 \, \text{Pa} \times \pi \times (4 \times 10^{-4} \text{m})^2$ *[1]*

$F = 1.7 \times 10^3 \, \text{N}$ *[1]*

3 $E = \dfrac{\sigma}{\varepsilon} \therefore \sigma = E\varepsilon = 2.1 \times 10^{11} \, \text{Pa} \times \left(\dfrac{1.4 \times 10^{-3} \, \text{m}}{2.0 \, \text{m}} \right)$

$1.47 \times 10^8 \, \text{Pa}$ *[1]*

$\sigma = \dfrac{F}{A} \therefore A = \dfrac{F}{\sigma} = \dfrac{52 \, \text{N}}{1.47 \times 10^8 \, \text{Pa}} = 3.53... \times 10^7 \, \text{m}^2$ *[1]*

Diameter of wire $= 2 \times \sqrt{\dfrac{3.53... \times 10^7 \, \text{m}^2}{\pi}} =$

$6.7 \times 10^{-4} \, \text{m}$ (2 s.f.) *[1]*

4 Writing length and cross-sectional areas of wires A and B as L_A, A_A; L_B, A_B, as both wires are the same material the Young modulus is the same for both.

So: $\dfrac{F L_A}{A_A x_A} = \dfrac{F L_B}{A_B x_B}$

$L_B = 3L_A \, , \, A_B = 9A_A$ *[1]*

$\therefore 9x_B = 3x_A$

$\therefore \dfrac{x_A}{x_B} = 3$ *[1]*

5 Area under F–x line $= F \, (\text{N}) \times x \, (\text{m}) = \text{energy} \, (\text{Nm} = \text{J})$

Area under stress–strain line $= \dfrac{F}{A} \, (\text{Nm}^{-2})$ *[1]*

$= \dfrac{\text{Nm}}{\text{m}^3}$ which are the units of energy per unit volume *[1]*

6 **a** % uncertainty $= \left(\dfrac{0.01}{0.8} \right) \times 100\% = 1.25\%$ *[1]*

   b Calculated value $= 5.03 \times 10^{-7} \, \text{m}^2$ *[1]*

   r^2 will have twice the % uncertainty of r. *[1]*

   2.5 % uncertainty of cross-sectional area gives an absolute uncertainty of $\pm 1.3 \times 10^{-8} \, \text{m}^2$. *[1]*

   c Calculated value of Young modulus

   $= \dfrac{FL}{Ax} = \dfrac{49 \, \text{N} \times 3.000 \, \text{m}}{5.03 \times 10^{-7} \, \text{m}^2 \times 2.00 \times 10^{-3} \, \text{m}}$ *[1]*

   $= 1.46 \times 10^{11} \, \text{Pa}$ *[1]*

   Taking % uncertainty in result as the same as the largest % uncertainty in the primary data gives a % uncertainty of 25% *[1]* which gives a final 2 s.f. value of $(1.5 \pm 0.4) \times 10^{11} \, \text{Pa}$. *[1]*

   OR:

   Adding all the % uncertainties gives a total % uncertainty of 27.6%. *[2]* This gives the same uncertainty in the final result (to 1 s.f.) *[2]*

   (This result shows the usefulness of concentrating on the largest source of uncertainty in experimental work.)

4.4

1 Stiffest polymer = 10 GPa, most flexible < 0.1 GPa *[1]*

ratio $\dfrac{10}{0.1} = 100$ *[1]*

2 **a** It is possible because the lowest density wood has a lower density than the highest density polymer. *[1]*

   b Some metals are less dense than water so can float. *[1]*

   Some woods are more dense than water and so would sink. *[1]*

3 **a** breaking stress $\sigma_b = \dfrac{\text{weight of human spider}}{\text{cross-sectional area of thread } A}$

   As the weight of the human spider is the same in both cases and $A = \pi r^2$:

   $\sigma_b(\text{steel}) \times \pi r_{steel}^2 = \sigma_b(\text{silk}) \times \pi r_{silk}^2$ *[1]*

   $\therefore r_{silk}^2 = \dfrac{\sigma_b(\text{steel}) \times r_{steel}^2}{\sigma_b(\text{silk})}$

   $\therefore$ diameter of silk thread = diameter of steel

   thread $\times \sqrt{\dfrac{\sigma_b(\text{steel})}{\sigma_b(\text{silk})}}$ *[1]*

   diameter of silk thread = 0.8 mm (1 s.f.) *[1]*

   (for information, 3 s.f. value = 0.789 mm)

   This value can be also found by calculating the weight of the human spider from the original data and using the value to calculate the cross-sectional area of the thread. This value leads to the radius and diameter.

   Either method is acceptable. The method shown is perhaps more elegant but if you are not confident about rearranging equations, use the numerical route.

   b For equal mass and length threads:

   $\dfrac{\text{cross-sectional area of spider silk}}{\text{cross-sectional area of steel thread}} = \dfrac{8000 \, \text{kg m}^{-3}}{1300 \, \text{m}^{-3}}$ *[1]*

   breaking force = breaking stress × cross-sectional area

   $\dfrac{\text{breaking force (spider silk)}}{\text{breaking force (steel thread)}} =$

   $\dfrac{1.3 \, \text{GPa} \times 8000 \, \text{kg m}^{-3}}{1.65 \, \text{GPa} \times 1300 \, \text{m}^{-3}}$ *[1]*

   $\dfrac{\text{breaking force (spider silk)}}{\text{breaking force (steel thread)}} = 4.8$, about five times the strength *[1]*

5.1

1 Number of atoms along length $= \dfrac{7.5 \times 10^{-4} \, \text{m}}{10^{-10} \, \text{m}}$ *[1]*

Number of atoms along length $= 10^8$ (order of magnitude) *[1]*

2 Order of magnitude size of

atom $(d) = \sqrt[3]{\dfrac{3.44 \times 10^{-25} \, \text{kg}}{11300 \, \text{kg m}^{-3}}}$ *[1]*

Order of magnitude size of atom $(d) = (3 \times 10^{-10}) = 10^{-10} \, \text{m}$ (order of magnitude) *[1]*

3 **a** $\pi R^2 h = \frac{4}{3}\pi r^3$

$$\therefore h = \frac{4}{3}\frac{\pi r^3}{\pi R^2}$$ [1]

$$\therefore h = \frac{4r^3}{3R^2}$$

b Order of magnitude estimate for height of the patch:

$$\text{height} = \frac{4 \times (5 \times 10^{-4}\,\text{m})^3}{3 \times (0.15\,\text{m})^2}$$ [1]

height = $(7.4 \times 10^{-9}\,\text{m}) = 10^{-8}\,\text{m}$ (order of magnitude) [1]

Major sources of uncertainty:

- Difficulty of measuring the diameter of drop (as the size is near the resolution of the measuring instrument). [1]

  As the value of the radius is cubed in the calculation, the percentage uncertainty of the final value is three times the percentage uncertainty in the original value of the diameter. [1]

- The oil doesn't spread into a uniform circle (making estimate of average diameter difficult). [1]

The uncertainties in the measured values are large enough to limit the precision of the calculated value to an order of magnitude. [1]

5.2

1 The microscopic structure of a crystalline material shows long range order. [1]

Polycrystalline materials have smaller regions of order (grains) which are randomly oriented with respect to each other. [1]

2 A scratch produces a stress concentration when the surface is put in tension. [1]

This allows a crack to propagate through the material [1]

as when the bonds are broken at the tip of the crack, the stress is transferred to the next set of bonds deeper into the material. [1]

3 Buildings are compressive structures [1]

and bricks are strong in compression. [1]

Compression forces will tend to close up cracks so they are less likely to propagate. [1]

5.3

1 Polymers have covalent bonds. [1]

Metallic bonding is non-directional. [1]

2 Metals have positive ions [1]

bonded together by a (negative) electron 'glue'. [1]

When the metal placed under tensile force the gap between the positive ions opens up a little. [1]

The gap closes when the tensile force is removed. [1]

3 Strain = $\frac{\text{extension}}{\text{original length}} = \frac{2}{6} = 33\%$ [1]

This cannot be explained by the distance between atoms increasing. The increase in length is due to the long chain molecules unravelling under the tensile force. [1]

6.1

1 number of rotations = $\frac{1}{0.25\,\text{s}}$ [1]

number of rotations = $4\,\text{s}^{-1}$ or Hz [1]

2 Check your answer against the bullet points given in the text: 1 mark for each bullet point [5]

3 $v = f \times 2(L_2 - L_1) = 440\,\text{Hz} \times 2(0.58\,\text{m} - 0.19\,\text{m})$ [1]

$v = 340\,\text{Hz}$ (2 s.f.) [1]

4 **a** Wavelength of lowest frequency note emitted from a tube of length L open at both ends = $2L$ [1]

$$f = \frac{v}{\lambda} = \frac{340\,\text{m s}^{-1}}{2 \times 0.28\,\text{m}}$$ [1]

$f = 610\,\text{Hz}$ (2 s.f.) [1]

b The wavelength of the note will not change [1]

as this is determined by the length of the tube. [1]

As $f = \frac{v}{\lambda}$, an increased speed of sound will lead to an increased frequency. [1]

6.2

1 $\sin r = \frac{(\sin 65°)}{1.6} = 0.566...$ [1]

$r = 35°$ (2 s.f.) [1]

2 $\frac{\sin i}{\sin r} = \frac{3.00 \times 10^8\,\text{m s}^{-1}}{2.04 \times 10^8\,\text{m s}^{-1}}$

$$\sin r = \frac{\sin i \times 2.04 \times 10^8\,\text{m s}^{-1}}{3.00 \times 10^8\,\text{m s}^{-1}}$$ [1]

$\sin r = 0.308...$ [1]

$r° = 18°$ [1]

3 $1.0003 = \frac{299\,792\,458\,\text{m s}^{-1}}{c_{\text{medium}}}$

Speed of light in air = $\frac{299\,792\,458\,\text{m s}^{-1}}{1.0003} =$

$2.997... \times 10^8\,\text{m s}^{-1}$ [1]

Difference = $8.9911 \times 10^4\,\text{m s}^{-1}$ [1]

OR:

Difference = $299\,792\,458\,\text{m s}^{-1} \times \left(1 - \frac{1}{1.0003}\right)$ [1]

Difference = $8.9911 \times 10^4\,\text{m s}^{-1}$ [1]

6.3

1 Wavelength $= \dfrac{340\,\mathrm{m\,s^{-1}}}{500\,\mathrm{Hz}}$ *[1]*

   Wavelength $= 0.68\,\mathrm{m}$ *[1]*

2 Where path difference $\left(n + \dfrac{1}{2}\right)\lambda$ *[1]* waves from

   coherent sources *[1]* will meet in antiphase *[1]*
   leading to a minimum at this point.

3 a Wavelength $= \dfrac{340\,\mathrm{m\,s^{-1}}}{850\,\mathrm{Hz}} = 0.4\,\mathrm{m}$ *[1]*

      Path difference $= 2.0\,\mathrm{m} - 1.8\,\mathrm{m} = 0.2\,\mathrm{m}$ *[1]*

      Path difference $= \dfrac{1}{2}\lambda$ *[1]* so minimum is formed

   b Amplitude is not zero as the amplitudes of
      the waves from the speakers meeting at the
      microphone are not equal. *[1]*

6.4

1 The amount of diffraction is dependent on the ratio
   of the width of the gap the waves pass through to
   the wavelength of the waves. *[1]*

   Light has a much smaller wavelength than sound so
   will diffract less through a gap of equal width. *[1]*

2 $\lambda = d \sin\theta = 4.0 \times 10^{-4}\,\mathrm{m} \times \sin 0.1°$ *[1]*

   $\lambda = 7.0 \times 10^{-7}\,\mathrm{m}$ (2 s.f.) *[1]*

3 $\sin\theta$ for 589.0 nm second order maximum $= 0.3534$,
   $\theta = 20.695...°$ *[1]*

   $\sin\theta$ for 589.6 nm second order maximum $=$
   0.35376, $\theta = 20.717...°$ *[1]*

   Separation at screen 3.500 m from the grating $=$
   $1.54 \times 10^{-3}\,\mathrm{m}$ *[1]*

7.1

1 $E = 6.6 \times 10^{-34}\,\mathrm{J\,s} \times 7.0 \times 10^{14}\,\mathrm{Hz}$ *[1]*

   $E = 4.6 \times 10^{-19}\,\mathrm{J}$ *[1]*

   $E = 2.9\,\mathrm{eV}$ *[1]*

2 Energy difference $= 10.2\,\mathrm{eV} \times 1.6 \times 10^{-19}\,\mathrm{J\,eV^{-1}} =$
   $1.6(32) \times 10^{-18}\,\mathrm{J}$ *[1]*

   Frequency $= \dfrac{1.6(32) \times 10^{-18}\,\mathrm{J}}{6.6 \times 10^{-34}\,\mathrm{J\,s}} = 2.5 \times 10^{15}\,\mathrm{Hz}$ *[1]*

3 Photon energy $= \dfrac{(6.6 \times 10^{-34}\,\mathrm{J\,s} \times 3.0 \times 10^{8}\,\mathrm{m\,s^{-1}})}{5.9 \times 10^{-7}\,\mathrm{m}}$ *[1]*

   Photon energy $= 3.35... \times 10^{-19}\,\mathrm{J}$ *[1]*

   Number of photons emitted per second $=$

   $\dfrac{\text{energy emitted per second}}{\text{energy per photon}} = \dfrac{12 \times 10^{-3}\,\mathrm{J\,s^{-1}}}{3.35... \times 10^{-19}\,\mathrm{J}}$

   $= 3.6 \times 10^{16}$ electrons s^{-1} *[1]*

4 Maximum kinetic energy $=$
   photon energy $-$ work function $=$

   $\left(\dfrac{(6.6 \times 10^{-34}\,\mathrm{J\,s} \times 3.0 \times 10^{8}\,\mathrm{m\,s^{-1}})}{3.1 \times 10^{-7}\,\mathrm{m}}\right) -$

   $(2.8\,\mathrm{eV} \times 1.6 \times 10^{-19}\,\mathrm{J\,eV^{-1}})$ *[1]*

   Maximum kinetic energy $= 1.9 \times 10^{-19}\,\mathrm{J}$ *[1]*

5 a $\phi = hf - E_{k(\max)}$

      As both frequencies strike the same surface the
      work function is the same

      $\therefore (h \times 6.90 \times 10^{14}\,\mathrm{Hz}) - 5.54 \times 10^{-20}\,\mathrm{J} =$
      $(h \times 6.40 \times 10^{14}\,\mathrm{Hz}) - 2.24 \times 10^{-20}\,\mathrm{J}$ *[1]*

      $\therefore h(6.90 \times 10^{14}\,\mathrm{Hz} - 6.40 \times 10^{14}\,\mathrm{Hz}) =$
      $5.54 \times 10^{-20}\,\mathrm{J} - 2.24 \times 10^{-20}\,\mathrm{J}$ *[1]*

      $\therefore h = 6.60 \times 10^{-34}\,\mathrm{J\,s}$ *[1]*

   b i $\phi = (6.60 \times 10^{-34}\,\mathrm{J\,s} \times 6.90 \times 10^{14}\,\mathrm{Hz}) -$
         $5.54 \times 10^{-20}\,\mathrm{J}$ *[1]*

         $\phi = 4.00 \times 10^{-19}\,\mathrm{J}$ *[1]*

      ii $f_0 = \dfrac{\phi}{h} = \dfrac{4.00 \times 10^{-19}\,\mathrm{J}}{6.60 \times 10^{-34}\,\mathrm{J\,s}}$ *[1]*

         $f_0 = 6.06 \times 10^{-14}\,\mathrm{Hz}$ *[1]*

7.2

1 Number of rotations s^{-1} = frequency $= \dfrac{E}{h}$ *[1]*

   Number of rotations s$^{-1} = \dfrac{2.0\,\mathrm{eV} \times 10^{-19}\,\mathrm{J\,eV^{-1}}}{6.6 \times 10^{-34}\,\mathrm{J\,s}}$ *[1]*

   Number of rotations s$^{-1} = 4.8 \times 10^{14}$ rotations s^{-1} *[1]*

2 Ratio $= \sqrt{3.2}$ *[1]* $= 1.8$ (2 s.f.) *[1]*

3 a Light travels more slowly in glass *[1]*

      so the time taken for the two paths can be/is
      the same. *[1]*

      As frequency does not change with change of
      medium *[1]*

      the number of rotations is/can be the same.

   b Phasor arrows line up at the detector creating
      maximum amplitude of resultant phasor arrow.
      [1]

      Greatest probability of arrival of photons at this
      point. *[1]*

7.3

1 a $\lambda = \dfrac{h}{p} = \dfrac{h}{mv} = \dfrac{6.6 \times 10^{-34}\,\mathrm{J\,s}}{9.1 \times 10^{-31}\,\mathrm{kg} \times 2.2 \times 10^{6}\,\mathrm{m\,s^{-1}}}$ *[1]*

      $\lambda = 3.3 \times 10^{-10}\,\mathrm{m}$ (2 s.f.) *[1]*

   b $v = \dfrac{h}{m\lambda} = \dfrac{6.6 \times 10^{-34}\,\mathrm{J\,s}}{9.1 \times 10^{-31}\,\mathrm{kg} \times 9.0 \times 10^{-9}\,\mathrm{m}}$ *[1]*

      $v = 8.1 \times 10^{5}\,\mathrm{m\,s^{-1}}$ (2 s.f.) *[1]*

2 Units of $\dfrac{h}{p}$ are $\dfrac{\mathrm{J\,s}}{\mathrm{kg\,m\,s^{-1}}} = \mathrm{J\,kg^{-1}\,m^{-1}\,s^2}$ *[1]*

   $= (\mathrm{N\,m})\mathrm{J\,kg^{-1}\,m^{-1}\,s^2} = \mathrm{N\,J\,kg^{-1}\,m^{-1}\,s^2} =$
   $(\mathrm{kg\,m\,s^{-2}})\mathrm{kg^{-1}\,s^2} = \mathrm{m}$ *[1]*

3 Your answer should include the following ideas:

   • Electrons explore all paths from the source to the
     screen. *[1]*

   • Each path contributes a phasor arrow at a point
     on the screen. *[1]*

   • The phasor arrows are added tip-to-tail. *[1]*

- The length² of the resultant phasor arrow is proportional to the probability of detection of an electron at that point. (probability of detection ∝ phasor amplitude²). [1]
- (Therefore) the pattern can be predicted – where there is a greater probability of detecting an electron the screen will be brighter... [1]
- ...because more electrons will strike the screen at this point than where the phasor arrows combine to produce a smaller resultant phasor arrow. [1]

8.1

1

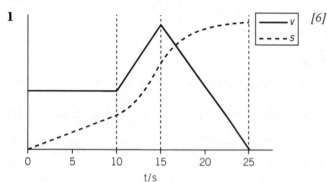

[6]

2 45 m [4]

3 Should obtain between 9.0 m s⁻² and 10.6 m s⁻² (900 cm s⁻² and 1060 cm s⁻²) [6]

8.2

1 39 km in a direction N 50° E / at a bearing of 50° (2 s.f.) [3]

2 290 m s⁻¹ in a direction N 32° W / at a bearing of 330° (all to 2 s.f.) [3]

3 9.6 m s⁻¹ in a direction W 16° S / at a bearing of 250° (all to 2 s.f.) [7]

8.3

1 In a typical laboratory, the time to fall from any reasonable height is much less than 5 s, so the model would not have even one step. [1]

2 Advantage: a much closer fit to the data that would be expected [1]

Disadvantage: 100 times as many calculations would be needed [1]

3 Each sideways step would no longer be two big squares, but would increase as the rocket accelerated sideways. The sum for each interval would be new v = previous v + Δv vertically (same as before) + Δv horizontally due to the rocket engine. The outcome would be that the rocket would travel much further horizontally than the simple projectile before it hit the ground. [3]

8.4

1 8.8 m s⁻¹ [2]

2 7.0 m (2 s.f.) [3]

3 24 m s⁻¹ (2 s.f.) [4]

9.1

1 a 30 000 kg m s⁻¹ [1]

 b 2.2 kg m s⁻¹ (2 s.f.) (1 mark for correct conversion of g to kg and for correct rounding to 2 s.f. and 1 mark for correct evaluation of answer.) [2]

2 a 2.5 kg m s⁻¹ (2 s.f.) [1]

 b 4.9 m s⁻¹ in the direction initially travelled by the bullet (2 s.f.) [2]

3 19 m s⁻¹ [4]

9.2

1 a 4.5 kg m s⁻¹ (or 4.5 N s) [2]

 b 180 N [2]

2 Moving the hand increases the stopping time Δt which makes the force less. By Newton's third law, the force the cricketer's hand exerts on the ball to slow it down is the same as the force the ball exerts on the hand. [2]

3 36 N, 1.1×10^4 s (about 3 hours) [6]

9.3

1 4.8 J [2]

2 170 kJ [1]

3 4.4 J [1]

4 41 m s⁻¹ assuming air resistance is negligible (which it would be here). (Can also use *suvat* equations for this sort of problem.) [4]

5 1.89 °C [6]

9.4

1 $u_h = 96$ m s⁻¹, $u_v = 72$ m s⁻¹ (2 s.f.) [3]

2 $t = 7.4$ s, height = s_v after 7.4 s = 270 m, range = s_h after 2 × 7.4 s = 1400 m, assuming no air resistance (2 s.f.) [6]

3 a 5.7 s (2 s.f.) [2]

 b 31 m s⁻¹ (2 s.f.) [2]

9.5

1 160 J (2 s.f.) [2]

2 110 kW (2 s.f.) [2]

3 9.3 [5]

4 a 27 kJ [2]

b 77 kJ [3]

5 a 17 kW [3]

b 5300 N [2]

10.1

1 Number of half-lives = 6 [1]

Percentage remaining = $100\% \times \dfrac{1}{2^6}$ [1]

Percentage remaining = 1.6% [1]

2 Three half-lives have passed. [1]

half-life = $\dfrac{60 \text{ minutes}}{3}$ = 20 minutes [1]

3 Activity = $3.8 \times 10^{-12}\,\text{s}^{-1} \times 6 \times 10^{14}$ [1] = 2 kBq (1 s.f.) [1]

4 a 70 s [1]

b Initial count rate (from graph) = $11.2\,\text{s}^{-1}$ [1]

decay constant = $\dfrac{11.2}{10^3}$ = $0.01\,\text{s}^{-1}$ (1 s.f.) [1]

5 a 1 mark for each correctly completed row in Table 1, that is, the values shown in bold. [3]

▼ **Table 1**

Time elapsed / s	Number of nuclei N	Number decaying $\Delta N = \lambda N \Delta t$	Number remaining $= N - \Delta N$
0.0	24 000	$0.4 \times 24000 \times 0.5 = 4800$	$24000 - 4800 = 19\,200$
0.5	19 200	3840	15 360
1.0	15 360	3072	12 288
1.5	12 288	2458	9 830
2.0	9 830	1966	7 864

b Graph: correct points [1]

correct quantities and units on axes [1]

straight lines between points (as the rate of decay is assumed to be constant between calculations) [1]

c method shown on graph [1]

value $1.52\,\text{s} \pm 0.2\,\text{s}$ [1]

d Model gives shorter half-life because it assumes constant rate of decay during each interval. [1]

This reduces the number remaining more quickly [1]

reducing the half-life.

10.2

1 Half-life = $\dfrac{\ln 2}{1.5 \times 10^{-4}\,\text{s}}$ [1] = 4600 s (2 s.f.) [1]

2 Method 1:

Decay constant = $\dfrac{\ln 2}{3.1 \text{ min}}$

Activity = $1.7 \times 10^3\,\text{Bq} \times e^{-(\ln 2/3.1\,\text{min} \times 0.75\,\text{min})}$ [1]

Activity = $1.4 \times 10^3\,\text{Bq}$ [1]

Method 2:

Activity = $\dfrac{1.7 \times 10^3\,\text{Bq}}{2^{0.75/3.1}}$ [1]

Activity = $1.4 \times 10^3\,\text{Bq}$ [1]

3 $\ln A = \ln A_0 - \lambda t$

$\lambda t = \ln A_0 - \ln A$

$\lambda = \dfrac{\ln A_0 - \ln A}{76 \times 60\,\text{s}} = 5.04\ldots\,\text{s}^{-1}$ [1]

$T_{\frac{1}{2}} = \dfrac{\ln 2}{\lambda} = \dfrac{0.693\ldots}{5.04\ldots\,\text{s}^{-1}}$ [1]

$T_{\frac{1}{2}} = 1.4 \times 10^3\,\text{s}$ (2 s.f.) [1]

4 a $1.7\,\text{kBq} = A_0\,e^{-(\ln 2/5.00\,\text{days} \times 4.00\,\text{days})}$ [1]

$A_0 = 3.0\,\text{kBq}$ (2 s.f.) [1]

b Activity = $\lambda N = \dfrac{\ln 2}{5.00 \times 24 \times 60 \times 60\,\text{s}} \times 2 \times 10^{11}$ [1]

Activity = $3.2\ldots \times 10^5\,\text{Bq}$ [1]

Ratio of activity to corrected count rate

$= \dfrac{3.2 \times 10^5}{1.7 \times 10^3} = 190$ (2 s.f.) = 200 (1 s.f.) [1]

Not all the decays are detected as (it can be assumed that) the detector does not completely surround the source and some of the emitted particles may be stopped within the source. [1]

10.3

1 1 mark for each correctly completed row in Table 1, that is, the values shown in bold. [3]

▼ **Table 1**

Capacitance / F	Potential difference / V	Charge / C	Energy / J
4700×10^{-6}	9.50	0.0447	0.212
4.70×10^{-4}	8.75	4.11×10^{-3}	0.0180
6.90×10^{-4}	4.60	3.20×10^{-3}	7.36×10^{-3}

2 $V = \sqrt{\dfrac{2E}{C}} = \sqrt{\dfrac{2 \times 9.47\,\text{J}}{1.85 \times 10^{-4}\,\text{F}}}$ [1]

$V = 320\,\text{V}$ [1]

3 Ratio = $\dfrac{\frac{1}{2}CV_{1.5}^2}{\frac{1}{2}CV_{6.0}^2} = \dfrac{1.5^2}{6.0^2}$ [1]

Ratio = 0.0625 (0.063 to 2 s.f.) [1]

10.4

1 a $Q = 470 \times 10^{-6}\,\text{F} \times 6.0\,\text{V}$ [1]

$Q = 2.8 \times 10^{-3}\,\text{C}$ [1]

b $\tau = 4500\,\Omega \times 470 \times 10^{-6}\,\text{F}$ [1]

$\tau = 2.1\,\text{s}$ (2 s.f.) [1]

c $Q = \dfrac{470 \times 10^{-6}\,\text{F}}{e^3}$ [1]

$Q = 2.4 \times 10^{-5}\,\text{C}$ [1]

2 a $V = \dfrac{0.021\,\text{C}}{4700 \times 10^{-6}\,\text{F}}$ [1]

$V = 4.5\,\text{V}$ (2 s.f.) [1]

b $Q = 0.021 \times e^{-3.0/2000 \times 4700 \times 10^{-6}}$ [1]

$Q = 0.015\,\text{C}$ (2 s.f.) [1]

3 Units of $RC = \Omega \times \text{F} = \text{V A}^{-1} \times \text{C V}^{-1}$ [1]

Units of $RC = \text{C A}^{-1} = \text{C C}^{-1}\text{s}$ *[1]* $= \text{s}$ [1]

There are many different ways of manipulating the units, this is just one example.

4 $V_C = V_0(1 - e^{-t/RC})$

$\therefore V_0 - V_C = V_0 e^{-t/RC}$ [1]

$3 - 2 = 3\,e^{-t/11000 \times 220 \times 10^{-6}}$

$\ln 1 = \ln 3 - \dfrac{t}{2.42}$ [1]

$\therefore t = 2.65\,\text{s}$ [1]

There are other routes through this analysis.

5 $60\,\text{s} = 2\tau$

after 2τ seconds, charge on capacitor $= \dfrac{\text{original charge}}{e^2}$ [1]

As energy on a capacitor is proportional to (charge on the capacitor)²:

after 2τ seconds, energy on capacitor $= \dfrac{E}{(e^4)}$ [1]

$= 0.018E$ [1]

11.1

1 $f = \dfrac{1}{T} = \dfrac{1}{2.5 \times 10^{-4}\,\text{s}}$ [1]

$f = 4000\,\text{Hz}$ [1]

2 a $x = A \sin 2\pi ft = 0.03\,\text{m} \times \sin(2\pi \times 1.2\,\text{Hz} \times 0.25\,\text{s})$ [1]

$x = 0.029\,\text{m}$ (2 s.f.) [1]

b Maximum acceleration $= -4\pi^2 f^2 A$ [1]

Maximum acceleration $= -4\pi^2 \times 1.2^2\,\text{Hz}^2 \times 0.03\,\text{m}$
$= -1.7\,\text{m s}^{-2}$ [1]

(When the pendulum has a positive displacement, the acceleration is negative. When the displacement of the pendulum is negative, the acceleration is positive.)

3 a Acceleration $\propto -x$ *[1]*, isochronous oscillations [1]

b Ratio $= \dfrac{4\pi^2 f_A^2 A_A}{4\pi^2 f_B^2 A_B}$ [1]

(where f_A, f_B, A_A, and A_B are the frequencies and amplitudes of pendulums A and B)

As $f_A = 2f_B$ and $A_B = 2A_A$, the ratio =

$\dfrac{4\pi^2 2^2 f_B^2 A_A}{4\pi^2 f_B^2 2A_A} = \dfrac{4}{2} = 2$ [1]

11.2

1 a $x = A \sin \omega t$ [1]

b Velocity: sinusoidal curve of same time period as the acceleration curve. Velocity is at its maximum negative value at time $t = 0\,\text{s}$.

Displacement: sinusoidal curve of same time period as the acceleration curve. Displacement is at its minimum at time $t = 0\,\text{s}$. The curve is the mirror image around the x-axis of the acceleration curve. [2]

2 a Maximum velocity $= 2\pi fA =$
$2\pi \times 0.90\,\text{Hz} \times 0.030\,\text{m}$ [1]

Maximum velocity $= 0.17\,\text{m s}^{-1}$ [1]

b Maximum acceleration $= 4\pi^2 f^2 A =$
$4\pi^2 \times 0.90^2\,\text{Hz}^2 \times 0.030\,\text{m}$ [1]

Maximum acceleration $= 0.96\,\text{m s}^{-2}$ [1]

3 1 mark for each correctly completed row, as shown in bold Table 1. [4]

a

▼ Table 1

t/s	x/m	$a/\text{m s}^{-2}$	$\Delta v/\text{m s}^{-1}$	$v_{new}/\text{m s}^{-1}$	$\Delta x/\text{m}$
0.00	0.12	−3.6	0.0	0.0	0.0
0.05	0.12	−3.6	−0.18	−0.18	−0.0045
0.10	0.1155	−3.465	−0.17325	−0.35325	−0.01333
0.15	0.102169	−3.06506	−0.15325	−0.5065	−0.02149
0.20	0.080675	−2.42025	−0.12101	−0.62752	−0.02835
0.25	0.052324	−1.56973	−0.07849	−0.706	−0.03334
0.30	0.018987	−0.5696	−0.02848	−0.73448	−0.03601
0.35	−0.01703	0.510768	0.025538	−0.70894	−0.03609

b One quarter of a cycle takes between 0.30 s and 0.35 s. [1]

This suggests a complete cycles takes about 1.3 s [1]

c The displacement is held at 0.12 m for the first 0.05 s [1]

so the velocity values calculated are all underestimates so the change in displacements are also underestimates, suggesting it takes longer for the mass to pass through the equilibrium point. [1]

11.3

1 $T = 2\pi \sqrt{\dfrac{4}{g}}$ [1]

$T = 4.0\,\text{s}$ [1]

2 a $k = 4\pi^2 \times 0.7\,\text{kg} \times 0.85^2\,\text{s}^{-2}$ [1]

$k = 20\,\text{N m}^{-1}$ [1]

b Maximum acceleration $= 4\pi^2 \times 0.85^2\,\text{s}^{-2} \times 0.020\,\text{m}$ [1]

Maximum acceleration $= 0.79\,\text{m s}^{-2}$ [1]

3 $T = 2\pi\sqrt{\dfrac{L}{g}} \therefore L = \dfrac{gT^2}{4\pi^2}$ as the length of the pendulum is constant:

$T_{Moon}^2 = \dfrac{g_{Earth}}{g_{Moon}} T_{Earth}^2$ *[1]* $= 6.2 \times 2.8^2\,s^2 = 48.6(08)\,s^2$

$T_{Moon} = 7.0\,s$ *[1]*

4 $v_{max} = 2\pi f A \therefore f = \dfrac{v_{max}}{2\pi A} = 0.69...\,m\,s^{-1}$ *[1]*

Use this value in $f = \dfrac{1}{2\pi}\sqrt{\dfrac{k}{m}}$ to calculate

$k = 3.8\,N\,m^{-1}$ *[1]*

OR:

Rearrange the two equations above to

show $k = \dfrac{v_{max}^2}{A^2} \times m$ *[1]*

$k = 3.8\,N\,m^{-1}$ *[1]*

11.4

1 At the top (maximum displacement) of the swing the energy of the mass is gravitational potential energy because its velocity is zero. *[1]*

At the bottom all the energy is kinetic energy and in between these values the energy mix changes from potential energy only (top) through to kinetic energy only (bottom). *[1]*

2 Resonance: increased oscillations of a driven oscillator *[1]*

when (for light damping) natural frequency of oscillator = driving frequency. *[1]*

Driven oscillator: oscillators which have a periodically varying driving force applied to them.*[1]*

These oscillators will always oscillate at the frequency of the driving force. *[1]*

Light damping: damping occurs when energy removed from an oscillator during its cycle which reduces the amplitude of oscillation. *[1]*

Lightly damped oscillators have (relatively) little loss of energy per cycle so will make a number of complete oscillations before coming to rest. *[1]*

3 a Total energy is proportional to amplitude². Total energy will decrease by a factor of $\sqrt{2}$. *[1]*

(It is less elegant but acceptable to state that the new energy value will be 71% of the initial energy value.)

b The maximum kinetic energy will halve. Therefore, the maximum velocity will decrease by a factor of $\sqrt{2}$. *[1]*

c Maximum acceleration will halve. *[1]*

4 Kinetic energy at 0.03 m = total energy – potential energy at 0.03 m = 0.16 J – ($\dfrac{1}{2} \times 60\,N\,m^{-1} \times 0.03^2\,m^2$) *[1]*

Kinetic energy at 0.03 m = 0.16 J – 0.027 J = 0.133 J *[1]*

Therefore, velocity = $\sqrt{\dfrac{2 \times 0.133\,J}{0.4\,kg}} = 0.82\,m\,s^{-1}$ *[1]*

12.1

1 a $\dfrac{2\pi}{T} = \dfrac{6.283}{1.2\,s}$ *[1]*

$\omega = 5.24\,rad\,s^{-1}$ *[1]*

b Speed = $\omega r = 5.24\,rad\,s^{-1} \times 2.0\,m$ *[1]*

Speed = $10.5\,m\,s^{-1}$ *[1]*

c i No change *[1]*

ii Double *[1]*

2 (centripetal) force required to break thread = 20.0 N *[1]*

$F = \dfrac{mv^2}{r} \therefore v = \sqrt{\dfrac{20\,N \times 1.5\,m}{1.8\,kg}}$ *[1]*

$v = 4.1\,m\,s^{-1}$ *[1]*

3 a $F = \dfrac{mv^2}{r} = \dfrac{1000\,kg \times 6.7^2\,m^2\,s^2}{25\,m}$ *[1]*

$F = 1800\,N$ *[1]*

b Centripetal force is proportional to mass *[1]*

so a vehicle travelling at the same radius and speed will require a larger centripetal force. *[1]*

The frictional force between the tyres and the road surface may not be great enough (to provide sufficient centripetal force to keep the vehicle moving in a circle) leading to skidding.*[1]*

12.2

1 $F_{grav} = -\dfrac{GMm}{r^2} \therefore G = \dfrac{F_{grav}r^2}{Mm}$ *[1]*

The units of these quantities are $\dfrac{N\,m^2}{kg^2}$ *[1]* so units of G are $N\,m^2\,kg^{-2}$.

2 The weight of Armstrong and suit is the force with which the Moon attracts him to the surface:

$F_{grav} = -\dfrac{GMm}{r^2}$

$= \dfrac{6.7 \times 10^{-11}\,N\,m^2\,kg^{-2} \times 7.3 \times 10^{22}\,kg \times 160\,kg}{(1.7 \times 10^6\,m)^2}$ *[1]*

$F_{grav} = 270\,N$ (2 s.f.) *[1]*

3 a Field strength at $1.5 \times 10^7\,m$ above the surface = $-0.8\,N\,kg^{-1}$ *[1]*

Force = $mg = 10\,kg \times -0.8\,N\,kg^{-1} = -8.0\,N$ *[1]*

b i An inverse square relationship is one in which the value of one variable is proportional to the square of the inverse (reciprocal) of the value of the other. *[1]*

ii The graph has an intercept (at 0, –9.8). *[1]*

An inverse-square graph is asymptotic to both axes. *[1]*

(An asymptotic curve approaches the axis but never reaches it.)

4 a $-\dfrac{GMm}{R^2} = -\dfrac{mv^2}{R}$ *[1]*

$\therefore v^2 = \dfrac{GMmR}{R^2 m}$ *[1]*

$v^2 = \dfrac{GM}{R}$

(Note that for these type of questions you should show every step.)

b $v = \dfrac{2\pi R}{T} \therefore v^2 = \dfrac{4\pi^2 R^2}{T^2}$ *[1]*

$\therefore \dfrac{4\pi^2 R^2}{T^2} = \dfrac{GM}{R} \therefore \dfrac{4\pi^2 R^3}{T^2} = GM$ *[1]*

$\therefore R^3 = \dfrac{GMT^2}{4\pi^2}$

c $R = \sqrt[3]{\dfrac{6.7 \times 10^{-11}\,\text{N}\,\text{m}^2\,\text{kg}^{-2} \times 6.0 \times 10^{24}\,\text{kg} \times ((23 \times 60 \times 60\,\text{s}) + (56 \times 60\,\text{s}))^2}{4\pi^2}}$ *[1]*

$R = 4.2 \times 10^7\,\text{m}$ *[1]*

Height above surface = $4.23 \times 10^7\,\text{m} - 6.4 \times 10^6\,\text{m}$
$= 3.6 \times 10^7\,\text{m}$ (2 s.f.) *[1]*

12.3

1 a Change in potential energy = $1.7\,\text{N}\,\text{kg}^{-1} \times 1.8\,\text{m}$ *[1]*
Change in potential energy = $3.1\,\text{J}\,\text{kg}^{-1}$ (2 s.f.) *[1]*

b $v = \sqrt{2g\Delta h} = \sqrt{2 \times 1.7\,\text{N}\,\text{kg}^{-1} \times 1.8\,\text{m}}$ *[1]*
$v = 2.5\,\text{m}\,\text{s}^{-1}$ (2 s.f.) *[1]*

2 Vertical component of velocity = $\sin 30° \times 40\,\text{m}\,\text{s}^{-1} = 20\,\text{m}\,\text{s}^{-1}$ *[1]*

$v = \sqrt{2g\Delta h} \therefore \Delta h = \dfrac{v^2}{2g}$ *[1]*

$v = \dfrac{400\,\text{m}^2\,\text{s}^{-1}}{(2 \times 9.8\,\text{N}\,\text{kg}^{-1})} = 20\,\text{m}$ (2 s.f.) *[1]*

3 a Change in kinetic energy = change potential energy = $30\,\text{J}\,\text{kg}^{-1} \times 0.09\,\text{kg}$ *[1]*
change in kinetic energy = $2.7\,\text{J}$ *[1]*

b i No change in horizontal velocity so horizontal velocity = $30\,\text{m}\,\text{s}^{-1}$ *[1]*

ii Vertical velocity = $\sqrt{\dfrac{2 \times \text{kinetic energy}}{m}} = \sqrt{\dfrac{2 \times 2.7\,\text{J}}{0.09\,\text{kg}}}$ *[1]*

Vertical velocity = $7.7\,\text{m}\,\text{s}^{-1}$ *[1]*

iii Speed² = (vertical velocity)² + (horizontal velocity)² = $(7.7\,\text{m}\,\text{s}^{-1})^2 + (30\,\text{m}\,\text{s}^{-1})^2$ *[1]*
Speed = $31\,\text{m}\,\text{s}^{-1}$ *[1]*

12.4

1 a Gravitational potential energy is the energy of a body at a position in a gravitational field. *[1]*
Gravitational potential is the gravitational energy per kg at a position in a gravitational field. *[1]*

b Work is done (energy transferred) to reach a point of zero potential at infinity. *[1]*
Therefore, the initial potential (potential at energy separation less than infinite) must be less than zero, i.e., negative. *[1]*

2 a Potential energy =
$-\dfrac{6.7 \times 10^{-11}\,\text{N}\,\text{m}^2\,\text{kg}^{-2} \times 7.35 \times 10^{22}\,\text{kg} \times 2.0\,\text{kg}}{1.74 \times 10^6\,\text{m}}$ *[1]*
$= -5.7 \times 10^6\,\text{J}$ *[1]*

b $+5.7 \times 10^6\,\text{J}$ *[1]*
The potential energy at a great distance is zero. The kinetic energy is just sufficient to climb out of the potential well. *[1]*

c $v = \sqrt{\dfrac{2E_k}{m}}$ *[1]*
$v = 2.4 \times 10^3\,\text{m}\,\text{s}^{-1}$ *[1]*

d Total energy = $-\dfrac{GMm}{r} + \dfrac{1}{2}mv^2 = 0$

$\therefore \dfrac{1}{2}mv^2 = \dfrac{GMm}{r}$ *[1]*

$\therefore v^2 = \dfrac{2GMm}{mr}$ *[1]*

$\therefore v = \sqrt{\dfrac{GM}{r}}$

3 a Area between line and x-axis *[1]*
area of one big square = $2.5 \times 10^6\,\text{m} \times 1\,\text{N}\,\text{kg}^{-1}$
$= 2.5 \times 10^6\,\text{J}\,\text{kg}^{-1}$ *[1]*
Number of big squares is roughly 6.5 *[1]*
Potential difference = $6.5 \times 2.5 \times 10^6\,\text{J}\,\text{kg}^{-1} = 1.6 \times 10^7\,\text{J}\,\text{kg}^{-1}$ *[1]*

b Calculation of V_g at height of $15 \times 10^6\,\text{m}$ gives value: $-1.878 \times 10^7\,\text{J}\,\text{kg}^{-1}$ *[1]*
Calculation of V_g at height of $5 \times 10^6\,\text{m}$ gives value: $-3.526 \times 10^7\,\text{J}\,\text{kg}^{-1}$ *[1]*
Potential difference = $1.65 \times 10^7\,\text{J}\,\text{kg}^{-1}$ *[1]*

13.1

1 a Distance in light-seconds $= \dfrac{1.5 \times 10^{11}\,\text{m}}{3.0 \times 10^8\,\text{m s}^{-1}}$ *[1]*

Distance in light-seconds $= 500\,\text{s}$ (8.3 minutes) *[1]*

b Distance in metres $= 8.6 \times 3.2 \times 10^7\,\text{s} \times 3.0 \times 10^8\,\text{m s}^{-1}$ *[1]*

Distance in metres $= 8.3 \times 10^{16}\,\text{m}$ *[1]*

2 10 minute walk covers about $10^3\,\text{m}$. Earth–Sun distance is about $10^{11}\,\text{m}$ *[1]*

time to walk from the Earth to the Sun $= 10^8 \times 10$ minutes *[1]*

time to walk from the Earth to the Sun $= 6 \times 10^{10}\,\text{s} = 1900$ years (2 s.f.) *[1]*

3 Suggested calculations:

- time delay between emission and detection:

$= \dfrac{2 \times 6 \times 10^{12}\,\text{m}}{3.0 \times 10^8\,\text{m s}^{-1}}$ *[1]*

$= 4 \times 10^4\,\text{s}$ *[1]* (about 11 hours)

- proportion of original energy incident per m²:

$= \dfrac{1}{(2 \times \pi \times (6 \times 10^{12}\,\text{m})^2)}$ *[1]*

$= 4.4 \times 10^{-27}\,\text{m}^{-2}$ *[1]*

Assuming that all the energy is released into a hemisphere in front of the emitter. *[1]*

Discussion points include:

- Problems arising from delay time (e.g., difficulty in detecting reflection because the Earth has undergone a half-revolution in the interval). *[1]*

- The signal will be further weakened on the return. *[1]*

13.2

1 $\dfrac{R_{\text{observed}}}{R_{\text{emitted}}} = 1 + z = 1 + 0.22 = 1.22$

$\therefore R_{\text{observed}} = 1.22\, R_{\text{emitted}}$ *[1]*

The Universe has expanded by about 22% since the light was emitted from the galaxy. *[1]*

2 Microwave background is red-shifted light from the time the Universe became transparent. *[1]*

This radiation has been travelling through the Universe for the longest time. *[1]*

3 Calculate age for lowest and highest value of H_0:

Lowest value of $H_0 = 67.00\,\text{km s}^{-1}\,\text{Mpc}^{-1}$

$= \dfrac{67\,000\,\text{m s}^{-1}}{3.09 \times 10^{22}\,\text{m}} = 2.168\ldots \times 10^{-18}\,\text{s}^{-1}$ *[1]*

Age $= \dfrac{1}{H_0} = 4.6\ldots 10^{17}\,\text{s} = 1.44 \times 10^{10}$ years *[1]*

Highest value of $H_0 = 70.12\,\text{km s}^{-1}\,\text{Mpc}^{-1}$

$= \dfrac{70\,120\,\text{m s}^{-1}}{3.09 \times 10^{22}\,\text{m}} = 2.26\ldots 10^{-18}\,\text{s}^{-1}$ *[1]*

Age $= \dfrac{1}{H_0} = 4.4\ldots \times 10^{17}\,\text{s} = 1.38 \times 10^{10}$ years *[1]*

Note that this gives the same answer to 2 s.f., the number of significant figures in the least precise value.

13.3

1 a The worldline is sloping. *[1]*

b The slope of the worldline is less than 45° from the vertical. *[1]*

2 $\gamma = \dfrac{1}{\sqrt{1 - \dfrac{v^2}{c^2}}} = \dfrac{1}{\sqrt{1 - \dfrac{(0.5c)^2}{c^2}}}$ *[1]*

$\gamma = \dfrac{1}{\sqrt{1 - 0.25}} = \dfrac{1}{\sqrt{0.75}} = 1.15$ *[1]*

3 $\gamma = \dfrac{1}{\sqrt{1 - \dfrac{v^2}{c^2}}} = \dfrac{1}{\sqrt{1 - \dfrac{(2.9 \times 10^8\,\text{m s}^{-1})^2}{(3.0 \times 10^8\,\text{m s}^{-1})^2}}}$ *[1]*

$\gamma = \dfrac{1}{\sqrt{1 - 0.934\ldots}} = 3.9$ *[1]*

4 observed half-life $t = \dfrac{0.7\,ns}{\sqrt{1 - \dfrac{(0.99c)^2}{c^2}}}$ *[1]*

observed half-life $t = \dfrac{0.7\,\text{ns}}{\sqrt{1 - 0.98}} = \dfrac{0.7\,\text{ns}}{\sqrt{0.0199}}$

$= 5\,\text{ns}$ (2 s.f.) *[1]*

5 $2.5 = \dfrac{1}{\sqrt{1 - \dfrac{v^2}{c^2}}} \therefore \sqrt{1 - \dfrac{v^2}{c^2}} = \dfrac{1}{2.5} \therefore 1 - \dfrac{v^2}{c^2}$

$= \dfrac{1}{2.5^2} \therefore \dfrac{v^2}{c^2} = 1 - \dfrac{1}{2.5^2}$

$\therefore v^2 = c^2 \left(1 - \dfrac{1}{2.5^2}\right)$ *[1]*

$\therefore v = \sqrt{c^2 \left(1 - \dfrac{1}{2.5^2}\right)} = \sqrt{(3.0 \times 10^8\,\text{m s}^{-1})^2 \left(1 - \dfrac{1}{2.5^2}\right)}$ *[1]*

$v = 2.75 \times 10^8\,\text{m s}^{-1}$ *[1]*

Note that there are a number of ways of performing this calculation and confident mathematicians might choose to do it all in one step. However, it is best to include intermediate steps so that you can gain credit from these even if you make an arithmetical error at some point.

14.1

1 a 298 K *[1]*

b Number of moles $= \dfrac{9.6\,\text{g}}{32\,\text{g mol}^{-1}} = 0.3\,\text{mol}$ *[1]*

c 1.8×10^{23} molecules of O_2 *[1]*

d $P = \dfrac{0.3\,\mathrm{mol} \times 8.31\,\mathrm{J\,mol^{-1}\,K^{-1}} \times 2.98\,\mathrm{K}}{2.5 \times 10^{-3}\,\mathrm{m^3}}$ *[1]*

$= 3.0 \times 10^5\,\mathrm{Pa}$ *[1]*

2 Initial number of moles of nitrogen = 2 mol

As $pV = nRT$ and V and T are constant:

$\dfrac{p_1}{n_1} = \dfrac{p_2}{n_2}$

$\therefore n_2 = \dfrac{p_2 \times n_1}{p_1} = \dfrac{4.7 \times 10^5\,\mathrm{Pa} \times 2\,\mathrm{mol}}{4.1 \times 10^5\,\mathrm{Pa}}$ *[1]*

$n_2 = 2.29\,\mathrm{mol}$ *[1]*

Gas added = 2.29 mol − 2.0 mol = 0.29 mol *[1]*

3 Total number of moles of gas = 0.5 mol + 2.5 mol = 3.0 mol *[1]*

$\text{Pressure} = \dfrac{3.0\,\mathrm{mol} \times 8.31\,\mathrm{J\,mol^{-1}\,K^{-1}} \times 300\,\mathrm{K}}{2.0 \times 10^{-2}\,\mathrm{m^3}}$ *[1]*

$\text{Pressure} = 3.7 \times 10^5\,\mathrm{Pa}$ *[1]*

14.2

1 a Kinetic energy $= \dfrac{3}{2}kT = 6.2 \times 10^{-21}\,\mathrm{J}$ *[1]*

b Mass of molecule $= \dfrac{32 \times 10^{-3}\,\mathrm{kg}}{6.0 \times 10^{23}} = 5.3 \times 10^{-26}\,\mathrm{kg}$

$\sqrt{\overline{c^2}} = \sqrt{\dfrac{2 \times 6.2 \times 10^{-21}\,\mathrm{J}}{5.3 \times 10^{-26}\,\mathrm{kg}}}$ *[1]*

$\sqrt{\overline{c^2}} = 4.8 \times 10^2\,\mathrm{m\,s^{-1}}$ (2 s.f.) *[1]*

2 a Mass of molecule $= \dfrac{29 \times 10^{-3}\,\mathrm{kg}}{6.0 \times 10^{23}} = 4.8 \times 10^{-26}\,\mathrm{kg}$

Kinetic energy of molecules $= 6.1 \times 10^{-21}\,\mathrm{J}$ *[1]*

$\sqrt{\overline{c^2}} = \sqrt{\dfrac{2 \times 6.1 \times 10^{-21}\,\mathrm{J}}{4.8 \times 10^{-26}\,\mathrm{kg}}}$ *[1]*

$\sqrt{\overline{c^2}} = 5.0 \times 10^2\,\mathrm{m\,s^{-1}}$ (2 s.f.) *[1]*

b $N = \dfrac{pv}{kT} = \dfrac{350\,\mathrm{Pa} \times 6.5 \times 10^{-4}\,\mathrm{m^3}}{1.38 \times 10^{-23}\,\mathrm{J\,K^{-1}} \times 295\,\mathrm{K}}$ *[1]*

$N = 5.6 \times 10^{19}$ molecules *[1]*

(about 0.0001 mol)

3 When the temperature doubles, the r.m.s. speed increases by a factor of $\sqrt{2}$. Therefore, the total distance moved in the same time increases by a factor of $\sqrt{2}$. Therefore, the number of steps N increases by a factor of $\sqrt{2}$.

As displacement $\propto \sqrt{N}$ the displacement will increase by a factor of $\sqrt{\sqrt{2}} = \sqrt[4]{2}$ *[1]*

so displacement $= \sqrt[4]{2} \times 0.05 = 0.06$ (1 s.f.) *[1]*

14.3

1 $\Delta\theta = \dfrac{1.2 \times 10^3\,\mathrm{W} \times 4.0 \times 60\,\mathrm{s}}{4.2 \times 10^3\,\mathrm{J\,kg^{-1}\,K^{-1}} \times 1.5\,\mathrm{kg}} = 46\,\mathrm{K} = 46$ *[1]*

Final temperature $= 20\,^\circ\mathrm{C} + 46\,^\circ\mathrm{C} = 66\,^\circ\mathrm{C}$ *[1]*

assuming no energy lost to surroundings *[1]*

2 $3.8\,^\circ\mathrm{C}$ per minute $= 0.063\,^\circ\mathrm{C\,s^{-1}} = 0.063\,\mathrm{K\,s^{-1}}$

$c = \dfrac{48\,\mathrm{J\,s^{-1}}}{0.8\,\mathrm{kg} \times 0.063\,\mathrm{K\,s^{-1}}}$ *[1]*

$c = 950\,\mathrm{J\,kg^{-1}\,K^{-1}}$ *[1]*

3 Increase of internal energy of cool water = decrease in internal energy of warm water

Therefore, indicating specific thermal capacity by c and final temperature by θ_f:

$1.4 \times c \times (\theta_f - 40\,^\circ\mathrm{C}) = 0.2 \times c \times (80\,^\circ\mathrm{C} - \theta_f)$

$\therefore 1.4(\theta_f - 40\,^\circ\mathrm{C}) = 0.2(80\,^\circ\mathrm{C} - \theta_f)$ *[1]*

$\therefore \theta_f = 45\,^\circ\mathrm{C}$ *[1]*

15.1 and 15.2

1 $\ln 1.0 \times 10^{-8} = -\dfrac{E}{kT}$ *[1]*

$\dfrac{E}{kT} = 18.4$ *[1]*

2 1 mark for each correct entry, shown in bold in Table 1. *[6]*

▼ **Table 1**

$E\,/\,\mathrm{J}$	$T\,/\,\mathrm{K}$	$\dfrac{E}{kT}$	$f = e^{-E/kT}$
3×10^{-19}	**870**	25	**1.4×10^{-11}**
3×10^{-19}	600	**36**	**1.8×10^{-16}**
1.9×10^{-19}	550	**25**	1.9×10^{-11}

3 Proportion dissociated $= f = e^{-3.5 \times 10^{-19}\,\mathrm{J}/1.38 \times 10^{-23}\,\mathrm{J\,K^{-1}} \times 298\,\mathrm{K}}$ *[1]*

Proportion dissociated $= 1.1 \times 10^{-37}$ *[1]*

4 Using $\ln\left(\dfrac{r_2}{r_1}\right) = \dfrac{E}{k}\left(\dfrac{1}{T_1} - \dfrac{1}{T_2}\right)$:

$\ln\left(\dfrac{0.16}{0.04}\right) = \dfrac{E}{k}\left(\dfrac{1}{900} - \dfrac{1}{1000}\right)$ *[1]*

$1.386... = \dfrac{E}{k}\left(\dfrac{1}{9000}\right)$ *[1]*

$E = 9000\,\mathrm{K} \times 1.4 \times 10^{-23}\,\mathrm{J\,K^{-1}} \times 1.386... = 1.75 \times 10^{-19}\,\mathrm{J}$ *[1]*

16.1

1 a $\dfrac{3.0 \times 10^{-4}\,\mathrm{Wb}}{600} = 5.0 \times 10^{-7}\,\mathrm{Wb}$ *[1]*

b $\dfrac{5.0 \times 10^{-7}\,\mathrm{Wb}}{2.2 \times 10^{-5}\,\mathrm{m^2}}$ *[1]*

$= 2.3 \times 10^{-2}\,\mathrm{Wb\,m^{-2}}$ *[1]*

2 4.0 V [1]

3 e.m.f. = rate of change of flux linkage [1]

$$= \frac{200(1.6\times10^{-6}\,\text{Wb} - 0.8\times10^{-6}\,\text{Wb})}{0.42}$$ [1]

e.m.f. = 3.8×10^{-4} V [1]

4 Area of coil = $5.0\times10^{-3}\,\text{m}^2$ [1]

Initial flux linkage through coil

= $500 \times 5.0\times10^{-3}\,\text{m}^2 \times 3.2\times10^{-4}\,\text{Wb}\,\text{m}^{-2} = 8.0\times10^{-4}$ Wb

Change in flux linkage during field

reversal = 1.6×10^{-3} Wb [1]

e.m.f. induced = $\dfrac{1.6\times10^{-3}\,\text{Wb}}{0.4\,\text{s}} = 4.0\times10^{-3}$ V [1]

16.2

1 ▼ Table 1

V_P	I_P	V_S	I_S
12.0 V	0.016 mA	150 V	0.20 mA

[2]

2 a 120 V [1]

 b Air has a much lower permeability than iron [1]
 so the permeance of the circuit is reduced [1]
 (maximum) flux in the core is reduced [1]
 e.m.f. across secondary is reduced. [1]

3 Remember that your answers to longer-response questions need to be clear and logical. You should not use bullet points as your answer should be more than a list of statements.

Here are some valid points of physics. Note that there are more than six. They have been given bullet points, but your answer should not be just a series of bullet points. You need to present a clear argument. An example is given below the bullet points.

 • Alternating current in the primary produces alternating flux in core

 • (which induces alternating e.m.f. in the core) which produces eddy currents which circle around the flux lines.

 • Eddy currents produce their own flux

 • which opposes the flux producing them.

 • Efficiency of transformer is reduced as energy transferred as thermal energy.

 • Laminations of thin sheets of insulation

 • placed between sheets of iron

 • reduce eddy currents and hence reduce power losses.

Example response gaining six marks:

The alternating current in the primary produces an alternating flux in the core of the transformer [1] which produces currents which circle the flux lines [1]. The flux produced by the eddy currents [1] opposes the flux which produced them [1]. Laminations reduce eddy currents as the laminations consist of layers of insulation [1] which cut across

the direction of the eddy currents and so reduce their effect which reduces the power loss in the transformer. [1]

16.3

1 a The induced e.m.f. has maximum magnitude at this point [1]
 because the gradient represents rate of change of flux linkage and $\varepsilon = (-)N\dfrac{\Delta\Phi}{\Delta t}$ [1]

 b Rate of change of flux linkage is (instantaneously) zero at maximum $N\Phi$. [1]
 This is shown by the gradient of zero at these (turning) points. [1]

 c $\varepsilon = -N\dfrac{\Delta\Phi}{\Delta t}$, induced e.m.f. is the negative of the rate of change of flux linkage. [1]

2 $\varepsilon = \text{v}LB \therefore B = \dfrac{\varepsilon}{\text{v}L} = \dfrac{2.4\,\text{V}}{3.2\,\text{m}\,\text{s}^{-1}\times0.4\,\text{m}}$ [1]

 $B = 1.9\,\text{Wb}\,\text{m}^{-2}$ [1]

3 a Flux linkage = $28.0\,\text{mWb}\,\text{m}^{-2}\times6.4\times10^{-3}\,\text{m}^2\times400$ [1]
 Flux linkage = $0.07(168)$ Wb [1]

 b Quarter of a rotation takes $\dfrac{1}{(30\,\text{s}^{-1}\times4)} = 0.0083\,\text{s}$ [1]

 Average e.m.f. = $\dfrac{\text{change in flux linkage}}{\text{time}}$

 $= \dfrac{0.07(168)\,\text{Wb}}{0.0083\,\text{s}} = 8.6\,\text{V}$ [1]

 This is an average because the rate of change of flux linkage is not constant over the time interval. [1]

16.4

1 $F = 2.3\,\text{A}\times0.28\,\text{m}\times4.8\times10^{-3}\,\text{T}$ [1]
 $F = 3.1\times10^{-3}\,\text{N}$ [1]

2 Force per centimetre = 1.6×0.14 [1]
 Force per centimetre = $0.22\,\text{N}\,\text{cm}^{-1}$ [1]

3 a Current in horizontal section is at right angles to the field. Current in vertical sections is parallel to the field. [1]

 b Force resolution of balance = $0.0001\,\text{kg}\times9.8\,\text{N}\,\text{kg}^{-1} = 0.0098\,\text{N}$ [1]

 Smallest detectable difference in current ΔI will produce a change of force = $0.0098\,\text{N}$ [1]

 $\Delta I = \dfrac{0.0098\,\text{N}}{(0.040\,\text{m}\times180\times10^{-3}\,\text{T})}$ [1]

 $\Delta I = 1.4\,\text{A}$ (2 s.f.) [1]

17.1

1 a 252 V (250 V to 2 s.f.) [1]

 b $F = Eq = 6000\,\text{V}\,\text{m}^{-1}\times1.6\times10^{-19}\,\text{C} = 9.6\times10^{-16}\,\text{N}$ [1]

2 Both lines curving [1] so that equipotential lines cross field lines at right angles. [1]

3 p.d. $= \dfrac{2.6\times10^{-18}\,\text{J}}{3.2\times10^{-19}\,\text{C}} = 8.1\,\text{V}$ *[1]*

4 a $E = \dfrac{V}{d} = 10^5\,\text{V}\,\text{m}^{-1}$ *[1]*

b $mg = \dfrac{qV}{d} \therefore q = \dfrac{mgd}{V}$

$= \dfrac{(9.8\times10^{-15}\,\text{kg}\times9.8\,\text{N}\,\text{kg}^{-1}\times5.2\times10^{-3}\,\text{m})}{520\,\text{V}}$ *[1]*

$q = 9.6\times10^{-19}\,\text{C}$ *[1]*

This is the charge of six electrons.

c The source will ionise the air in between the plates. *[1]* The ions will be attracted towards the charge on the oil drop *[1]* and will neutralise the charge. *[1]* This will reduce the upward force on the drop *[1]* so the weight of the drop is greater than the upward force   *[1]*

17.2

1 Kinetic energy of electron (E_k) =
$700\,\text{J}\,\text{C}^{-1}\times1.6\times10^{-19}\,\text{C} = 1.12\times10^{-16}\,\text{J}$ *[1]*

$v = \sqrt{\dfrac{2E_k}{m}} = \sqrt{\dfrac{2\times1.12\times10^{-16}\,\text{J}}{1.9\times10^{-31}\,\text{kg}}}$ *[1]*

$v = 1.6\times10^7\,\text{m}\,\text{s}^{-1}$ *[1]*

2 a $r = \dfrac{mv}{qB} = \dfrac{1.9\times10^{-31}\,\text{kg}\times2.0\times10^6\,\text{m}\,\text{s}^{-1}}{1.6\times10^{-19}\,\text{C}\times0.0012\,T}$ *[1]*

$r = 0.002\,\text{m}$ (2 s.f.)   *[1]*

b The radius will be $1800\times$ the answer to **a** = 3.6 m   *[1]*

c The speed of the particle is decreasing.   *[1]*
$v = \dfrac{qBr}{m}$ and r is decreasing whilst the other variables are held constant.   *[1]*

3 a Kinetic energy of electron (E_k)=
$900\,\text{J}\,\text{C}^{-1}\times1.6\times10^{-19}\,\text{C} = 1.4(4)\times10^{-16}\,\text{J}$ *[1]*

$v = \sqrt{\dfrac{2E_k}{m}} = \sqrt{\dfrac{2\times1.44\times10^{-16}\,\text{J}}{1.9\times10^{-31}\,\text{kg}}}$

$= 1.79\times10^7\,\text{m}\,\text{s}^{-1} \approx 1.8\times10^7\,\text{m}\,\text{s}^{-1}$ *[1]*

b $F = qE = q\dfrac{V}{d} = 1.6\times10^{-19}\,\text{C}\times\dfrac{300\,V}{0.090\,m}$ *[1]*

$F = 5.333\times10^{-16}\,\text{N} \approx 5.3\times10^{-16}\,\text{N}$ *[1]*

c This part requires you to remember the equations of accelerated motion. Time for electron to travel through the deflection region at constant horizontal velocity of $1.79\times10^7\,\text{m}\,\text{s}^{-1}$

$= \dfrac{\text{distance}}{\text{speed}} = \dfrac{0.12\,\text{m}}{1.79\times10^7\,\text{m}\,\text{s}^{-1}} = 6.7\times10^{-9}\,\text{s}$ *[1]*

$\text{acceleration} = \dfrac{F}{m} = \dfrac{5.3\times10^{-16}\,\text{N}}{1.9\times10^{-31}\,\text{kg}}$

$= 2.789...\times10^{15}\,\text{m}\,\text{s}^{-2}$ *[1]*

$s = ut + \dfrac{1}{2}at^2$

Initial velocity is zero so:

$s = +\dfrac{1}{2}at^2 = \dfrac{1}{2}\times2.789...\times10^{15}\,\text{m}\,\text{s}^{-1}\times(6.7\times10^{-9}\,\text{s})^2$ *[1]*

$s = 0.063\,\text{m} \approx 0.06\,\text{m}$ or 6 cm   *[1]*

17.3

1 a $F_{electric} = k\dfrac{Qq}{r^2} = 9.0\times10^9\,\text{N}\,\text{m}^2\,\text{C}^{-2}$

$\times \dfrac{+1.6\times10^{-19}\,C \times(-1.6\times10^{-19}\,C)}{(1.0\times10^{-10}\,\text{m})^2}$ *[1]*

$F_{electric} = 2.3\times10^{-8}\,\text{N}$ *[1]*

b Potential energy $= k\dfrac{qQ}{r} = 9.0\times10^9\,\text{N}\,\text{m}^2\,\text{C}^{-2}$

$\times \dfrac{+1.6\times10^{-19}\,C \times(-1.6\times10^{-19})C}{1.0\times10^{-10}\,\text{m}}$ *[1]*

Potential energy $= = 2.3\times10^{-18}\,\text{J}$ *[1]* $= 14\,\text{eV}$ *[1]*

2 Remember, the radius of the sphere is 0.10 m.

a Potential $1/r$ where r is the distance to the centre of the sphere. At a distance of 0.1 m from the surface the distance of the sphere has doubled so the potential will halve: $V = 400\,\text{V}$ *[1]*

b At a distance of 0.3 m from the surface the distance of the sphere has increased by a factor of fours, so the potential will quarter: $V = 200\,\text{V}$ *[1]*

3 a $V_{electric} = k\dfrac{Q}{r} = 9.0\times10^9\,\text{N}\,\text{m}^2\,\text{C}^{-2} \times \dfrac{+1.2\times10^{-9}\,C}{0.054\,\text{m}}$ *[1]*

$V_{electric} = 200\,\text{V}$ *[1]*

b Potential energy of electron at the surface of the sphere $= 200\,\text{V}\times(1.6\times10^{-19})\,\text{C}$

Potential energy of electron at the surface of the sphere $= -3.2\times10^{-17}\,\text{J}$ *[1]*

Potential energy of electron when a great distance from sphere = 0 J

Therefore, work done in moving electron to a great distance from sphere $= 0\,\text{J} - (-3.2\times10^{-17})\,\text{J}$
$= +3.2\times10^{-17}\,\text{J}$ *[1]*

18.1

1 charge $= 26\times1.6\times10^{-19}\,\text{C}$ *[1]* $= 4.2\times10^{-18}\,\text{C}$ (2 s.f.)   *[1]*

2 a Less deflection than original path   *[1]*
Maximum curvature at nearest point to nucleus *[1]*

b Greater deflection   *[1]*
Greater charge on nucleus so greater (repulsive force)   *[1]*

c No change to deflection *[1]* as no change in charge of nucleus   *[1]*

3 Potential energy of alpha particle at closest approach to nucleus = $k\dfrac{Q_{alpha}Q_{nucleus}}{separation}$ ∴

$3.84 \times 10^{-13}\,J =$

$\dfrac{8.9 \times 10^{9}\,N\,m^{2}\,C^{-2} \times 1.6 \times 10^{-19}\,C \times 79 \times 1.6 \times 10^{-19}\,C}{r}$ [1]

$r = \dfrac{8.9 \times 10^{9}\,N\,m^{2}\,C^{-2} \times 1.6 \times 10^{-19}\,C \times 1.264 \times 10^{-17}\,C}{3.84 \times 10^{-13}\,J}$ [1]

$r = 4.7 \times 10^{-14}\,m$ [1]

18.2

1 $E_{rest} = mc^{2} = 6.64 \times 10^{-27}\,kg \times (3.0 \times 10^{8}\,m\,s^{-1})^{2} =$
$5.976 \times 10^{-10}\,J$ [1]
(no intermediate rounding)
Convert joules to GeV $= \dfrac{6.0 \times 10^{-10}\,J}{1.6 \times 10^{-19}\,J\,eV^{-1}} = 3.7\,GeV$ [1]

2 a Kinetic energy = 0.9 MeV =
$0.9 \times 10^{6}\,MeV \times 1.6 \times 10^{-19}\,J\,eV^{-1}$ [1]
Kinetic energy $= 1.4 \times 10^{-13}\,J$ [1]

b Relativistic factor $= 1 + \dfrac{kinetic\ energy}{rest\ energy}$

$= 1 + \dfrac{0.9\ Mev}{0.51\ MeV}$ [1]

Relativistic factor = 2.8 [1]

c $2.8 = \dfrac{1}{\sqrt{1 - \dfrac{v^{2}}{c^{2}}}}$ ∴ $\sqrt{1 - \dfrac{v^{2}}{c^{2}}} = \dfrac{1}{2.8}$

∴ $1 - \dfrac{v^{2}}{c^{2}} = \dfrac{1}{2.8^{2}}$ ∴ $\dfrac{v^{2}}{c^{2}} = 1 - \dfrac{1}{2.8^{2}}$

∴ $v^{2} = c^{2}\left(1 - \dfrac{1}{2.8^{2}}\right)$ [1]

∴ $v = \sqrt{c^{2}\left(1 - \dfrac{1}{2.8^{2}}\right)} = \sqrt{(3.0 \times 10^{8}\,m\,s^{-1})^{2}\left(1 - \dfrac{1}{2.8^{2}}\right)}$ [1]

$v = 2.8 \times 10^{8}\,m\,s^{-1}$ [1]

3 1 mark for each bold answer in Table 1. [2]

▼ **Table 1**

$\dfrac{v}{c}$	γ
0.1	1.005
0.4	**1.1**
0.75	1.5

4 $\sin\theta \approx \dfrac{1.22\lambda}{nuclear\ diameter}$

As this question concerns high energy electrons you can also write $\lambda \approx \dfrac{hc}{E}$

∴ nuclear diameter $\approx \dfrac{1.22hc}{E\sin\theta}$ [1]

Electron energy in J $= 280 \times 10^{6}\,eV \times 1.6 \times 10^{-19}\,J\,eV^{-1}$ [1]

Nuclear diameter
$\approx \dfrac{1.22 \times 6.6 \times 10^{-34}\,J\,s \times 3.0 \times 10^{8}\,m\,s^{-1}}{280 \times 10^{6}\,eV \times 1.6 \times 10^{-19}\,J\,eV^{-1} \times \sin 22°}$ [1]

Nuclear diameter $= 1.4 \times 10^{-14}\,m$ [1]

18.3

1 a 1 mark for each value: $^{220}_{86}Rn$ [2]

b $224 - 88 = 136$ [1]

2 $224 \times 3 = 672$ [1]

3 Proton: uud [1]
Neutron: ddu [1]
Antiproton: $\bar{u}\,\bar{u}\,\bar{d}$ [1]
Antineutron: $\bar{d}\,\bar{d}\,\bar{u}$ [1]

18.4

1 Nucleon number before decay: 90. Nucleon number after decay : 90 + 0 + 0 = 90 [1]
Lepton number before decay: 0. Lepton number after decay : 0 + 1 + −1 = 0 [1]
Proton number before decay: 38. Proton number after decay : 39 + −1 + 0 = 38 As proton number and lepton number have been conserved, the charge has been conserved [1]

2 If the electron and positron collide with kinetic energy greater than zero the total energy of the particles is bigger. [1]
If the kinetic energy of the annihilating particles is great enough, particles of greater rest energy than the annihilating particles can be created. [1]

3 Rest energy of tau–antitau pair =
$2 \times 3.2 \times 10^{-27}\,kg \times (3 \times 10^{8}\,m\,s^{-1})^{2}$ [1]
Rest energy of tau–antitau pair $= 5.7 \times 10^{-10}\,J$ [1]

18.5

1 Energy change $= -2.6 \times 10^{-19}\,J - -6.0 \times 10^{-19}\,J$
$= 3.4 \times 10^{-19}\,J$ [1]

$\lambda = \dfrac{hc}{e} = \dfrac{6.6 \times 10^{-34}\,J\,s \times 3 \times 10^{8}\,m\,s^{-1}}{3.4 \times 10^{-19}\,J}$ [1]

$\lambda = 5.8 \times 10^{-10}\,m$ [1]

2 a $-13.6\,eV = -13.6 \times 1.6 \times 10^{-19}\,J = -2.18 \times 10^{-19}\,J$ [1]

b This is the energy when the electron is at the $n = 1$ level (or at the ground state). [1]
The ionisation energy is the required to remove an electron from the ground state. [1]

c $n = 1$: energy $= -2.18 \times 10^{-19}\,J$
$n = 2$: energy $= -5.45 \times 10^{-20}\,J$ [1]
$n = 3$: energy $= -2.42 \times 10^{-20}\,J$ [1]
$n = 4$: energy $= -1.36 \times 10^{-20}\,J$ [1]
correct diagram [1]

3 a $E_k = \dfrac{h^2}{2m\lambda^2}$

$$= \dfrac{(6.6 \times 10^{-34}\,\text{J s})^2}{2 \times 9.1 \times 10^{-31}\,\text{kg} \times (3.2 \times 10^{-10}\,\text{m})^2}$$ *[1]*

$E_k = 2.4 \times 10^{-18}\,\text{J}$ *[1]*

b Wavelength of electron in atom of radius
$8.0 \times 10^{-11}\,\text{m} = 3.2 \times 10^{-10}\,\text{m}$ *[1]*

E_p of electron $8.0 \times 10^{-11}\,\text{m}$ from proton =

$\dfrac{1}{4\pi\varepsilon_0} \times \dfrac{1.6 \times 10^{-19}\,\text{C} \times (-1.6 \times 10^{-19}\,\text{C})}{8.0 \times 10^{-11}\,\text{m}}$ *[1]*

E_p of electron $= -2.9 \times 10^{-18}\,\text{J}$ *[1]*

Total energy $= -2.9 \times 10^{-18}\,\text{J} + 2.4 \times 10^{-18}\,\text{J} = -5 \times 10^{-19}\,\text{J}$

Negative total energy shows electron can be bound in the atom. *[1]*

19.1

1 Number of ionisations $= \dfrac{5\,MeV}{14\,eV}$ *[1]*

Number of ionisations $= 3.6 \times 10^5$
ionisations (2 s.f.) *[1]*

2 Remove the source or ensure that any sources are far from the detector. *[1]*
Record the number of counts over a given time interval (a few minutes). *[1]*
Divide the counts recorded by the time interval in seconds to find the background count rate. *[1]*

3 Alpha particles are absorbed by a few centimetres of air *[1]*

so the alpha particles will transfer their energy to the air (and become helium atoms) before reaching the body. *[1]*

Alpha particles from a source within the body will be absorbed in the region close to the source, *[1]*
transferring energy to body tissue and causing cell damage. *[1]*

4 $I = I_0 e^{-\mu x} \therefore \ln I = \ln I_0 - \mu x$ *[1]*

$\therefore \ln\dfrac{I}{I_0} = -\mu x$

When the count rate falls to half its original value
$\dfrac{I}{I_0} = \dfrac{1}{2}$

This happens after one half-thickness, $x_{1/2}$.

$\ln\dfrac{1}{2} = -\mu x_{1/2}$ *[1]*

So, $x_{1/2} = \dfrac{\ln 2}{\mu}$ or $\mu = \dfrac{\ln 2}{x_{1/2}}$ *[1]*

5 a $\ln\dfrac{I}{I_0} = -\mu x \therefore \ln\dfrac{520}{600} = -\mu \times 0.002\,\text{m}$ *[1]*

$\therefore \mu = -\dfrac{\ln\dfrac{520}{600}}{0.002\,\text{m}} = 72\,\text{m}^{-1}$ *[1]*

b $x_{1/2} = \dfrac{\ln 2}{\mu} = \dfrac{\ln 2}{72\,\text{m}^{-1}}$ *[1]*

$x_{1/2} = 9.7 \times 10^{-3}\,\text{m}$ *[1]*

19.2

1 Absorbed dose $= \dfrac{\text{energy absorbed}}{\text{mass of tissue exposed}}$ *[1]*

Effective dose = absorbed dose × quality factor *[1]*

2 Energy deposited $= 1.5 \times 10^3\,\text{Bq} \times (24 \times 60 \times 60)\text{s} \times (0.5 \times 10^6 \times 1.6 \times 10^{-19})\,\text{J}$ *[1]*

Dose $= (1.5 \times 10^3\,\text{Bq} \times (24 \times 60 \times 60)\text{s} \times (0.5 \times 10^6 \times 1.6 \times 10^{-19}))\,\text{J}/0.09\,\text{kg}$ *[1]*

Dose $= 0.12\,\text{mGy}$ *[1]*

3 Risk $= 1 \times 10^{-4}\,\text{Sv} \times 0.05\,\text{Sv}^{-1}$ *[1]*

Number of cases per million =
risk per individual $\times 10^6 = 1 \times 10^{-4}\,\text{Sv} \times 0.05\,\text{Sv}^{-1} \times 10^6$

Number of cases per million = 5 cases *[1]*

4 There are a number of ways to tackle this question. This method separates each element of the calculation so that you can see each step.

Decay constant in $\text{s}^{-1} = \dfrac{(\ln 2)}{(11.4 \times (24 \times 60 \times 60)\text{s}}$
$= 7.0 \times 10^{-7}\,\text{s}^{-1}$

Initial number of radium-223 nuclei =
$\dfrac{\text{initial activity}}{\text{decay constant}} = \dfrac{2000\,\text{Bq}}{7.0 \times 10^{-7}\,\text{s}^{-1}} = 2.8 \times 10^9$ *[1]*

Number remaining after 6 days =
$2.8 \times 10^9 \times e^{-7.0 \times 10^{-7} \times 24 \times 60 \times 60 \times 6}) = 1.95 \times 10^9$

Alpha particles emitted in 6 days =
$2.8 \times 10^9 - 1.95 \times 10^9 = 0.85 \times 10^9$ *[1]*

Energy deposited =
$0.85 \times 10^9 \times (5.8 \times 10^6 \times 1.6 \times 10^{-19})\,\text{J} = 7.9 \times 10^{-4}\,\text{J}$ *[1]*

Dose equivalent $= \dfrac{(7.9 \times 10^{-4}\,\text{J})}{0.04\,\text{kg}} \times 20 = 0.4\,\text{Sv}$ *[1]*

19.3

1 a $^{32}_{15}\text{P} \rightarrow ^{32}_{16}\text{S} + ^{0}_{-1}\text{e} + ^{0}_{0}\nu$ *[1]*

b $^{230}_{90}\text{Th} \rightarrow ^{226}_{88}\text{Ra} + ^{4}_{2}\text{He}$ *[1]*

2 Mass difference between original nucleus and products $= 13.00189\,\text{u} - (13.00005\,\text{u} + 0.00055\,\text{u}) = 1.29 \times 10^{-3}\,\text{u}$ *[1]*

Mass difference between original nucleus and products $= 2.1427 \times 10^{-30}\,\text{kg}$ *[1]*

Energy released $= \Delta mc^2 = 1.93 \times 10^{-13}\,\text{J}\ (= 1.2\,\text{MeV})$ *[1]*

3 Mass difference Δm between nucleus and individual nucleons = $238.00016\,u - (92 \times 1.00728\,u) - (146 \times 1.00867\,u) = -1.935\,u$ [1]

$= -3.2 \times 10^{-27}\,kg$ [1]

$E = \Delta mc^2 = -2.89 \times 10^{-10}\,J$ [1]

Binding energy per nucleon = $-2.89 \times 10^{-10}\,J/238 = -1.216 \times 10^{-12}\,J = -7.6\,MeV$ [1]

4 Binding energy per nucleon = $-1.408 \times 10^{-12}\,J$ [1]

Total binding energy = $56 \times -1.408 \times 10^{-12}\,J = -7.8848 \times 10^{-12}\,J$ [1]

Mass difference $= \dfrac{-7.8848 \times 10^{-12}\,J}{9 \times 10^{16}\,m^2\,s^{-2}} = -8.76 \times 10^{-28}\,kg = -0.527\,u$ [1]

Mass of unbound nucleons = $56.44938\,u$

Mass of iron nucleus = $56.44938\,u - 0.527\,u = 55.9\,u = 9.29 \times 10^{-26}\,kg$ [1]

19.4

1 a The average binding energy per nucleon of the products is more negative than the binding energy per nucleon of the original nucleus. [1]

b The average binding energy per nucleon of the more massive nucleus is more negative than the binding energy per nucleon of the original particles. [1]

2 Total binding energy of $^{236}_{92}U = -1.21 \times 10^{-12}\,J \times 236 = -2.8556 \times 10^{-10}\,J$ [1]

Total binding energy of products = $(-1.35 \times 10^{-12}\,J \times 146) + (-1.37 \times 10^{-12}\,J \times 87) = -3.1764 \times 10^{-10}\,J$ [1]

Energy released = $-2.8556 \times 10^{-10}\,J - (-3.1764 \times 10^{-10}\,J) = 3.21 \times 10^{-11}\,J\ (= 200\,MeV)$ [1]

3 Difference in mass Δm between initial nuclei and products = $(2.0136\,u + 3.0155\,u) - (4.0015\,u + 1.00867\,u) = 0.01893\,u$ [1]

$= 3.14 \times 10^{-29}\,kg$ [1]

$E = \Delta mc^2 = 3.14 \times 10^{-29}\,kg \times 9.00 \times 10^{16}\,m^2\,s^{-2} = 2.8 \times 10^{-12}\,J\ (2\ s.f.)\ (= 18\,MeV)$ [1]

Data, Formulae, and Relationships

Data

Values are given to three significant figures, except where more – or fewer – are useful.

Physical constants

speed of light	c	$3.00 \times 10^8 \, \text{m s}^{-1}$
permittivity of free space	ε_0	$8.85 \times 10^{-12} \, \text{C}^2 \text{N}^{-1} \text{m}^{-2} \, (\text{F m}^{-1})$
electric force constant	$k = \dfrac{1}{4\pi\varepsilon_0}$	$8.98 \times 10^9 \, \text{N m}^2 \, \text{C}^{-2}$ $(\approx 9 \times 10^9 \, \text{N m}^2 \, \text{C}^{-2})$
permeability of free space	μ_0	$4\pi \times 10^{-7} \, \text{N A}^{-2} \, (\text{or H m}^{-1})$
charge on electron	e	$-1.60 \times 10^{-19} \, \text{C}$
mass of electron	m_e	$9.11 \times 10^{-31} \, \text{kg} = 0.000\,55 \, \text{u}$
mass of proton	m_p	$1.673 \times 10^{-27} \, \text{kg} = 1.007\,3 \, \text{u}$
mass of neutron	m_n	$1.675 \times 10^{-27} \, \text{kg} = 1.008\,7 \, \text{u}$
mass of alpha particle	m_α	$6.646 \times 10^{-27} \, \text{kg} = 4.001\,5 \, \text{u}$
Avogadro constant	L, N_A	$6.02 \times 10^{23} \, \text{mol}^{-1}$
Planck constant	h	$6.63 \times 10^{-34} \, \text{J s}$
Boltzmann constant	k	$1.38 \times 10^{-23} \, \text{J K}^{-1}$
molar gas constant	R	$8.31 \, \text{J mol}^{-1} \text{K}^{-1}$
gravitational force constant	G	$6.67 \times 10^{-11} \, \text{N m}^2 \text{kg}^{-2}$

Other data

standard temperature and pressure (stp)		$273 \, \text{K} \, (0\,^\circ\text{C})$, $1.01 \times 10^5 \, \text{Pa}$ (1 atmosphere)
molar volume of a gas at stp	V_m	$2.24 \times 10^{-2} \, \text{m}^3$
gravitational field strength at the Earth's surface in the UK	g	$9.81 \, \text{N kg}^{-1}$

Conversion factors

unified atomic mass unit	1 u	$= 1.661 \times 10^{-27} \, \text{kg}$
	1 day	$= 8.64 \times 10^4 \, \text{s}$
	1 year	$\approx 3.16 \times 10^7 \, \text{s}$
	1 light year	$\approx 10^{16} \, \text{m}$

Mathematical constants and equations

$e = 2.72$ $\qquad$ $\pi = 3.14$ $\qquad$ 1 radian = 57.3°

$\text{arc} = r\theta$ $\qquad$ circumference of circle = $2\pi r$

$\sin\theta \approx \tan\theta \approx \theta$
and $\cos\theta \approx 1$ for small θ

area of circle = πr^2

surface area of cylinder = $2\pi rh$

$\ln(x^n) = n\ln x$

volume of cylinder = $\pi r^2 h$

$\ln(e^{kx}) = kx$

surface area of sphere = $4\pi r^2$

volume of sphere = $\frac{4}{3}\pi r^3$

Prefixes

10^{-12}	10^{-9}	10^{-6}	10^{-3}	10^{3}	10^{6}	10^{9}
p	n	μ	m	k	M	G

Formulae and relationships

Imaging and signalling

focal length $\qquad$ $\dfrac{1}{v} = \dfrac{1}{u} + \dfrac{1}{f}$

linear magnification $\qquad$ $m = \dfrac{v}{u}$

refractive index $\qquad$ $n = \dfrac{\sin i}{\sin r} = \dfrac{C_{\text{1st medium}}}{C_{\text{2nd medium}}}$

noise limitation on maximum bits per sample $\qquad$ $b = \log_2\left(\dfrac{V_{\text{total}}}{V_{\text{noise}}}\right)$

alternatives, N, provided by n bits $\qquad$ $N = 2^b,\ b = \log_2 N$

Electricity

current $\qquad$ $I = \dfrac{\Delta Q}{\Delta t}$

potential difference $\qquad$ $V = \dfrac{W}{Q}$

power and energy $\qquad$ $P = IV = I^2 R,\ W = VIt$

e.m.f and potential difference $\qquad$ $V = \varepsilon - Ir$

conductors in series and parallel $\qquad$ $\dfrac{1}{G} = \dfrac{1}{G_1} + \dfrac{1}{G_2} + \ldots$
$G = G_1 + G_2 + \ldots$

resistors in series and parallel $\qquad$ $R = R_1 + R_2 + \ldots$
$\dfrac{1}{R} = \dfrac{1}{R_1} + \dfrac{1}{R_2} + \ldots$

potential divider $\qquad$ $V_{\text{out}} = \dfrac{R_2}{R_1 + R_2} V_{\text{in}}$

conductivity and resistivity $\qquad$ $G = \dfrac{\sigma A}{L}$

$R = \dfrac{\rho L}{A}$

capacitance $\qquad$ $C = \dfrac{Q}{V}$

energy stored in a capacitor $\qquad$ $E = \dfrac{1}{2}QV = \dfrac{1}{2}CV^2$

discharge of capacitor $\qquad$ $\dfrac{dQ}{dt} = -\dfrac{Q}{RC}$

$Q = Q_0\, e^{-t/RC}$

$\tau = RC$

Materials

Hooke's law $\qquad$ $F = kx$

elastic strain energy $\qquad$ $\dfrac{1}{2}kx^2$

Young modulus $\qquad$ $E = \dfrac{\text{stress}}{\text{strain}},$

$\text{stress} = \dfrac{\text{tension}}{\text{cross} - \text{sectional area}},$

$\text{strain} = \dfrac{\text{extension}}{\text{original length}}$

Gases

kinetic theory of gases $\qquad$ $pV = \dfrac{1}{3}Nm\overline{c^2}$

ideal gas equation $\qquad$ $pV = nRT = NkT$

Motion and forces

momentum $\qquad$ $p = mv$

impulse $\qquad$ $F\Delta t$

force $\qquad$ $F = \dfrac{\Delta(mv)}{\Delta t}$

work done $\qquad$ $W = Fx$ $\qquad$ $\Delta E = F\Delta s$

power $\qquad$ $P = Fv,$ $\qquad$ $P = \dfrac{\Delta E}{t}$

components of a vector in two perpendicular directions

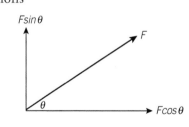

Data, Formulae, and Relationships

equations for uniformly
accelerated motion
$$s = ut + \frac{1}{2}at^2$$
$$v = u + at$$
$$v^2 = u^2 + 2as$$

for circular motion
$$a = \frac{v^2}{r}, F = \frac{mv^2}{r} = mr\omega^2$$

Energy and thermal effects

energy
$$\Delta E = mc\Delta\theta$$

average energy approximation
average energy $\sim kT$

Boltzmann factor
$$e^{-\frac{E}{kT}}$$

Waves

wave formula
$$v = f\lambda$$

frequency and period
$$f = \frac{1}{T}$$

diffraction grating
$$n\lambda = d\sin\theta$$

Oscillations

simple harmonic motion
$$\frac{d^2x}{dt^2} = a = -\left(\frac{k}{m}\right)x = -\omega^2 x$$
$$x = A\cos(\omega t)$$
$$x = A\sin(\omega t)$$
$$\omega = 2\pi f$$

Periodic time
$$T = 2\pi\sqrt{\frac{m}{k}}$$
$$T = 2\pi\sqrt{\frac{L}{g}}$$

total energy
$$E = \frac{1}{2}kA^2 = \frac{1}{2}mv^2 + \frac{1}{2}kx^2$$

Atomic and nuclear physics

radioactive decay
$$\frac{\Delta N}{\Delta t} = -\lambda N$$
$$N = N_0 e^{-\lambda t}$$

half life
$$T_{\frac{1}{2}} = \frac{\ln 2}{\lambda}$$

radioactive dose and risk
absorbed dose = energy
deposited per unit mass
effective dose = absorbed
dose × quality factor

mass–energy relationship
$$E_{\text{rest}} = mc^2$$

relativistic factor
$$\gamma = \sqrt{\frac{1}{1 - v^2/c^2}}$$

relativistic energy
$$E_{\text{total}} = \gamma E_{\text{rest}}$$

energy–frequency
relationship for photons
$$E = hf$$

de Broglie
$$\lambda = \frac{h}{p}$$

Field and potential

for all fields
fields strength $= -\dfrac{dV}{dr} \approx -\dfrac{\Delta V}{\Delta r}$

gravitational fields
$$g = \frac{F}{m}, E_{grav} = -\frac{GmM}{r}$$
$$V_{grav} = -\frac{GM}{r}, F = -\frac{GmM}{r^2}$$

electric fields
$$E = \frac{F}{q} = \frac{V}{d},$$
electrical potential energy $= \dfrac{kQq}{r}$
$$V_{electric} = \frac{kQ}{r}, F = \frac{kQq}{r^2}$$

Electromagnetism

magnetic flux
$$\Phi = BA$$

force on a current carrying conductor
$$F = ILB$$

force on a moving charge
$$F = qvB$$

Induced e.m.f
$$\varepsilon = -\frac{d(N\Phi)}{dt}$$